Dr Alex Comfort was born in  in medicine at Trinity College, his doctorate at London Univ numerous other medical degre the United States in 1974. He geriatric psychiatry at Brentwo sor at UCLA, and clinical lecturer at Stanford. Best known to the public as the editor of *The Joy of Sex* and *More Joy* he has written many works of fiction and poetry.

ALEX COMFORT

Tetrarch

PALADIN
GRAFTON BOOKS
A Division of the Collins Publishing Group

LONDON GLASGOW
TORONTO SYDNEY AUCKLAND

Paladin
Grafton Books
A Division of the Collins Publishing Group
8 Grafton Street, London W1X 3LA

Published in Paladin Books 1989

First published in Great Britain by
Wildwood House Ltd 1981

ISBN 0-586-08772-9

Printed and bound in Great Britain by
Collins, Glasgow

Set in Palatino

Contents

BOOK ONE
A Fearful Symmetry
9

BOOK TWO
A Grain of Sand
145

BOOK THREE
Beyond the Night of Beulah
263

BOOK FOUR
The Fourth Journey
387

Appendix
391

The Losian Religion
Losian Grammar
The Losian Script
A Losian Vocabulary

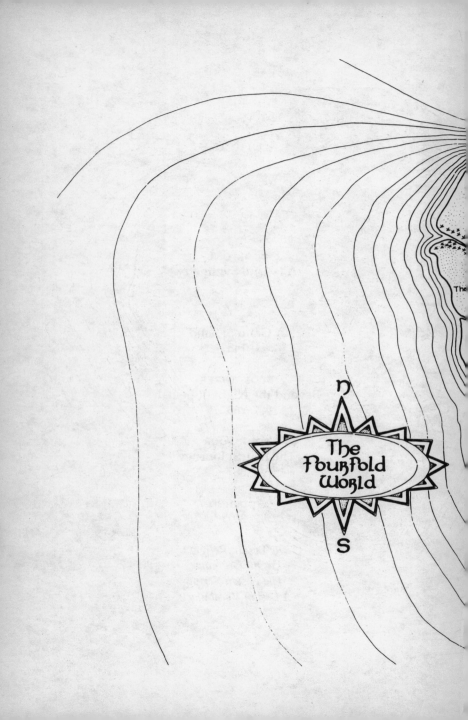

The

N

The
Fourfold
World

S

BOOK ONE
A Fearful Symmetry

There Is a Place
where Contrarieties Are Equally True . . .

1

We Find a Gate in Albion

Rosanna had moved in to live with me seven days previously. It was rewarding but still prickly, probationary, on both sides, and wild, tender and distant by turns. She brought her china and shared the double bed I already had. We were in my apartment in Edinburgh, and I bought it before suggesting the arrangement. Both of us were in systems theory – she programming, to save enough cash to get into medical school; I, of all things, assigned to finding a general program to translate linear 'A'. The idea was to find the beginning and ending of words by statistical analysis, then compile a terminal syllabary, and run a random phonetic transliteration until we got a fit with the syllabaries of Greek, Sanskrit, Luvian, Hittite and a lot more. I heard about this in Cambridge and thought it feasible. The first thing I saw on landing at the airport in Edinburgh was a sign at the side of the taxi-way which read:

CLRNC BEF XING RNWY

After that I wasn't so sure. Linear 'A' didn't itself of course matter – these ancient writings are commonly laundry lists, or the equivalent – but the general principle of decipherment did.

Rosanna wandered all round the place like a new cat. When they'd divided the old Victorian family house to make apartments, they'd crammed two into the ground floor. Our bedroom had been a hallway. In consequence there was a piece of passageway about ten feet long running out of it, which went nowhere and ended in a papered-over partition, bang opposite the end of our bed, so that we lay in bed and looked down it. I found it had a bad effect on our sense of privacy. Rosanna clearly didn't like it either.

'I'll put a curtain across that,' said Rosanna. 'It should go somewhere and doesn't. It's untidy and disturbing.'

We then set out in search of curtains and found some. The passage was promoted to wardrobe, store and playroom.

'Still not right,' said Rosanna – twice: once when we woke in the morning, again in the afternoon when I was in the middle of loving her.

'I'll board it over,' I said, 'and paper it.'

'No – we need the cupboard.'

Our facing neighbor was a junk and furniture store. In summer it blossomed onto the pavement, in winter it drew itself in and closed the door. This was summer. Rosanna called me to the apartment window on the seventh morning of our mutual investigation.

'Look,' she said, 'they've got a door.'

'It's a wardrobe-front,' I said.

'It's a door. With the frame. Have you got a rule?'

We measured the offending space, went down the steep stairs into the wynd, and looked more closely.

The door itself was divided into smaller panels set between heavy dividers. It was of long-standing unstained oak. The handle and lock were heavy. In the four top panels were carved animals, very well done, but modern and not matching the apparent antiquity of the wood – bull, lion, eagle, and man. In the lower four the carvings were star, sun, moon, and a mountain. The frame was more complex, a tree on one side and a snake on the other, intertwining at the top, and each extending to the bottom on the side opposite to its beginning, the snake's head by the tree's roots.

'A historiated door. It's not old, I think.'

'It's beautiful,' said Rosanna. 'Where did they get it?'

'Possibly a church – more likely a local artist.'

The storeman knew nothing of its history, beyond that it had been brought in from a demolished house, wanted twenty-five good Scots pounds and helped us take it across and (with problems) up into the apartment. All that it lacked was a key, and it was at the present time locked.

The back was less interesting – plain board with a cheap brass door-knob. We set it in place.

'Fix it,' said Rosanna. 'It might fall.'

I drilled and plugged it at four points. The wood was fragrant, like incense cedar. When the locksmith came, it could easily be turned if necessary. We needed a playroom accessible at minimum notice.

'It's the door of our bridal chamber,' I said, 'guarded by dwarfs on the other side.'

'It's the door of something,' said Rosanna.

There was more detail than I had noted. At the top, in the branches of the serpent-wound tree, was a hollow sphere, inside it a male and a female figure embracing. On the left was a circle in which a woman was spinning, and from her spinning a veil, carved with great fineness, seemed to encompass the whole frame. On the right was a falling figure, whether male or female I could not tell.

'Let Sandy see it,' said Rosanna.

'Sandy,' I said, 'is a professor of anthropology, not an art critic.'

'Call him up all the same,' said Rosanna.

Professor Alexander McPherson was our tap for some living languages, including the Gaelic, which we'd put in the syllabary. He was also a kind of mental amphibian. They'd had him over at Lawrence Berkeley, talking about ethnographic reality-models to the particle physicists and scoring heavily with them on explicate-implicate field theories, diverging time-streams, and so on. He was a resource man but a very odd customer. Back home in the Isles he'd have been the local seer. He seemed unsurprised to be asked to look at a door. 'It is,' he said, 'a verra fine example.'

'Of what?' said Rosanna.

'That I would not know precisely. It is designed as a portal.'

'What about the iconography?'

'The Tree of Life, I see, and the Serpent of Eternity. The other symbols you can see as well as myself.'

'Any suggestions?'

'It is not, I think, of any culture with which I am familiar.'

Sandy was Highland-hedging in precisely the way he did when anyone talked about second sight. He reminded me on these occasions of a psychiatrist trying not to overinterpret, and of knowing far more than would be good for us.

'I'll get it opened tomorrow, but the back's quite plain. Any advice about it?'

I was thinking of a suggestion as to who might identify it, if the symbolism wasn't quite arbitrary.

'I think on the whole,' said Sandy, 'that I would give great consideration before opening such a door.' He was evidently thinking on other lines.

'It's perfectly robust,' I said. 'Opening it can't hurt it. It's been opened enough times before.'

'It well may have been,' said Sandy, 'but I would give great consideration before opening such a door. And still greater, I think, before stepping through it. I will see you tomorrow, I hope.'

'He's a great chap, with a great sense of humor,' I told Rosanna, 'but I wish he didn't sound like the village wise man. He's spent too much time with shamans.'

Rosanna said absolutely nothing. She ran her forefinger over all parts of the design, as if the finger were a metal detector, or she were going to trace the pattern onto paper. She tried the handle. She said, 'There could be two ways of opening it. You could lay it down for the man to work on and it would be just a door. Or you could open it where it is.'

I may have been flippant with Sandy, but he was a man with his own personal radar, and he and I, and I am sure Rosanna, were getting the same signal. 'Which will it be?' said Rosanna. 'If you're willing to open it where it is, I'm game.'

'So am I.'

We said no more at all about it. It was borne in on me, however, that we should have to have a locksmith, and he would open it, and probably oil it, and his presence would kill stone dead any of the fantasy games Rosanna and I were learning to play. When he'd gone we would have a ceremonial opening, close it to get total darkness, and I would learn what her fantasy was on this occasion – probably to be hunted and caught in the dark. It was a fantasy door, there were endless possibilities, and it was clearly going to enrich our lives. Rosanna's silence made me sure I had read her wishes.

About midnight I suddenly woke and missed her. She was moving about.

'You feel all right?' I said.

'Yes, all right. Edward, the door isn't locked any more.'

'Let me wake up,' I said. She hadn't wanted this in mid-sleep before. The whole room was full of the aromatic scent of the wood. 'I won't ask questions,' I said, 'and spoil it, but I'll feel more vigorous in the morning.' The chase-and-ravish sequence was apt to be rather boisterous.

'How did you get it open?'

'I didn't. It's just not locked.'

We had woken, after all, from deep sleep, and at such times one is a little changed. I had filed away the second signal from Sandy's and my own radar because it was troubling. In this out-of-sleep state it was no longer so. I moved the handle and pulled a little. It creaked, and would open. It had unlocked itself.

'Sandy said we should consider carefully,' said Rosanna. 'Also, do we close it after us?'

I thought a moment. 'Yes, we can – if it sticks I can push the whole thing over – it's only held at four points.'

We were both naked and the room full of moonlight. She traced the patterns, which seemed deeper, and took my hand. 'Come in with me,' she said.

2

Warlike Men Who Rise in the Silent Night

She opened the door and went in. I followed, closed it and waited for the whispered scenario.

What came then was an interval, featureless, followed by recollection. All that happened was that thought was gently suspended, or moved momentarily elsewhere.

We were not in the alcove, nor now in darkness, but in a small arched stone chamber, a little like a church crypt. Its floor was of shiny black marble, not flagged, but in a single gray-veined slab. The stone of which the vault was built was semitransparent in the manner of alabaster or onyx, pale like a candle, and like the wax of a candle near to the lighted wick, it was internally luminous, but yet there was no flame.

It was dim there, but each could see that the other had changed.

Rosanna held hard to my hand, almost crushing it. We turned together towards the door.

It was reversed – or rather, the plain inner face with its cheap hardware knob had been replaced by a carved surface, the twin of the other face, but its reverse, and there was a handle as on the other side. It was now locked.

'You knew,' said Rosanna.

'We both knew,' I said – 'you went in and I followed you.'

Either the light brightened or our eyes had adapted. As Rosanna tried the door again I realized that she was in fancy dress. Her long hair was unchanged, but she was wearing a tuniclike costume which seemed to come from the wardrobe of a Roman film. Between her ankles, joining two yellow metal anklets, was a thin chain.

Rosanna stared at it, holding up an ankle.

'Take this thing *off*,' she said.

I tried. It had minute keyholes in each anklet. It too was locked.

'Where is this?' said Rosanna.

'I haven't the remotest idea.'

'On our way to a fancy dress party.' She was shaken and giggling, unusual for Rosanna.

'It's a game,' I said. 'Let's play it.'

'Yes.'

I followed Rosanna's eye and looked down. My feet and calves were in boots of a soft, shiny material, reaching to the knee. I had large round iron spurs with starred rowels. My own garment was shorter than hers, and so light that I did not at first realize that it was covered with overlapping metal scales like those of a carp. It was belted with a belt of mottled, hair-covered hide. There was a frog for a sword on my left hip, but no sword.

'Tools,' said Rosanna, 'or a key.'

'The door?' I asked.

'No. This chain.'

'Can you walk?' I asked her.

'Just. I feel like a slavegirl.'

I did not say that she looked like one, and beautiful at that. I was surprised at her intensity – it was one of her favorite games, but it wasn't turning her on.

'What next?' said Rosanna.

'The other door, evidently,' I said. 'We don't have any choice. And stay behind me this time.'

It opened, inwards, easily, into a far larger hall, lit by the same subdued glow but brighter. Two soldiers were guarding it at ease, with lances crossed before it. Their uniforms were like my own but simpler. On a stool sat another soldier – he was unarmed, but wore a foxtail attached to his left shoulder which hung in front like a lanyard. All were dark, short-built men, not more than four foot six in height, but thickset and strong, like robust dwarfs.

As the door opened in front of us, the guard came smartly to attention. The man with the foxtail jumped from the stool and clapped the back of his right hand with a flourish against his forehead, under his round metal helmet brim. I did the same, and we passed between them into the hall. The guards recrossed lances and stood at ease. It was a long hall. In it were two green transparent stone basins with fountains playing and floating plants. We threaded between them, Rosanna stumbling over the chain.

'Take shorter steps,' I said.

'If those goons are friends of yours, tell them to let me loose,' said Rosanna. 'My ankles are hurting.'

'We have to play along,' I said, over my shoulder. 'I'm getting the scenario, I think. I'm some kind of warrior, and you're my slavegirl – it's your usual trip.'

'Thanks,' said Rosanna.

We reached the end of the hall. The doors here (they were double) left us no choices, but flew open before we reached them. The hall beyond, bathed in the same light, ceiled in the same waxy stone, was enormous. The roof, forming a total wall-less arch to the floor, was like a vast hangar. Drawn up in two sets of two files were a full hundred or more of the dark spearmen. There were copper drums and a banner. As we appeared, there was a yell, and a hundred spear butts hit the floor with a crash. It was clearly a guard of honor.

I gave the salute I had learned at the former door, and the spears hit the floor again.

To a drumbeat a man marched up the files. On his left shoulder like the half of a pelisse hung what appeared to be three foxtails. Beside him another, with one foxtail, carried before him, across his two hands, a sheathed sword. They marched up like a color party and halted face to face with me, insofar as such short men could be said to do so. We exchanged salutes. Then Three-Tails bawled, in a voice common to sergeants and chief petty-officers the world over, a phrase in a strange language.

It took me a moment to realize that I understood him. It was not precisely '*Idou to xiphos sou, Kyrie*' but close enough to have meaning: and anyhow he made it sound like 'Your sword! Sir!!' I took the sheathed sword and slipped it into the frog. The sword party took one pace to the rear. I drew the thing (fortunately it came out of the sheath easily) and presented it in front of my nose. The weapons party did the same. Then we all replaced swords in sheath, the weapons party about-faced and quick-marched back to stations, about-faced again and waited.

It was my next move.

'When you've finished playing soldiers – ' said Rosanna fiercely.

'Sshh!' I said, and chanced my arm on information so far received. Orders sound much alike in any tongue. I wasn't risking creaky Greek – the English for 'slope arms' is 'yawp . . . hipe!' – no time now for linguistics.

'Colonel's guard – shun!' I bawled, amazed at my own voice.

Crash went the spears.

'Hoplitai – emprosthen – pros to dexion – choreite!!'

It worked like a charm. The weapons party about-faced, files faced forward into column, the drums struck up, and huge doors opened into blinding sunlight. Then we were off at the quick-march.

'Short steps,' I said to Rosanna. 'Don't try to keep step – you'll fall.'

'Edward, my ankles are killing me. Enough is enough.'

'Sshh!'

'Cut this thing with your sword!'

'Keep going,' I hissed. 'As soon as I can.' The chain looked thick for a steel blade, and for all I knew the sword could be bronze. Not much chance of freeing Rosanna in a quick swipe, unless the thing was pure gold.

We were marching along a causeway through wide, tree-filled garden beds between high white walls like city walls, set perhaps three hundred yards apart. They had towers and parapets on which I could see round helmets and cross bowmen looking down. At the end of the vista was a round white building with columns. We appeared to have filled in the Reflecting Pool and be marching up it to the Jefferson Monument – I looked for the Washington obelisk. It was there, or almost – there was a high mast with wicker crow's-nests from which hung climbing ropes. In them were more squat troops looking down. The dwarfs marched like marines or guardsmen, with the style and smartness of professional soldiers bulging with regimental pride – I found myself whistling 'Colonel Bogey' unawares.

We halted at the round building: files faced inward, the sergeant and lance-corporal faced me.

If it worked once it should work again. I needed, 'Carry on, Sergeant, parade dismissed.'

'*Kalōs, hekatarche, soi to epos!*' I bellowed.

It was lousy Greek, but it worked. Parade saluted, the doors opened, and we entered.

'My ankles!' cried Rosanna and stumbled on all fours, looking up wildly. The doors closed.

At a table facing us, the only major furniture of the rotunda, a gray-haired man was sitting in a large chair of hide slung on crossed, curved wooden members. He rose smiling.

'Greetings!' he said, and extended his hand.

I took it. 'Thank God someone speaks English,' I said.

'What did you expect me to speak?' said the gray-haired man.

'I don't know. Look, help me to get this off the lady's ankles,' I said, pulling out the sword.

'I don't understand.'

'Key, file, hacksaw,' I said, ceasing to saw at the chain and making signs. 'Hold still, or I'll cut you – this thing is sharp.'

'Who put these things on me?' said Rosanna, close to tears.

'But you put them on yourself,' said the gray-haired man, 'in the Time of Choice: and in any case they are not locked. You can take them off when you wish.'

It was true, and we looked remarkably foolish. After a little fumbling I removed the anklets. Rosanna, to my surprise, put them in the pocket of her tunic, as if for reference. Then she sat on the floor, rubbing her ankles.

'Where is this?' said Rosanna.

'The Other Side,' said our host gravely.

'Side of what?'

'Of earth, of course.'

'I see,' said Rosanna.

'You look surprised – you came through the door, didn't you?'

'I don't understand you,' said Rosanna. 'Say again?'

'I think I'm beginning to understand,' I said. 'And the Time of Choice – I don't recall it.'

'People never recall it,' said the gray-haired man. Then, as if I had asked a question: 'I am Thapsis, an undersecretary to the Council, under the Archon.'

The last words, from the way he delivered them, were clearly a religious formula, not an administrative description.

'Which Archon?' said Rosanna, suddenly straightening.

'Urthona is our Archon, whose earth name is Los.'

'Thank goodness,' she said. 'I thought it might be Urizen.'

Thapsis looked at her sharply. 'You understand much, lady,' he said. 'You aren't by chance an Adept?'

He seemed alarmed by the idea.

'No,' said Rosanna, rising from the floor, 'but among other things I'm a poet.'

'We have a caste of poets held in great honor,' said Thapsis. 'Why in the Four Heavens did you choose to come here as a slavegirl?'

I had caught up with Rosanna's mind. 'Is slavery an institution in the City of Los?' I asked.

'Yes and no. Not an institution – we didn't institute it – it's purely voluntary. It depends on the Time of Choice.'

'The Time of Choice?'

'Yes. Of course we know there are people who seem to want to belong absolutely to other people: there are people who want to own other people. Seems to be an obsession on Your Side: people keep turning up here with that sort of hang-up – forgive me, I mean sexual preference – we don't let them do it politically, of course, but in sexual relationships it's their option and we wouldn't dream of being judgmental about it. We've just had to make a few rules to regularize matters and see they don't get out of hand. Losians are extraordinarily tolerant, even of things they don't understand and can't empathize. Excuse me for being surprised at your choice. I didn't mean to imply any criticism.' Poor old Thapsis was looking as embarrassed as a straight doctor trying to be nice to a gay patient. I told him we were less like that than most. He didn't seem convinced.

'Can we sit down?' said Rosanna.

'Certainly. Pardon me.' He rang a silver desk bell, and two soldiers, minus side-arms and helmets, brought in chairs for us.

'The door,' said Rosanna, 'was it the Veil of Ulro that we passed through?'

Thapsis looked shocked, as if she had asked a bishop, 'Are you Jesus Christ?' – crazy and slightly impious.

'Nobody passes through the Veil of Ulro, Lady,' said Thapsis, 'or ever will. Not in the sense you're speaking of it.'

There was another pause. Wheels spun in all our heads.

'Or behold Beulah, Allamanda, Cathedron or Golgonooza?' said Rosanna.

'Why did you not frankly tell me,' said Thapsis, 'that you were Adepts? I think you should have said. If you wish to be unknown, that is your right, but surely it's a lot better if I know. Nobody else will, except the Council, I promise you.'

'What we said is true,' said Rosanna. 'Technically we are not Adepts. But we have read much in the book of an Adept.'

'I see,' said Thapsis. Obviously he didn't see. But his style was getting noticeably more conversational, and less like Sarastro and splash. Either the fantasy was about to run out, or this unaccustomed world was becoming real.

'Is there death here?' said Rosanna, after another awkward pause.

'Yes, of course there is death. And most people here believe in another world, a belief which sustains them when death must be faced.'

'What other world?' said Rosanna.

'Yours, Adept.'

'So there are two ways, death, and the door?'

'Yes. But not many people know this – Adepts, not the people.'

'Passing from Here to There,' said Rosanna, 'do they remember?'

'In part they may,' said Thapsis. 'Do you remember your dreams, or do they scatter?'

'Mostly they scatter,' said Rosanna.

'So too with this,' said Thapsis. 'Adepts however remember.'

'They do?'

'Everything. If you remember Your Side, then you are Adepts.'

'You said that you're not an Adept?' said Rosanna.

'I didn't,' said Thapsis, 'but I am not an Adept.'

'But you know. And you remember.'

'I am instructed by Adepts,' said Thapsis, looking uncomfortable, 'but I have to live life literally. I've no control over its course – you can see I have no ring.'

There was yet another pause, of the kind which makes the Russians say that a little policeman is being born.

My turn to bat.

'Try it the other way, Ros,' I said: 'this is the alternative explicate, am I right?'

'Thank goodness,' said Thapsis. 'Thought you'd never ask. You are science people, not professional mystics, aren't you? I thought for a moment we'd got the wrong pair.'

Rosanna started to say that the two weren't conflicting paradigms.

'I know, I know,' said Thapsis. 'Please don't lecture. Let's get back. It's *an* alternative explicate. Right.'

'Any chance we get to have a look at the implicate, while we're here?' I asked.

'I rather think,' said Thapsis, 'that for the moment you'd better stick to settling in – to the alternative explicate, that is. Plenty of time for other experiences later. You know,' he said, 'the lady had me really confused. But I'm relieved to find she's so far along, if you'll excuse the comment. I was afraid we'd have to start in the first grade, with quantum logic, and here you are, talking like Adepts. That's a great relief. No blackboard needed!

'You're both tired,' said Thapsis briskly, 'and I am very remiss. Let me send for refreshments and then you can rest. I'll have your room made ready. You are not chaste Adepts?'

'Indeed not,' I said.

'Good. I'll tell them to prepare a love bed.'

They brought yellow pancakes like chapatis and hot aromatic herb tea in tall glasses, and we sipped it in silence.

Finally a side door opened and a girl in a rainbow-pattern apron came in. She had waist-length black hair and a kind of dirndl-bodice of Minoan pattern which left her bare-breasted. She was taller than my troops, of another people no doubt, and she smiled and motioned us to follow her.

I shook Thapsis's extended hands. 'See you later,' I said.

'I will come to you at the Fourth Fire. We will talk more then of the future,' said Thapsis. 'Love well.' He returned to his papers. I had the impression that in importing us he'd got slightly more than he had bargained for.

'When's the Fourth Fire?' said Rosanna, as we followed the housekeeper.

'Your guess is as good as mine, but you heard what he said. It should leave us time,' I answered, reading her mind. 'And for a sleep as well.'

The room was cool, built and ceiled with the luminous stone. It seemed underwater in the greenish light. It had two ogival windows, hangings and chairs like those of Thapsis. The love bed was a pile of skins, very soft but hairy rather than furry, mottled in a pepper and salt pattern. The housekeeper motioned to it and smiled. She was pretty, with little dark nipples of the typical Losian brunette, and I would have looked longer at her, but I was staring at the skins. They were seamless, cut square, with no visible limbs or quarters flayed into them, and each was bigger than a king-size bed.

'There's a beautiful bath,' said Rosanna. 'What's the matter?'

'Nothing. Just that I wonder what that skin came from.'

'Why?'

'It's enormous.'

'Does it matter? Come on.'

The bath was a deep luminous onyx tank, the water perfumed.

'They're doing us extremely proud for unannounced visitors,' I said as we dried ourselves. Rosanna pulled me towards the pile of skins. Her discarded clothes were on the floor with mine.

'This turns you on,' I said, taking hold.

'Oh, stop talking!' said Rosanna. I did.

When we had done, she put her head on my shoulder. There was a traffic noise outside unlike the noise of our cities, a sound of people, not machines: voices, steps, creaking, rattling, children shouting or crying. A squad marched past.

'You know,' said Rosanna, 'I've been thinking about the Time of Choice. This place is full of soldiers – they're probably at war.'

'Looks very like it,' I said.

'And you chose a macho trip with instant promotion to colonel and a sword. Iron Age colonels have to lead their men in battle, right?'

'Right – I hadn't thought of that.'

'And you volunteered.'

'I'm as like a soldier,' I said, 'as a Chinese admiral. I don't recall volunteering. It happened.'

'Nobody recalls it, that man said. But you must have.'

'And you – you did some volunteering yourself,' I said. 'You may have to deliver on these.' The slave chains had fallen out of Rosanna's pocket. I picked them up and dangled them.

'Want to try again for size?' I asked her.

'I imagine I'll be yours,' said Rosanna.

'You can't be.'

'What?'

'You heard Thapsis. Here it's a voluntary arrangement. Some people want to be owned like property.'

'I do, occasionally,' said Rosanna.

'But they can only be owned by someone who wants to own people. I don't want to own people.'

'So?'

'So I rather think that Thapsis will put a small ad in the Losian gazette, "One or Possibly Two Careful Owners."'

Rosanna looked alarmed.

'It's like you said,' I told her. 'We both volunteered. I have the feeling we might have to live with the consequences, until this is over.'

She thought for a moment. 'What *is* this?' she asked.

'The dream. Or whatever else it is. The alternative explicate.'

'To go back,' said Rosanna, 'it's either death, or the door?'

'That's what Thapsis said.'

'Let's get dressed,' said Rosanna, pushing it away. 'The bath will still be hot, we don't know when the Fourth Fire is, and we're making a mess on these beautiful furs.'

She got up and went back to the onyx tank.

I adjusted my military monkey suit before a polished bronze mirror, and went to the window.

Outside in a small square, surrounded by market baskets and crates of what seemed to be brightly-colored poultry, was a gigantic statue of a horseman. The rider was small, one of the lancers of Los's kingdom. But what struck my eye was his mount.

It was enormous, standing nearly twice as high at the withers as any horse. Its neck was longer than a horse's neck but thicker. It had a huge rather squirrel-shaped head which wore a muzzle in the form of an iron cage riveted to the stone. Inside the carved stone teeth were ungulate – denture, that is, rather than dog, but the canines, spaced back from the incisors, were pointed, not rudimentary, and showed in the lips. It had large camellike feet, and its hind legs were shorter than the huge forelegs, so that it sloped and appeared perpetually to crouch, like a hyaena. It also had enormous claws, weirdly out of key with its tooth arrangements. Rosanna was at the window beside me, fetchingly Minoan.

'What is it?' she said. 'Do you *know* what it is?'

'I can guess,' I said. I remembered the mottled skins of our love bed.

'It's not a horse.'

'No, but it's an ungulate, in spite of the claws. If it's what I think, it's the only ungulate *with* claws – in that case it's called Chalicotherium. Some people call it the Nandi bear.'

'Is it special?'

'It's supposed to be a partially carnivorous primitive horse. It's also probably extinct – on Our Side. And I'm not overpleased to see it here, though that statue looks as if they've domesticated it. Probably eats cabbages after all.'

'It might eat people?'

'Judging from the reputation of the Nandi bear, I imagine it might. Which is probably why it's muzzled. It could certainly bite like all hell. That neck's nearly as long as a camel's – it could probably get at its rider.'

'Colonels,' said Rosanna the slavegirl, 'ride at the head of their men.'

'Not this one. Not on that. God bless the infantry!'

'Those troops all had spurs. You've got spurs,' said Rosanna.

'I won't be Bishop.'

'Well, fair's fair,' said Rosanna. 'I may have problems too, with my choice.'

'We might have had to face those anyhow,' I said.

'I think so,' said Rosanna. 'I didn't know I wanted to be owned.'

'By me you can't, not like that.' I dangled the ankle fetters: 'For kicks, now and then, but not permanently. People don't own people in my book.'

'So we may be going to be separated.'

'Leaving me,' I said, 'in a strange land, without pussy, galloping around on a chalicothere at the head of a regiment of dwarfs.'

Rosanna's eyes twinkled with mischief. 'Slaveboy, you want to be owned,' she said.

'Like a hole in the head I do.'

Somebody knocked cautiously.

'That'll be Thapsis. Come in!' I said.

Nothing happened. He knocked again.

'Come in already!'

Thapsis entered after some fiddling – he'd been slow because his arms were full of a bronze tray. On it stood a phial of a violet liqueur – Parfait Amour, or wood alcohol – and two crystal glasses, also a flat black leather case of the kind which might hold a diamond necklace.

'Did you love well?' he said, gravely, and without a trace of snigger.

'Very well.'

'Between Adepts it is always so. May we talk business?'

'Fire away.'

'First and most important, I bring you these.' He took the jewel box. 'I fully respect your incognito, but the Council absolutely insists you wear them. We just can't face the responsibility of having Adepts at risk. I can assure you they won't be recognized – the legend is on the inside.'

He snapped open the box. In it were two perfectly plain electrum rings, like broad wedding bands. Thapsis proffered it to each of us as if it were full of candy.

Rosanna slipped hers on her wedding-ring finger. I eyed mine with suspicion.

'Is this a caper of yours?' I asked her.

'No, it isn't. Don't be so scared, Colonel – they aren't slave chains.'

I put mine ostentatiously on my right index finger. Both fitted perfectly and automatically.

'Now,' said Thapsis, 'as to the future. You have three days' adjustment, as newcomers – then you're on your own.'

'In a strange city not speaking the language?' I said.

'That won't be a problem.'

'Doing what exactly?' I asked.

'What you elected at the Time of Choice. Now, about this.' He pointed to the purple decanter. 'It's nepenthe. You can drink it now, or later, or not at all. Most people find it helpful. But of course I couldn't speak for Adepts.'

'If we drink it,' said Rosanna slowly, 'we shall forget the – other explicate?'

'Oh no,' said Thapsis, 'it's nothing dramatic. All it does is to alter the backdrop of consciousness slightly. So that the real feels more real.'

'This is the real?' asked Rosanna.

'Of course. To you it must still be a little dreamlike, I can understand. With nepenthe, There would be more dreamlike and Here a little more actual. Please yourselves. You may find it alters you a little, but not much, and the change is not unpleasant.'

'We'll think it over,' I said.

'Good,' said Thapsis. 'Now I will leave you. Dinner will be served very shortly. Ask for what you want. I'll call again promptly at First Fire tomorrow – that's four human hours after sunrise. Love well.' And he left.

The tray with the nepenthe stayed where it was, with a spot of purple light in the little decanter.

We looked at one another, and as if by consent at the two rings. There was a tap at the door.

It was the bare-breasted girl, smiling and pleasant. 'You loved well? I'm glad. Would you care to order, Sir?' She held a small wax tablet and a stylus.

Suddenly we both, simultaneously, I think realized that she had spoken in Losian, but we had understood her.

'If it's inconvenient . . .' she began.

I slipped off the ring. I no longer understood. Rosanna saw and comprehended in one. I put the ring back.

'Fine,' I said. 'What's on the menu?'

And my words, though foreign, were familiar.

3
Tour of a Merciful Order

We slept for a few hours on the skins, but then woke irrevocably and watched the dawn come up in the two ogival windows with little pillow talk or discussion of what had passed, being both of us too busy with self-preparation. Street noises began early, the sounds of any unmechanized city. The moment of sunrise was marked by a large bell, but it did not ring long. When it was light we took a window each and watched the city wake. At first the passers were chiefly growers bringing produce. Some fruits and vegetables were familiar, others not – they were carried on the head by men and women alike. Next there appeared children, the smallest quite naked, the older wearing tunics, the girl children bare-breasted even before they had breasts. Later still came men in leather aprons – surprisingly, since these were artisans: their working day began far later than ours. The maidservant knocked and brought food, unembarrassed to find us both naked – which seemed from her response to be the normal mode of Losian domesticity. She brought me clean linen, and for Rosanna another Losian bodice in the Minoan style. Four hours after sunrise a red glow lit the city as the First Fire was ignited on the roof of a building the body of which we could not see. Within one minute Thapsis arrived. He had now abandoned English, no doubt to see how our rings were working, and gave the Losian greeting 'You loved well?' the normal good-day to a couple in Adambara.

'Yes,' we answered.

'Splendid. Then I think we should take a look at Adambara. You'll need to find your way, and I think it will give you a rough idea of our institutions and of how people behave. By the way, make no reference to Your Side: to the folk here you are foreigners – we have adjusted your rings to give you an accent. Any other reference would have the same effect as if, on Your Side, a Frenchman in London announced that he was really a ghost.'

We followed him down a winding stair into the street. It was clear to me from the start that Adambara was a 'low technology' society, and we seemed to be in for a day's march over cobbles, but Thapsis had brought a minute governess cart, drawn by a long-necked sheep, not quite an alpaca but like it, which he introduced as a choreb and encouraged Rosanna to feel its softness. They are bred in the mountains, he told us, and produce wool for the looms. It was an affectionate creature. I for my part was relieved that these people had invented the wheel – this was the first vehicle I had seen anywhere.

'If this is a choreb, what's that?' I said, pointing to the statue.

'An asva,' said Thapsis. 'It's the normal mount of a warrior.'

Rosanna was eyeing me, being revenged for her passage with the Time of Choice. Thapsis seemed artificially off-hand.

'Fierce?' I said.

'Oh, very – after all, it's a battle animal. We feed them on hyasa,' said Thapsis, 'fat, garbage-eating lizards. Nasty things. Asvaya love them.'

We trotted off, drawing little attention. I had expected a rough ride, but the little cart was sprung on what appeared to be sinews, and rode well. We attracted little notice.

'The city's roughly circular,' said Thapsis, 'so you can get your bearings – it was perfectly circular, but there have been additions outside the walls. The wall of Bowmen runs round the old city – the old moat is inside, not out, and forms a modern canal.'

'It has four gates,' said Rosanna, 'at the points of the compass – that to the South, gilt, with a lion over it; that to the East is studded with brass; that to the West is silver; and that to the North is iron or clay or both, and one of them, I'm not quite sure which, will be permanently shut.'

'It's the West Gate,' said Thapsis, rather sharply, as if he were the courier dealing with a tourist who has read the *Michelin Guide*.

The streets were narrow and winding here, but with a general curvature imposed by the shape of the city, the houses whitewashed and contiguous, sharing walls and balconies, in the style of most Italian hill-villages. A few walls, quite arbitrarily placed, were covered with shining white ceramic.

'This part's residential,' said Thapsis, 'aside from the Rotunda. We came out the back way from the guestrooms. We're now in the northeast quadrant moving east and south.'

There were now stalls, but still few public buildings. Everything appeared handmade, from pots to cleavers – the only singularity was the beautiful and varied wrought iron.

'This is the City of the Smith,' said Thapsis. 'You'll see much beautiful craft work – jewelry, window bars, weapons – look at this inexpensive bridle.'

'Adambara,' I said, trying to finesse Rosanna and the mandala gates, 'is a low-technology society – paleotechnic, I mean?'

Thapsis burst out laughing. 'Excuse me, please,' he said, 'the short answer is yes. But I see I'm going to have trouble explaining. You are referring to what we make, how we carry it and that kind of thing.'

'You evidently know what *we* make and how we carry it.'

'Oh, yes, but most folk here don't. As to your question, give it a little time and you'll understand easily. This lady understands.'

'I think I do,' said Rosanna.

'He is about to ask me how many transistors there are in his ring that it transdicts languages,' said Thapsis. 'A shaman on Your Side would ask how many spirits are in your computer. A Losian would ask neither, but quite another question.'

'Such as?'

'How high is the inner-space technology on Your Side?'

'Actually,' I said, 'in many cultures it's quite high. But in technical cultures, until recently, it's been uniformly scoffed at. But now when it's started to mesh with neurology, quantum logic and computer science, it's begun to get a hearing on a limited scale. Most workers still think of it as fringe science.'

'That's precisely what you'll find on This Side in regard to thinging,' said Thapsis, 'meaning, doing things the hard way with hardware. You find it in semi-backward places like Verula – they think of things as toys, precisely as on Your Side. The joke is,' he added, 'all their major component patterns are made here, by our Smiths – the patterns, mind you – our men are craftsmen pattern makers; everything by hand to better than one part in 10^5. Rather as the yogi's mat is made in your Birmingham nine times out of ten.'

At this point, as was inevitable, since Thapsis was talking rather than attending, we hit a stall of what seemed to be pumpkins. By the time we had picked up the produce, apologized to the owners, discussed the time of day and shaken hands – both hands, in Adambara – all round, the palaver on technology was over.

We emerged from the casbah into wider streets, rather like those of Washington, but trafficless save for walkers and a few choreb carts. There were white stone buildings, distant still, shimmering in parkland. We had seen only one public building in the casbah area – in a small square had stood a stone chapel surmounted by a spire, and that surmounted in turn by a cluster of bronze stars, but Thapsis made no comment on it, and I divined that it wouldn't be our place of worship.

'I thought,' said Thapsis, 'that we would go past the Hall of Council in this sector, and the baths, and the House of Play – which is roughly the Losian cinema or theater, and the College of Physicians and Surgeons: they're all pleasant buildings, which you'll get a chance to enter later, all except the Hall of Council, of course – I should stay out of the House of Play until I've explained how it operates, though as Other-Siders you'll probably love it. This is the Hall of Council coming up.'

It looked uncommonly like any other courthouse, Greco-pompous, steps, columns, two men in high caps on guard.

Its compound was walled and contained a white, apparently ceramic, tower – the building on which the Fires are ignited. The Second Fire was not yet due. I was a little disappointed in Losian architecture, apart from the wrought iron, and puzzled by the one-piece ceramic tower, which looked technically impossible. Before I could inquire of Thapsis, he pulled his choreb and chaise to the curb. There was a loud padding, more vibration than hoofbeat, accompanied by a rattle of claws, and two soldiers rode by. I saw asvaya in the flesh. The statue had indeed been lifesize, for they stood at least twice as high as horses. Their massive legs were feathered, their color pepper-roan, with the roaning in spots. Their long necks were held erect in moving, and they ran at a crouching lope, flat nostrils inside their iron muzzles, mouths closed, large eyes staring forward with a stupefied air, unlike the nervous eloquence of horse eyes. Their passing was in fact almost noiseless, but it shook the ground like the passing of a freight train. The stocky hindquarters and small tails disappeared round the curve of the avenue.

'Now those,' said Thapsis, 'are your asvaya.'

Rosanna, who had been very quiet on the ride, began to giggle hysterically. 'I made my bed and I must lie on it,' she said. 'You made your asva and you must sit on it. Quits?'

'Quits.'

The House of Play was quiet – it was too early for it to be patronized – and it seemed an illogical construction, for it was small, far too small for any sizeable audience: not much larger in fact than the Rotunda housing Thapsis's office. Yet the entrances seemed capable of handling a stadium crowd.

'Big audiences?' I asked.

'A lot of people use it on rest-day,' said Thapsis.

'We have two more days,' I said. 'When are the shows?' A culture's entertainment is an excellent entry to its state of mind.

'All the time,' said Thapsis. 'I misled you by my comparison. This is not mechanical entertainment, it's rather the theater of participation. And if I may suggest, you'll like it rather later on, not now. Now you'd find it confusing. The best way to put it is that the House of Play is what I suspect you were looking for when you opened the door. It involves a mini Time of Choice without permanent effects, and without snags. If you, Edward' – it was Eda in Losian – 'wanted for example to be a hero, you could choose what sort of hero. If you, Rusana, wanted to be a slavegirl, you could dictate the erotic context. And go home to dinner.'

'We used to do that on Saturday nights,' said Rosanna.

'Psychodrama, I believe you call it,' said Thapsis. 'We call it svamaya, do-it-yourself illusion. Only, our feeble technology provides all the props.

'Later,' said Thapsis, as an afterword. 'I strongly recommend not now. One trip at a time is sufficient? Try a bhin recital at the House of Arts. Our Losian music is excellent.'

Again, the palaver was obviously finished. I noted, from the stone benches, that in Adambara both men and women smoke pipes, longer than ours. I asked Thapsis what they smoked.

'Yes,' he said, 'good question. You're sure to be offered it. It's called blach, and there are two kinds, both made from the kalpalata plant. It comes in a box divided into two halves, and it's offered lid to donor. When you – since you are the recipient – face the open edge, the blach on the left is intoxicant blach, the blach on the right is our tobacco. If you're wise you won't get blached at this early stage. I never touch the left-hand stuff; prefer my head straight. Some of them get stoned out of their minds on left-hand blach and then go to the House of Play to enjoy getting the horrors. It's not my notion of civilized entertainment. You can say "Tolk dakshi blach" – only right-hand blach – it's perfectly courteous to do so. And if you must try the other stuff, mix it one in ten with right-hand blach. That's the College of Physicians.'

It was large, and a mosaic in brilliant, almost dazzling, colors, rayed with black, occupied all of the front wall above two small doors. It was a mandala or yantra in a brilliant hollow-cone pattern, so that it gave a trompe l'oeil illusion of a receding pyramid which almost drew one in. I saw it was not attached, but erected on a hoarding.

'What's that?' asked Rosanna.

'A general tonic for the city. We've all been much healthier since it was put up. There was an epidemic of chhota nos, the small disease, due this spring, but the Council ordered general immunization. So the college was refaced with that.'

Patients were coming and going at the right-hand door, and physicians in white tunics at the left. Both the physicians and the emerging patients often carried what appeared to be large canvases wrapped in cloth.

'It looks more like an art sale,' I said.

'No, those are all prescriptions. The patients get them at the dispensary,' said Thapsis. 'You hang them in the living room, or put them on an easel.'

The buildings grew scarcer again and the parkland opened with flowering trees and walking couples. Beyond shone the wall of Bowmen, faced with the same seamless ceramic and glossy. Below it ran the green canal, flanked by a street, with waterbirds and floating lilies. A boatload of produce was poled along. Beside it was another chapellike structure, larger than the last, topped with an iron spear of great size, to the top of which was affixed a blazing golden sun. A couple of nuns disappeared into its porch, followed by another, escorted by a man in conspicuous gold bracelets.

'I think probably, Rusana,' said Thapsis, 'this will be your place of worship.'

'Who goes there?'

'Owners, owned and the Council.' Once again the palaver was obviously finished.

Rosanna looked thoughtful and a little alarmed. 'It's the south point,' she said.

The Baths of Adambara were unremarkable – under a high ceramic roof on wall-less columns, men, women and children splashed about naked in an onyx-lined tank. Coming into the southwest quadrant we were among stodgy municipal buildings, the Halls of Record, Justice and the like – guarded in two cases by asva-mounted ceremonial lancers in vast sentryboxes who were in turn surrounded at a safe distance by sightseers from the outlying country.

'The rustics,' said Thapsis, 'think of asvaya as wild beasts.

On Your Side you really should mount your Guardsmen on lions – they'd look magnificent.'

There was a moon chapel here, standing by itself under a silver crescent. Beyond were the barracks, behind their high mud-brick wall, guarded at a heavy arch by dismounted lancers who, to my alarm, presented lances to me.

'Your future place of work,' said Thapsis to me.

'Where's mine?' said Rosanna.

'It's in the process of negotiation. We're held up for the notary to finish the paperwork,' said Thapsis.

We were reentering narrower streets when we ran into what appeared to be an eviction. Commotion, as opposed to bustle, is so rare in Adambara that we had trouble getting through the crowd. An angry woman, followed by an expos-tulating husband and bawling children, was being dragged out of a house by four of my troops. She was giving a good account of herself, to the point that after taking some casual-ties the corporal in charge handcuffed her; the crowd hissed; the troopers were embarrassed and tried to keep their lances, two-handed, between themselves and the bystanders.

'Dear me,' said Thapsis. 'Unfortunate lady – two children, too.'

'Why is she being arrested?' said Rosanna. 'What did she do?'

'She probably didn't do anything,' said Thapsis. 'I think you are witnessing an election.'

'You mean an eviction?'

'No, an election. One-third of the Council, excluding Adepts, is replaced today. There are more or less heartbreak-ing scenes of this sort all over the city. It's not so bad for the unattached, though the Smiths complain that they lose their skill, but with a family . . .'

'Let me get this right,' said Rosanna. 'Your Council are conscripts, and they don't want to serve.'

'Would you? If you are chosen for the Council of One Hundred, you not only have all the cares of the city on your shoulders, you have also to take power over other people. It's a stigma. You have very little time for ordinary living, you're exposed to a constant display of your defects of character, and you are apt to be ostracized when your term runs out – as if you were an owner, which you are. Fancy being forced to wear the gold!'

'On Our Side,' said Rosanna, 'people spend their entire lives using knees and elbows to get that.'

'I know,' said Thapsis, 'I know. And we have sick people too, I assure you. But if the lot fell on someone who was overpleased at the idea, he'd be sent to the College of Physicians and get a prescription to look at. Besides, you don't have the House of Play – or rather you do, and you conduct all your important business there, which is crazy. Mind you, they aren't all as violent as that lady. She has a lot to lose, having her family life disrupted. How would you like to be hauled out of whatever you were doing and told you'd been elected executioner? or town scavenger? You'd be as mad as she is, poor lady. But she'll make a good member – better than if she were willing.'

'I shall command soldiers,' I said.

'Yes,' said Thapsis, 'but they're all volunteers.'

The narrow street contained one public building, of plain appearance. It might have been a university club. 'The House of Adepts,' said Thapsis. 'There you can enter but not I. Inside you can say what you like, and they'll understand you, but our Adepts only answer questions in the course of grade rituals – I imagine yours are the same. Shall we eat?'

The tavern was comfortable, with oak beams, at the sign of the Iron Choreb. The lunch was copious: for two small iron coins of Adambara, pulse with spices, sour choreb milk, marvelous vegetables and copious herb tea or sherbet, served by friendly bare-breasted daughters of the elderly owner, who stood at the charcoal stove as chef.

'No meat,' I said to Rosanna.

'Unlike asvaya,' said Thapsis, 'in this city we don't feast on corpses. We leave that to the people of Verula who worship the Unnameable like the bloody pagans they are.'

Blach was brought for all three of us, and we took from the right-hand compartment. Thapsis nodded approval. 'In Verula they even eat choreb,' he said, as we remounted. 'And,' he added, 'I believe, people.'

'I thought I saw people fishing,' said Rosanna.

'Adepts, probably. All Adepts fish. Don't ask me why – it's conducive of meditation, I suppose. When they catch one, which isn't often, they measure it and put it back. Pretty damn pointless, I always think. Now Tharmians eat fish – that's largely ritual: anything out of the sea is kosher for Tharmians. And then there's dried fish; that's a natural product – out on the shore of the plains they get millions of alewives washed up every year, and those dry in the sun, and you can pick them up by cartloads. We don't eat them, we feed them to our message-birds. A bit like Bombay Ducks.'

'No further questions,' said Rosanna, catching his eye. I was glad to see Thapsis had a sense of humor too – probably quite a good one, though he had that section pat and gave it with a dead straight face. I didn't ask a supplementary about shellfish.

We passed a stunning little garden with fountains, moss and flowering vines. There were also stone pillars among the flowers. 'That's beautiful,' said Rosanna. 'It's the Losian burial ground.' And, indeed, it was.

There was one more building, the largest we had seen, a windowless Albert Hall of shining white ceramic. 'That,' said Thapsis, 'is our most important religious edifice, and the only place where sacrifice is offered.'

'What gets sacrificed?' said Rosanna. 'Not choreb? Or is it people? I thought this city was too good to be true.'

'Lady,' said Thapsis severely, 'Verulans sacrifice choreb, Verulans occasionally sacrifice people, when they want to intimidate the poor or boost the prestige of their priesthood. All Adambara sacrifices here, some many times in a life, some once.'

'No windows,' I said.

'It's dark inside.'

'You haven't said what gets sacrificed,' said Rosanna.

'Blood is an abomination to our Mother,' said Thapsis, 'except the few drops a virgin sometimes sheds when she becomes a woman. That and the seed of the man are what we offer to Enitharmon.'

'On festivals?'

'Continuously. In the darkness there is continuous sacrifice going on. If you want to sacrifice together you had better do it in the next couple of days – that is perfectly orthodox. At each fire a man and a woman sacrifice on the actual altars with one of the sons or daughters of the House of Enitharmon. I'll come with you if you find it strange. It's an uplifting experience for me, and I think for everyone.'

People were entering singly or in couples, of all ages after puberty, and leaving with the illuminate expression of worshippers. 'Yes,' said Rosanna.

The street ended at the north before a chapel wholly of wrought iron and a great brick wall. This was the industrial heart of Adambara, the Smithies, and behind it could be heard the deep booming of hammers which seemed to be underground. 'We have no time,' said Thapsis, 'to go in. Drop by my office. We're back at the Rotunda.'

We sat in the same room and took the same refreshments. Rosanna was deeply silent. It seemed longer than yesterday. Adambara was already moving into reality and replacing what had preceded it. We seemed in no need of nepenthe.

I told Thapsis that I liked the sound of the Adambaran electoral system.

'Yes,' he said, 'that's why, unlike Verula and the politics on Your Side – I trust I don't give offense – we don't invariably get our affairs run by the scum of the earth. Giving authority to people who want it for its own sake is insane. It absolutely guarantees constant control by psychopaths. Play, yes – in Adambara, you'll find we value and use it. But government is one kind of play therapy no community can tolerate.'

'I'd noticed there didn't seem to be any public sports here,' I said, 'except playing at soldiers.'

'Sports of your kind, no. They remind us too much of the sports of Verula, which are gladiatorial and revolt us. But when you have any time for recreations other than each other there are a couple of games you might as well learn. You'll find them helpful.'

He pointed to a small table which had in it an onyx

chessboard. 'The pieces are in the drawer.' They were Asvin, a Tower of each color, the Sun, the Moon, the Star and the Mountain, and the Four Living Things.

'It is the Game of the Asvin,' said Thapsis, 'inculcating tactics. Get them to teach it to you in the mess – it's not unlike chess on Your Side but easier. Soldiers play it for money – Adepts say it gives you a grounding. I think you'll find it instructive. Now this' (he opened a drawer of his desk) 'is different, and I personally can't play it. I borrowed it to show you. It's the Game of the Adepts.'

Rosanna is bored by chess. She was standing with her back to us, gazing out of the window. Thapsis brought out a wooden base, about a foot long and half as wide. On two pillars was supported a metal band about three inches wide and three feet long. It had been welded end to end, flatwise, and in it was a single twist. Thapsis got out the pieces and put them at random on the surface of the band. They adhered, whether erect or inverted, held by little magnets.

'The game is simple. You make any move you like, and transfer your pieces to the other surface of the board. The winner is the first to move all his pieces to the other surface. It's simple.'

'But that,' I said, 'is a Möbius loop, and it has only one surface.'

'That,' said Thapsis, 'is the point of the game.'

We spent the second day in loitering, and upon the skins, with little conversation, as people aware of time running out. The morning of the third day passed similarly. It was after the midday meal that Rosanna said: 'We haven't made sacrifice.'

'How about last night? And this morning?'

'At the House of Enitharmon.'

'How about the House of Play?' I said. 'Sounds more our mark.'

'Later, Thapsis said. Today I'm not playing.'

We walked uninterrupted through the stalls and the children and approached the eye of the mandala which was Adambara. It was walled and guarded. The wall was low, and in it was an open space of unreclaimed, original desert, perhaps a quarter of an earth mile across.

'Nobody,' said Rosanna, 'would go to the center.'

We could see the Temple, like a great marble breast, and made our way towards it. We climbed the steps between an old bearded Losian and an anxious young girl. The entry was another onyx bath. Girls took our clothes and we were naked among the naked. I saw the clothes folded and placed in the niches of a columbarium. We passed through the bath. 'Pause at the threshold,' said the girl attendant, taking our towels. 'The light is dim and you will stumble.'

The interior of the House of Enitharmon was like the British Museum reading room, with low marble walls for bookcases, dividing its space into concentric circles. The light that entered fell from embrasures, designed so that while the outer circle was dimly lit, the darkness grew deeper centrally and became almost total. Rosanna pulled me after the flow of worshippers, a few of whom turned aside to the outer circle while the rest went on, naked, to openings in the low wall, topped with invisible statues. At each wicket stood two girls of Enitharmon; as each approached, they were binding the wrists of the worshippers behind them tightly with short cords.

Rosanna paused and stopped.

'Don't be afraid,' said the girl of Enitharmon. And then, 'To enter the presence of the Goddess one must be bound. Would you rather stay in the outer circle?'

'Yes,' said Rosanna. 'Today I don't feel like that.'

And she pulled me back into the brighter but still dim circle, and we fell upon skins next to another couple, deeply engaged. We had completed our worship when the Fourth Fire was approaching. A metal tube was struck, a cover removed at the apex of the dome, and we saw extended upon skins, on the raised central altars of Enitharmon, in the light of that Cyclopean eye, the anxious girl and the old Losian man, hands behind them, and eyes closed. Over her stooped a Temple boy, over him a Temple girl, commencing the hierogamy, which they completed as the light of the ignited Fourth Fire was reflected from the cover of the impluvium. The cover closed. There was no chanting or invocation, but the whole temple was full of the small individual cries of generation, like the lights of innumerable matches among a crowd in a winter stadium. We touched hands with the couple next us, silently exchanged partners, and resumed our worship.

'That was good timing by the hierophants,' I said to Rosanna, as we went down the steps.

'Don't,' she said, 'spoil it.' I too was moved.

That night, after supper, she went to the cupboard. 'It's time for the nepenthe,' she said. 'Tomorrow we begin.'

'Tomorrow we begin. You're sure you want nepenthe.'

'Yes – if you do.'

She poured two crystal glasses of the purple stuff. It was anise-flavored, not spirituous, and produced, in the hour that we waited before returning to the asva skins, no evident change.

Next morning it was the First Fire when the hostess opened our door. We were dressed and ready. A boy entered, completely hidden by a bunch of flowers. 'Did you love well?' he said.

'Very well. And you?'

'Very well.' He smiled, and obviously had done so, despite his thirteen or so years. 'Rusana, a Smith of the Smiths awaits you at the office of the notary of persons.'

'This,' said Rusana the slavegirl, 'is it.' She kissed me, looked back, headed for the door.

'Break a leg,' I said, 'and be expensive.'

'I will. I love you, Edward.' She was gone with the flowers and the boy.

Feet tramped up the stairs. Two corporals of my asvin marched in and saluted.

'Colonel Eda, Sir!'

'I am Colonel Eda.'

'Escort to your quarters, Sir. On foot, I'm afraid, but it's not that far.'

'Your names, Corporal.'

'1732 Corporal Eka of Asvin, 1645 Corporal Kar of Asvin. Sir!'

'Carry on,' I said. 'I'm ready.'

4

In Which Contrarieties are Equally True

I was not ill-pleased with the Colonel's quarters – in fact, they were not unlike the guest-room I had shared with Rosanna, save that there were crossed lances over the fire-place, and figurines of asvaya, together with books, ranged in iron tubes like wine-racks, a long pipe and the two-chambered box for blach, its left compartment, I noted, empty, the board with pieces for the playing of the Game of the Asvin, and, in a crystal-fronted press, the metal pathway and magnetic pieces for the Game of Adepts. There was also the same onyx bathtub, a cot, but, not unexpectedly, no love bed. I inspected it, found nothing wanting, and called my batman. What came was another bare-breasted girl, waist-length black hair in a wrought-iron ring, sandals on her feet, and rather fetching trousers in the Sikh manner.

'Sir?'

I had had a bedder, not a scout, at Cambridge, but she was sixty and protective.

'I called the batman,' I said.

She giggled. 'I'm the bat woman, Sir. I am Ayah.'

'You're not military?'

'Beg pardon, Sir, I am military. My whole family is military, Sir, and with this regiment.'

'Your mother's a bat person too?'

'No, Sir, a ferry pilot. She ferries asvaya to outlying garrisons.'

'I wanted my bath.

'Yes, Sir.'

When she had not only drawn it but placed me in it, brought the blach and pipe, dried me on getting out of it and helped me into my boots, all without embarrassment and to

militarily respectful small talk, my pleasure at the standard
of comfort for senior officers in the Losian forces had grown,
but I found it necessary to repeat frequently to myself, 'Cross-
cultural complications' – after all, Rosanna had been missing
for less than a day. Then Ayah withdrew to fetch up my
dinner (evening mess is optional above the rank of major)
while I puffed at the blach, not liking it overmuch, and
examined the books, which were uniformly on tactics, regimental tradition, and the like. In none could I find an account
either of the military position of Adambara or of an actual
military action in which its forces had taken part. This I
found odd, and determined to repair the deficiency as soon
as possible.

General Kari, Master of Asvaya, was as short as his men,
bronzed and composed entirely of whipcord. On his face, a
saber cut had closed one eye. We walked through the
corridors of the barracks towards the riding school in step.

'Sergeant Takis the riding master knows you're a novice,'
said Kari, 'but as I don't like my officers to look like idiots, I
want to tell you a few things myself. First, you can't kill an
asva outright with a sword thrust. So in close action engage
the man – leave the mount to your mount: he's trained to
handle it. Second, we fight asvaya unmuzzled – the muzzle
is simply to stop them chewing on civilians. So stay on your
mount at all costs. In a hot engagement there are riderless
battle-crazy animals rushing around, and if you're dismounted, wounded or not, you're as good as finished. And
in any other emergency, stay in your saddle – you can't bail-
out. If you do you'll break your neck for a start and be
trampled or eaten for finishers. And watch it when you turn
in the saddle – you lose control. Thirdly, good luck. Any
questions?'

'Yes, Sir. I'd like to be briefed on the general military
situation. I don't even know with whom we're at war.'

'We're at war,' said the General, 'with a fiddlestick. What
foolery is this? Haven't been at war in a century. Our
assignment, Colonel, is to maintain a high state of general

military readiness. In the absence of an enemy, armies get soft and grow bellies. Not this regiment.'

'So in fact,' I said, 'none of my men have ever seen action?'

'Correct. And your job is to see that if and when they do, they put up a good show.'

I was about to ask him where he collected the saber cut, but refrained. 'Any other assignments, Sir?'

'Plenty – do you take us for idlers? Ceremonial, guard, individual special missions. Those go to officers, so cultivate individual initiative and tactics, but not at the expense of formation, mind you.'

'The officers ride off on their own on special missions?'

'Correct.'

'Like the knights of old – rescuing maidens and serving as peripatetic goons?'

'Colonel Eda!' said Kari. 'That is the last joke you will make, in or out of my presence, about this regiment. It's now your regiment, and don't you forget it.'

'Beg your pardon, Sir.'

'Granted. Here's the riding school.'

On the tan, muzzled asvaya on lunges were loping in circles. On two leather trestles, side-by-side, and the height of a saddle, men were practicing saber cuts.

Takis was as short and as wiry as my commander. He saluted and reported, and I stood him easy. 'I gather, Sir, you haven't ridden an asva before?'

'Correct, Sergeant.'

'Well, Sir, with permission, I won't give you a lesson.'

'Why not?'

'No time, Sir. You have to post the guard this afternoon. So I've given you Herod. Don't try to ride him, Sir – just leave it to the beast. He knows the drill and can do it in his sleep. With your permission we'll start riding lessons and saber tomorrow.'

'As you say, Sergeant.'

'And, Sir, the cornet of asvaya on your left will stay near enough to grab your bridle if – if Herod were to stumble, so keep up with him. The cornet on your right will have the guidon and can't bear a hand.'

46

Even with the bare-breasted waitresses, I had less appetite than usual for lunch when the mess call blew.

Herod, I think, was old. He was imposing – a black asva is unusual, though some breeders specialize in them and they command high prices. The detachment was already drawn up, so I had to mount in front of them.

'Now, Sir,' said Takis, 'when you mount, settle, fix the saddlebelt – never ride without that – and leave everything to Herod. Hold the reins, but don't guide him. Down!'

He tapped Herod's flank, and the beast knelt with his forelegs. Takis stooped and joined his hands with locked fingers. I stepped in them, taking care not to grab the bridle. I was up. I buckled the saddlebelt. My legs were wide apart. It was like bestriding a skin-covered omnibus. 'Mount!' I said. There was a brief clatter behind me, and the cornets cantered up on each side. On my right was the guidon, red with the black hammer of the Smiths.

'Forward!'

We moved off into the street. Behind me I could hear the rest of the guard, and turning a corner I saw the farrier riding last, his huge ax at the present. Children and Minoan girls stared, men stopped working and turned. Herod moved with a gait like nothing else I have ridden. It was not the gait of a horse, or the tottering lurch of an elephant, or the jolting of a dromedary, but a slow loping undulation which does not change from the trot to the gallop, for the asva changes speed by lengthening his stride. It was my first taste of the gait of a chalicothere.

The saddle was of asva hide, with a back pommel and a wide waiststrap. On the left was my saber, on the right the battle-ax, two-bladed, and the ankus, a hooked goad as for an elephant but lighter. It is used to tap, and its point, as a final resort, to blind the mount if it turns uncontrollably on the rider.

At the Council House Herod stopped, and I held up my hand. The last two men in the squadron detached, cantered up, wheeled, and backed their beasts into the sentry boxes. The guidon cornet rode to face them, read the orders and rode back. 'Forward' I ordered, before Herod could start on his own. At the Hall of Justice and the Hall of Record and before the gates of the Smithy the performance was repeated for small interested crowds. Then with two troopers and the farrier we cantered back through the arch, halted and dismounted as the grooms caught our reins.

'Very good indeed, Sir,' said Takis. It was he who had ridden farrier.

'Thanks to Herod, I think.'

'With respect, Sir, I'm glad you said that. There is more to learn, Sir.'

'I know that, Sergeant. And you're going to teach me, starting tomorrow. Is Herod my regular mount?'

'No, Sir. He's not even a war asva. You'll have a charger, Sir. Every gentleman has one charger from the regiment, and every officer below the rank of major has to buy a second at his own charge. They often buy hunters, Sir, which can't behave on parade, but that of course won't apply to you, Sir.'

'Quite so,' I said.

There was a terrible sound in the manège, a screaming whinny most like that of a horse caught in a burning stable, but louder. On lunge chains held each by ten troopers and affixed to iron rings, two asvaya were snapping and kicking at one another, held watchfully just out of contact. Your mount will take care of his mount, I thought – he's trained to handle it. I had heard the battle cry of the asva and found it chilling.

The extraordinary, loping, stiff-rear-legged gait of the Losian asva, like the beast, is unique. It is not the fossil chalicothere of earth, hyaena-shaped and more, indeed, like a cross between a baboon and a compressed, sloping, longer-necked bear. That species, or one like it but smaller, is the dog-like, domestic, chalicothere of Adambara. The asva is perhaps even of a different genus, as its functional canines suggest. It runs with its hind legs part-extended and its body still sloping, as if on points. Its leap is unique too – unlike any other mammal, it seems to launch itself with its lighter hindquarters and propel itself with its immense forequarters, the reverse of horse procedure, so that to the rider it almost appears to fly, landing on rear claws first. In fighting with conspecifics it rises on its hind legs and thrashes with its forward claws, like a bear, or rises on its forefeet, brings its body level, and kicks backward, like a stallion, but its kick is clawed. The first finders of an earth chalicothere thought that the feet belonged to a pangolin and the skull to an ungulate, so strange is the combination. It is omnivorous, eating leaves which it claws down when it must, but its natural food is the hyasa, and the meat of these in carts came in daily to feed my stables. Asvaya run wild in the Losian plain, or feed in great tended herds around Or-Cu, and the sight of those sloping, giraffelike backs, sailing in groups in the dusty Losian light, is something once seen and not forgotten.

Sergeant Takis started his ministrations on time – to him, I was another raw recruit, and his handling of the colonel-recruit was a masterpiece of military tact. For saber, which is what we began with, Herod was brought out again, and cantered me past the wooden asva-sized frames with dummies mounted on them, while Takis bawled, 'Number one cut, Number four cut, sheathe saber and draw battle-ax, now, about wheel.' (Herod did so with the resignation of an old performer.) 'And let him have it, Sir. Halt. Now that was good, Sir, for a start, but a few points. If you lean out of your saddle and follow the stroke, the next man's mount will get you with his teeth. So you're a dead man, Sir. Repeat exercise.'

After two days of this I was reasonably confident on an asva, and was promoted to a more military model accustomed to recruit training, and for another two days I mounted, dismounted and generally handled the animal, which seemed surprisingly obliging in view of its bulk, and surprisingly agile. Then Takis fired his shot: 'You're making good headway, Sir. That's as well, because we have another deadline. Two weeks, Sir, Third Tasuranga. You command parades, Sir.'

'On Herod?'

'No, Sir, we can't parade a black asva on Third Tasuranga. You'll have something quiet. And in any case you know enough to manage a mount on a straightforward circuit patrol, which is what this is.'

The Tasuranga festivals, or Four Parts, fall at the Losian quarters and represent in three cases the union of the Sons of Los with their śaktis or female emanations – Palambron with Elynittria for spring, Rintrah with Ocalythron for summer, Theotormon with Oothoon, which was coming now, for summer; Bromion, at the winter quarter, has no female emanation. Apart from the riding, which left me stiff and glad of the onyx bath, I was working on Losian, for fear of accidents with the translating ring. It was an odd language, reminiscent of Maltese in being a hybrid – not between Arabic and Italian but between Ionic Greek and Sanskrit. Words are from both sources but the grammar is closer to Greek, and unlike both there is no dual in Losian. Instead, there is a complete paradigm for things in fours, a double dual, not much used in common speech, but wholly in religious matters, rather as we commonly pray in archaic English. Thus the plural of *asva*, steed, is indifferently *asvaya* and *asvai*; the tessaract number *asvat*, however, means not four-in-hand but exclusively four steeds of mythological significance, the team of Fuzon for example. 'Four mounts,' as for *asvin*, hussars, is *asvabhi* (genitive plural) *tasur*: 'of steeds four.' I did not memorize the tessaract – the only part I needed was *Ma tasurat* – 'by the Fourfold' – for purposes of swearing. I longed for the quickest route of all, a sleeping dictionary. Instead I had a saluting and bath-filling dictionary which had to serve instead, and I cultivated the knack of hearing twice – the words said and my inner translation provided by the ring.

By the morning of Third Tasuranga I was in fine form. Asvaya already felt smaller and less difficult to manage – clearly those of the regiment, for all their fighting performance, were skilled circus animals not war chargers. I came on parade jauntily rather than apprehensively.

I was slightly less jaunty when I saw my mount. For a start it took four men to bring him out. He was an enormous brute, pepper-and-salt like the skins on that much lamented love bed, and a swift comparison with horses spelled trouble from the look of eye and nostril. 'Is that my mount?' I asked Takis.

'Yessir. He's big. But he's quiet. Quieter than usual today. You can handle him, Sir.'

I mounted the enormous upholstered back. An engine seemed to be running inside the beast. 'Mount!' I ordered, and put him into first gear.

5

Moving by Compulsion

The Festival proper takes place in the Iron Chapel, and ends
at midnight with a hierogamy in which the Son and Śakti are
impersonated – I meant to be out of riding dress to see this if
possible. The afternoon parades are purely secular and an
excuse for shutting up shop. The whole place was consequently packed, but our circular route was being cleared
ahead by my lancers, dismounted, who were holding their
lances two-handed to push back sightseers and joking with
the crowd.

Takis had obviously been right. My mount was as steady
as old Herod, though his motion was different, which I put
down to his bigger size. With a clear road ahead I changed
up a gear from the asva equivalent of trot to the asva
equivalent of canter, the trumpeter calling the pace without
further orders, then to a hand-gallop: a splash was needed,
and cavalry looks best on the move. We only lacked a
mounted band to play 'Garryowen'. As we got going I looked
momentarily back and caught a frown on the face of the
farrier, or thought I did, but it was lateish to change down,
and I reckoned to do so when we struck the narrower streets.

As we went along, at the loping gait of the asvaya, the
town looked festive enough. All the curved balconies were
packed. I never saw so many Minoan-style girls. Some were
leaning, some jumping up and down and clapping. One
blew me a kiss, and I turned to blow one back, forgetting
Kari's instruction. It would have been safe enough on a
horse, and probably, nine times out of ten on an asva. But as
luck would have it, she leaned too far. An alabaster pot of
trailing lata came off its perch dead in front of my mount and
shattered with a crash. The animal reared, and, unlike a

horse, threw its head forward, not back, after the manner of chalicotheres. The girl screamed, my mount reared again, and instead of reins I was holding a piece of unattached leather. Then we were off like the clappers of hell.

Citizens and troopers scattered, houses flashed past, I beat the runaway over his broad head with the ankus, which was supposed to slow him. It seems I beat the wrong area. I tried pulling on the muzzle straps, but could get no purchase.

We were at the end of the city. The broad canal and the wall of Bowmen were ahead. I recalled Kari's instruction: 'The one thing you can't do with an asva is bail-out – you have to stay with your mount.' For a moment the brute slowed, then, gathering, he took canal and wall in one vast Olympic leap. I saw bowmen ducking, heard a voice shout 'Flaming bloody idiot!' and Adambara was behind us. In two, it was out of sight; in another four, it was dark.

The night was perfectly starlit – other stars, other constellations. I felt like Mazeppa. The beast was going with the smooth motion of a locomotive. I could not control him, but I attempted to calm him. It was then I realized that he had no name, and began to pass the time in naming him, hoping that he would soon tire and return to base. A moon came up. Hermit, Galopin, Hampden – I had a wide knowledge of past Derby winners; they were names borne by the old Great Northern Pacific locomotives of my boyhood: Harvester, St Simon, Minoru, Flying Fox, Woolwinder, Crusader, Galtee More. None fitted this spotty monster.

We came to a ravine, a vast crack in the ground, and he took it in his stride. As he landed, smoothly as an aircraft, I got it – The Tetrarch. I sincerely hoped I was going to need a name for him.

It was now bright moonlight, and I could see the shadows of boulders and dry plants. There was a range of low mesas to which the Tetrarch was headed. The night was full of noises, mostly insect, but suddenly my mount heard something else, and his ears shot up. Almost at once I heard it too, a screaming whinny, and simultaneously I saw them, three bounding shadows on a nearly parallel course – wild chalicotheres. This was a complication I had not expected and did not relish. The Tetrarch at least was muzzled. He wheeled towards them and we were closing fast. I grasped the ankus.

The leading chalicothere was a dun-colored wild-type beast. His head came alongside and above me, and in a leisurely manner he prepared to pick me out of the saddle.

As his mouth opened, The Tetrarch came round in full stride, reared and struck him with both forefeet. There was a squeal of pain, and the chalicothere veered off with wheals on his side that rapidly darkened with blood.

The second beast came up, smaller than the Tetrarch, a female. The Tetrarch struck with his muzzled head, spun suddenly as if on a dime, and kicked with both hind feet. There was a hollow thump, and the second chalicothere went sprawling in a cloud of dust, rose to her feet and bolted. The Tetrarch put down his head and charged screaming at the last and largest enemy. As he did so I sheathed the ankus, drew my saber and cut the muzzle straps. It fell and rolled behind us.

The last chalicothere, nearly as large as mine, waited for the charge, spun and aimed his kick, but the Tetrarch was too quick, and took him in the right side, the collision nearly throwing me. Then the Tetrarch's teeth were in the back of his neck.

For a full minute the screaming tussle continued. I felt my mount stagger and begin to lose his tooth-hold. I thrust my drawn saber into the spotty hide of the enemy. It was like stabbing an upholstered submarine. The Tetrarch reared, pawed, and screamed his victory, whinny after whinny. Then he subsided, I felt the muscles slacken and heard the bellows-like breathing slow, and he turned his unmuzzled head towards me, with the flat nostrils and the unforgiving eyes. I remained perfectly still, not even raising the saber. The Tetrarch snorted gently and contentedly, put out a long tongue and licked at my boot, then my hand. It seemed we were not going to have trouble after all. As the rough tongue touched the Adept ring, he stared at me.

'Home, boy,' I said.

54

The great head was raised. He snorted, wheeled and set off at a full gallop for the City of Los.

'You were damned lucky,' said Kari, 'that none of those wild asvai was killed outright. Yours would have stopped to tear it, and might then have torn you.'

He poured out more sherbet. 'You know,' said the General, 'you're either the bloodiest young fool or the coolest customer in this bloody regiment. By rights you should be lying on a marble slab with a bunch of parsley up your ass. Does nothing scare you, man?'

I meditated coming on with the 'I am a warrior' number, but Kari didn't seem quite the right audience at that moment. Also this had stopped being a costume piece, ever since the nepenthe, and the words didn't fit the new script. Before the nepenthe it was all high camp. Now I was simply an officer on the carpet, and for real.

'I fear a number of things, Sir, but, as it happens, not getting killed,' I said.

'What?'

'I have a firm belief in the afterlife, Sir.'

'Death is not the end, eh?'

'Yes, Sir.'

'In this regiment,' said Kari, 'we now have not only an idiot in command but a religious nut to boot – all I needed. Colonel Eda!'

'Sir!'

'I consider this disgraceful caper a bloody poor show. I had my men scouring the country. I will not have parades disrupted by buffoons. You, Sir, are severely reprimanded. The reprimand will be entered in your record. You may be a religious lunatic if you like, but your fellow officers value their necks.'

'Sir!'

'If you can't control your mount, go and shovel shit with the purple-pissing pioneers!'

'Sir!'

'And, incidentally, where the devil did you learn to ride like that?' General Kari was grinning.

'When I was a student, Sir, I rode to hounds with the Galway Blazers,' I boasted.

'With *what??*'

I suddenly felt a burning sensation in my index finger, where the ring enclosed it.

'I used to ride as a young man, Sir.'

'Chorebs, I suppose,' said Kari. 'Ah well, many a good asvin started on chorebs. Cheers. I'm about to get blached.'

As for myself, I went to find Ayah and the onyx bath.

Next day, she brought in a letter from Thapsis, rolled up in a little iron cylinder with my name in it, requesting me to call on him immediately.

Ayah had been impressed and a bit reproachful. 'You might have been killed, Sir,' she said. I had spent the night thinking what a pity it was that she was under my orders, and about cross-cultural complications, and feeling guilty about Rosanna – albeit she was doing her thing, probably with someone else and quite possibly in general.

Anyhow, in full dress order, I set out through the streets of Adambara, stiff from that infernal ride and wishing that cabs were a Losian institution.

The people were immensely various – men seemed to wear leather, often leather aprons (this was after all the City of the Smith, and it was lunch hour). Among women the bare-breasted fashion was general at all ages, but there were other costumes. There were even a few nuns, in black shoes, long white robes with girdles and yashmaks. They were not numerous, and it took a while for me to realize that nuns in Adambara all had dogs, and longer still, meditating on the oddity and similarity of the dogs they kept, that each nun was in fact followed at a respectful distance by a small hyaena. Furthermore, just about the time this unusual fact sank home, I passed my first hyaenaless nun.

'Psst!' said the nun.

I took no notice. Presently I realized that I was being chased by a nun. It was a nun which rattled if it hurried. It grabbed my belt and hurried me into an alleyway behind a market stall.

'Edward,' said the nun, 'I've got to talk to you.'

I kissed the yashmak. 'Great to see you,' I said, 'but how did you manage to switch choices? I was hoping to see you in Minoan topless. I suppose they made you a chaste Adept.'

'I'm a slavegirl,' said Rosanna. 'This is the uniform. Only free women dress Minoan.'

'Why no hyaena, and what are the hyaenas for anyway?'

'To watch us. If we talk to men or smile at them. If I talk to you I'll be punished. I left my hyaena outside a jeweler's and left by the back door.'

At that moment, her hyaena arrived, like a tawny rocket, with a growl which was also a whinny. I realized it was a small species of chalicothere.

'Steady,' I said. 'If he tries anything there'll be a small chalicothere on earth. I've got a sword and shield.'

'Don't kill it!' yelled Rosanna. 'There'll be endless trouble. It'll obey an Adept.'

'Kathiso!' I bawled, parade style. The chalicodog sat, then lay. I was showing it the ring, but it didn't seem to need credentials and took no further interest in the proceedings.

'You have your ring?'

'Yes. But gold is sacred to Urizen – I told my master it was part of my religion, but as electrum has some gold in it, it had to be covered with iron and I don't think it works as well.'

'But it sounds as if you got what you wanted. Is he nice?'

'Very,' said Rosanna. 'His name's Faesto, he's in the Guild of Smiths – we don't use his name, it's unlucky, and he must be addressed as Smith by everyone except slaves.'

'Did he like the ankle-chain touch?'

'We don't wear them. We wear these. And that dog-oid thing follows us around.'

'I'm glad,' I said, 'that you got a nice master – quite apart from the fact that Smiths are traditional cuckolds. No doubt that's why he wants slaves.'

'Yes, it is, precisely,' she said.

'How did you fix it? I thought you'd enjoy being tied naked to a pillar and looked over by handsome financiers.'

'I wasn't – it wasn't erotic at all, not ever – it was all done in a notary's office.'

'Duties?' I asked. 'You dance for him?' She nodded. 'And get laid?'

'A lot – he's strong and gentle but terribly short on confidence. I feel more like a surrogate therapist.'

'And chores?'

'Not a lot – he's rich: I was expensive. We hire free help. I'm a pleasure slave – it's called kamini in Losian.'

'What you are,' I said, 'is called in English, wife.'

'Ouch,' said Rosanna, 'but I take your point.'

'And if you talk to men and the chalicodog reports you, you get chained up and flogged?'

'No, boycotted – I keep telling you it never gets kinky or erotic or anything, except when it gets to literal sex. All that stuff belongs in the House of Play.'

'No other men?'

'My master has the right to give me to guests. But then I have to be blindfolded so that there's no follow up.'

'You said it never gets erotic.'

'It's not. Not even that. It's called parakiyamarga – the custom.'

'In English it's called blind swinging,' I said.

'In English it's called artificial insemination, donor,' said Rosanna, 'except here it isn't artificial.'

'Would Faesto invite me to one of his parties?'

'You stay away. He doesn't give parties – he's insanely jealous, and if you fool about he'll either strangle me or become totally impotent or both. Please, Edward, no fooling about – I want to make it work.'

'I believe you do,' I said.

'And the Colonel?' said Rosanna.

'Doing fine. My only desperate deed so far was getting on a steed which bolted. I nearly got repatriated. There's no war and never will be – we're all very, very good at playing soldiers.'

'You know,' said Rosanna, 'I think everyone here is playing at something.'

The dog-oid looked up knowing and whinnied. 'He's

right,' said Rosanna. 'I'll be missed and we shall have questions. Faesto's crazy about me and I won't have him upset.'

And she was gone, followed, after a knowing look and a tailwag at me, by the chalicothere. 'Be careful,' Rosanna said, as she departed, 'I don't want to be left here.'

6

The Idiot Questioner

The two foot guards at the Rotunda stood to attention while I straightened their equipment – harder on a dwarf than on a guardsman – and I went in.

Thapsis was waiting for me.

'You did well, very well,' said Thapsis, in English.

'If you mean the caper with the runaway asva,' I said, 'General Kari thinks differently. I had the reprimand of a lifetime.'

'General Kari himself informed me how well you carried yourself,' said Thapsis, 'but it was in any case unnecessary. You've become something of a city hero – all the markets are talking: it happened at a festival and in full view of the city.'

'You're very kind, but all that happened was that I was run away with, on parade. I'm not the first commander to whom that happened, but I never heard that any of them were decorated for it,' I said.

'You rode a very nearly unbroken asva on parade, you tamed it and you brought it back without a bridle. That's about enough for the city – I know now you are an Adept, but they don't. And from what I know of asvaya it would have been sufficient for an Adept simply to stop the beast devouring him.'

'A very nearly unbroken asva, you said?'

'That animal,' said Thapsis, 'had been saddled twice previously.'

'When I find out who did that,' I said, 'I'll have his testicles for doorknockers. What a filthy trick! Who was it?'

'I'm afraid,' said Thapsis, 'I did it. Before you become angry, consider this: I had to be sure, and there could be no harm. If you had failed in this test, you would only have been returned to earth from which you came, after a dream about wild asvaya which you would have attributed to overeating. Had I known you were an Adept I would never have proposed this kind of test; as it was, the Council had adopted it and decided to let it go ahead, on the grounds stated. But then if I'd known you were an Adept I would never have unlocked the door. And you wouldn't have needed it. Many Adepts cross practically at will.'

'You unlocked the door?'

'Yes. It didn't appear that you knew precisely how to do it for yourself. Not all Adepts can – and that's probably why we never realized your status.'

'You have it wrong,' I said. 'The woman is the Adept – not I.'

Thapsis looked puzzled. 'But you lay with her, didn't you, on the love bed?'

'Certainly I did – several times.'

'And before that?'

'Often.'

'And sacrificed?'

'Yes – in the outer circle.'

'Then you are an Adept. You know that as well as I do.'

'You mean that it's catching?'

'I'm not deceived by jesting, my Adept,' said Thapsis. 'How could she not initiate you? That is how it is done.'

'With what object, if you had an object, did you unlock that door to us, Thapsis?' I said. 'Was it simply because we got possession of it?'

'No, you got possession of it because we would open it to you.'

He rubbed his chin, wondering how much to say. 'Yet again, you actually defeated us – an Adept would have found it in any case, at least if he knew how to look for it. There are many such doors.'

'All of that kind?'

'Identical – but of course their physical form isn't fixed – it depends on who looks at them. You saw woodwork – a shaman would probably have seen the same door as the smokehole of his hut, or even felt it as the Door in the Top of the Head.'

'Let us now,' I said, 'get to the object of the exercise. We were brought here?'

'Encouraged to come here. You knew perfectly well, as Adepts or not as Adepts, that it wasn't a common door.'

'By whom?'

'Unanimous vote of the Council,' said Thapsis. 'And my personal decision.'

'How the hell did I get on that brute, and why did it bolt?' I said, harking back – partly because of saddlesoreness on Thapsis's chair – 'It was quite quiet for over an hour.'

'It had had,' said Thapsis, 'nepenthe in its feed – we had to get you in the saddle, after all. But in asvaya it wears off rapidly.'

'That flowerpot could have hit my skull.'

'That was a genuine accident. The asva would have bolted anyhow sooner or later. And you had an excellent helmet on.'

'So now?'

'I think I owe it to you to drop pretenses. I am an undersecretary to the Council, as I told you. But I'm also chief of secret operations.'

'Since this seems to be revelation time,' I said, 'you've been on Our Side – Our Side of earth, I mean. You must have been.'

'Three times,' said Thapsis, 'briefly. But enough.'

'Did you use the door, or get clobbered here?'

'Well, naturally, the door. The route by death is irreversible.'

'They never come back?'

'They can, but it complicates things. If they go that way, in that direction, the only return has to be by way of birth. Death is destructive to the body, after all.'

'In that case,' I said, 'what crosses over? A program?'

'I think,' said Thapsis, 'that really you should present your ring at the College of Adepts. I'm not a psychobiologist. But there's really nothing occult about it. We are after all in both places already.'

Listening to Thapsis, and wishing Rosanna had heard this useful intelligence, I formed two impressions – one, that he was disguising his voice; and two, that some of his vowels I had heard before – for example, he said 'irrevairsible.' I filed that.

'Of course you're curious,' said Thapsis, 'and I'm sure the college will satisfy you if you're of high enough *dan*, or whatever you Adepts call it. But I didn't get you here to talk transpersonal psychology.' Not having heard another English-speaking native, I did not know what a Losian accent would sound like, but I did not think this was one, and wondered where exactly Thapsis had learned our language.

'So?'

'I want to know if you accept the mission. I promise there will be no more practical jokes – you're an Adept, and a practically efficient Adept, which is a huge and quite uncovenanted bonus for us, and I'm fully satisfied.'

'What mission?' I said.

'Well, that will unfold.'

'I do not,' I said, 'steal uranium spheres, kill the head of the Mafia, dress as a girl and screw foreign agents, or any other clown stuff. And on principle I never do anything for anybody which involves secrecy – it's invariably discreditable.'

'Neither,' said Thapsis, 'do we. I have the impression that you confuse me with characters from your own political behavior and your imaginative literature: which, incidentally, always amazes me – I think at first I am reading the work of Adepts, and it suddenly evaporates in sexual play. Acting out, like hardware technology, belongs to your world.'

I thought about the army that had no enemies, but held my peace.

'On the other hand, although most people here, particularly the Adepts, think of scientism and acting-out as crass superstitions and a lot of nonsense, it happens I don't entirely. I think all worlds contain insights, and I wouldn't entirely dismiss several thousand years of your experience. Let me put it around in outer-earth terms. Imagine you are a doctor – you have an educated African patient who believes he is bewitched. You can't cure him. Perhaps, however, a shaman could. You think shamanism is superstitious nonsense, taken as real-time fact: but you suspect that three thousand years of human imaginative experience may not be quite void of medical uses. So you send him to a shaman. And the shaman cures him in one. At that point you realize, if you're an Adept, that the shaman's technology belongs to This Side: if you're not an Adept you call it suggestion, and probably demean the African for getting bewitched in the first place, instead of collecting a gunshot wound from a technology you do understand. I once said to you, you would probably ask how many transistors are in your ring, that it translates all tongues; a shaman would ask how many spirits are in your computer. Now do you understand? Now, at the moment I think we need a consultant shaman. But we need one who embodies the superstitions, or the wisdom, whichever you like, of Your Side.'

Thapsis sat back and rang for the herb tea. When it arrived he continued: 'My one worry, and I'll be frank with you, is the Buck Rogers tendency of Your Side. We put you in the Time of Choice and you emerged as a thick-ear military hero – Your Side's version of maleness – and an erotic slavegirl, which is apparently part of Your Side's version of femaleness, though I must say that that is becoming complicated. Doesn't she realize she is an initiatrix? Even Adepts – I was amazed.'

'Losians don't have fantasies?'

'We live for fantasy, except that we call it Vision, and divide it from play. Is not Los the Ancient Prophet?' said Thapsis. 'But we know we're doing it. Of course, I don't mean to be hard on you. You opened the door half-planning a sexual kick, and you entered the Time of Choice in that state of mind – she was going to be ravished by a warrior, and so on. It was unfortunate, I think – if you'd been better prepared you'd have come frankly as Adepts, graduates of both worlds. The sexual playfulness we fully understand – you and the lady should both visit the House of Play – but acting-out gets into everything on Your Side: the last earth woman who came here wanted to be an Amazon and kill men – your government is play-therapy, you spend billions on going to the moon by hardware methods and you find a lump of rock. A shaman would have gone there for a present of two skins and brought back healing. Nothing you do is practical – in fact, you two with your play-cupboard make better Losians than most, but why can't all of you call play, play?'

'This cast of mind,' I said, 'is one thing you're buying in importing a shaman from Our Side. I offer no guarantees. Taming wild asvaya is about as psychosymbolic as it gets.'

'I know,' said Thapsis. 'So you will remain a colonel of asvin. I won't say too much and upset things, but we realized you have to combine play-therapy with purpose, being of Your Side, so we'll arrange it that way. All I ask you to understand is that just as all the serious projects on Your Side tend to be at root Buck Rogers fantasies made to look serious, any Buck Rogers project we ask you to undertake will be purposive. It will simply take that form to motivate you at our level.'

'Any instructions or details?' I asked.

'Details later – instructions, simply continue to play. We will make purposive use of the game.'

'That,' I said, 'takes care of me. Now what about Rosanna – or is this exclusively a macho trip?'

'Certainly not,' said Thapsis. 'She has skills similar to yours, but with the addition of Vision.'

'That's a relief,' I said. 'I was afraid she only got involved in this because for some reason you wanted me.'

'On the contrary,' said Thapsis, 'you only got involved in this because, for a very weighty reason we wanted her. Well,' he added, 'let's say we wanted you both for different reasons. You can each do things the other can't. Incidentally, can you read back crystal geometry from an X-ray scatter diagram?'

'I can compute it if I have the program,' I said.

'Ah, but can you read back a program from a computer output?'

'Not with certainty – it depends on the program, and the machine, and how complicated it is. One could usually guess how a programmer would have thought,' I said.

'She can.'

'Rosanna?'

'She has the gift of thinking in both directions, back and forward.'

'Precognition, do you mean?'

'Well, retrospective precognition. We can all see the flower in the seed. She intuitively sees the seed in the flower. Show her a pattern of light on a wall and she knows immediately the shape of the decanter-stopper which made it. It's a rider, of course, to the Game of the Adepts, but it's still an unusual ability. Many Adepts look straight in front, like an asva. You do.'

'Have you told her she's been coopted?' I asked.

'Not yet. Like you, she needs time to settle. And she has other problems, unlike yours – or not precisely like them; complementary, say.'

'So,' I said, 'I gather.'

'I understand you've talked to her,' said Thapsis.

'That was quick work; I only just did. She was wearing a flour sack and a yashmak and being escorted around by a Baskerville hound. Somehow I don't think that's what she intended. I don't see why she didn't go straight to the House of Play – her slavegirl number is simply for kicks, and she seems to have got marriage for real.'

'You see,' said Thapsis, 'that's exactly what I mean about Your Side. Her mind was, I think, deeply divided – only in her case it was the other way around. She fantasized being possessed, as you put it, for kicks, and actually desired possession for real, and the confusion confused her too. She may not like what she has.'

'She won't be unique there,' I said. 'It happens on Our Side – in fact, it would probably have happened to her anyway if I didn't agree to put a collar on her. And if I had agreed, I should have been on the receiving end when she got the two fantasies straight and realized that people don't own people and shouldn't attempt to do so.'

'And precisely for that reason,' said Thapsis, 'don't try any funny jokes, I do beseech you. Let her play her game in real time. If you don't own her, you don't own her.'

'On the other hand, I both want her and care about her. Furthermore, I want a definite understanding that you won't repatriate us separately, or I return now.'

'That seems perfectly reasonable, on one condition.'

'What condition?'

'That she wants to leave when you do.'

'If I don't own her, I don't own her.'

'I'm glad,' said Thapsis, 'that you see it that way.'

'Meanwhile,' I thought, 'no pussy. Cross-cultural complications.' I would wait until I thoroughly knew the ropes – ritual sex is one thing, but probably the penalty for purely secular fornication or adultery is being fed to an asva as a savory. Thapsis, however, was evidently psychic.

'As for what I believe you call pussy,' he said, 'let me give you a hint. How do you set about dancing with a girl on Your Side, if you lack a partner?'

'You just ask her,' I said.

'Precisely. Here you simply say "May we have the pleasure of sharing a love bed?" She will say "Certainly" or "Thank you, I have a partner," or even simply "No."'

'Any girl?'

'Except, obviously, the minority of slaves. They march to a different drummer, so it isn't fair to embarrass them.'

'Husbands, boyfriends?'

'You're still with Other Side thinking,' said Thapsis. 'No free person here is owned, not of either sex. The minority who are into ownership dress distinctively to show it – the owners wear gold bracelets, the owned wear veils if they're female and collars if they're male.'

'I thought gold was sacred to Urizen,' I said.

'It is,' said Thapsis. 'So are power and humbug. Faesto wouldn't want to see her wear gold – she's owned, not owning.'

'He sounds a louse,' I said.

'He's an extremely nice guy,' said Thapsis, 'and brilliant in his field. You have to remember, this is a society of choices; learn to be non-judgmental. Obviously he's got problems – but equally obviously, Rosanna volunteered.'

'So you don't have marriage at all?'

'Rubbish; of course we have marriage. What we don't have is proprietorship – outside the minority which chooses it.'

'Any penalty for laying slavegirls?' I asked.

'Yes indeed. You become their property, creating a three-tiered structure which makes life a constant ongoing complication and excludes you from most of the good things of life,' said Thapsis. 'I've told you already to abstain from funny jokes. Unless you care to declare yourself an owner and buy Rosanna from Faesto – it's a way of life, but it almost precludes Adepthood, and it's difficult to get public employment. It's only recently that owners were able to come out publicly at all – they used to be punished, they were constantly exposed to blackmail and they still find it hard to get jobs, say, in the police. I think their rights should be respected more, but it takes time to change attitudes.'

'If I were her owner I wouldn't spoil Rosanna by putting her in that Maltese faldetta thing. Faesto's an idiot not to dress her Minoan simply to add to the gaiety of nations.'

'If you were an owner,' said Thapsis, 'you wouldn't want to add to the gaiety of nations.

'Of course,' he added, 'you and she can always manage to be at the House of Play together, though it might be sensible to arrive at different entrances. Each of you is likely still to be a part of the game the other chooses, though of course you can't count on that absolutely. Also I fear a little for the consequences, in her case, of wholly divorcing the erotic from the social fantasy.'

'That's happening already,' I said. 'Rosanna has this shtik about being subdued and ravished – by someone she likes, of course – and here she is acting as a sex therapist to a two-hundred-pound blacksmith with premature ejaculation.'

'Then,' said Thapsis, 'a visit to the House of Play won't alter things much. You may as well enjoy it, and anything that happens there is socially acceptable. But no follow-up, I do implore you, not with Rosanna or anyone else. The House of Play carries the secrecy of your confessional.

'You know,' he added, 'I sometimes think it was an appalling blunder that in order to have babies, or even to have fun, men have to get erections and women have to get penetrated. Pity it wasn't, well, less of a performance.'

'Always struck me as a great idea,' I said. 'What's wrong with it?'

'The immense Freudian fuss you make,' said Thapsis. 'Even Adepts. All your games are about masculinity or violation – castrating mother figures, sensible girls who want to play slaves, sensible men who come on like Nietzsche, the whole kindergarten trip. It would be funny if it wasn't so bloody serious sometimes.'

'I suppose so,' I said, 'but we can't help our turn-ons. I suppose they're functional – at least they're built-in. And I thought you found the hero fantasy useful: how about your asvin?'

'Oh yes, it's useful all right,' said Thapsis, 'as play. And as myth – Perseus and Andromeda are fine. But dammit, on Your Side you live the thing out. Live heroes are mostly thick-skulled goons like Achilles and the Vikings, or cowardly scum like the Nazis. Usually the second. Why do they do it?'

'Attempting to be more than man we become less,' I said.

'Precisely. But I apologize,' said Thapsis. 'Shouldn't have started on the subject. Don't introspect about it now, or you'll overinterpret and spoil the game. Just play it. We have to work with what we've got.'

'For whose good?' I said.

'Everyone's. Yours and ours. You won't turn into a hero – any more than your lady really wants to be a slave. At the moment we want you to play. Agreed?'

'All right,' I said, 'but with reservations: why not just in the House of Play?'

'Because,' said Thapsis, 'this is Los's city. With imagination, even play is holy. So you see, your odd biology has gains as well as dangers. People wouldn't be holy if they weren't driven to be playful.'

'Say again?'

Thapsis shook his head. 'We're going too fast. That comes later.'

'Meaning when?'

'Later comes later. And don't press me for answers because I don't know them. This isn't enlightenment time, it's play-time, right?'

'The Verulans, I take it, aren't playing,' I said.

'No,' said Thapsis, 'they aren't. I doubt if there's a playful child in Verula, let alone a playful adult – they'd crucify him. Only genuine slaves, and genuine scum who think they're heroes; you see what happens when human toys get put in the wrong boxes. Go on back with you. And remember, here you just ask.'

'I will,' I said. 'It's the most useful intelligence I've received since I came here. But I warn you I'm doing nothing blind – I'm going to want the whole story. Including why you wanted someone from Our Side – couldn't you trust your own people?'

'Because,' said Thapsis, 'on Your Side you have the gift of Urizen.'

'I thought he was the archenemy,' I said.

Thapsis looked genuinely shocked. 'For an Adept you have much to learn – never, never take sides among the Archons. It is our task to bring the Four together, not to divide them.'

'Isn't he Nobodaddy? And don't the Verulans worship him?'

'Yes,' said Thapsis, 'but that *is* dividing the Archons. Look, either read your own Great Adept carefully, or ask Rosanna and she'll explain. And Urizen's gift to you is science, objectivity, wanting to know how and why, verification. Don't underrate it. Now get gone, stay out of trouble and I'll send for you. Dismiss!'

When I got back to barracks, I viewed Ayah in quite a different light. She brought my dinner, asked where I had been, and looked impressed when I told her 'To the Rotunda, for a consultation.' When she came back to light the lamps, I took the chalicothere by the forelock.

'Ayah?'

'Yes, Colonel?'

'Call me Eda. May we have the pleasure of sharing the love bed?'

'You don't have to take me because I'm your personal attendant, you know,' said Ayah.

'I'd like to take you because you are Ayah, and very beautiful,' I said.

'Then in that case I'd love it. Let me get the skins,' said Ayah.

My only precaution was to ask her to remove a necklace she wore. It was mostly beautiful Losian wrought iron, but I spotted a tiny gold charm on it.

It was next day before exercise that Ayah came in to announce: 'There is a Smith to see you, Colonel.'

'Show him in.'

He was a big, anxious, kindly man, who sweated excessively, as if still at his forge. He wore the leather apron of his guild. I shook two enormous hands and noted the gold bracelets he wore. I offered him blach, and he took it copiously from the left-hand box, which Ayah had filled but I had left unsampled. He puffed before speaking.

'I can't of course give my name, being a Smith, but I am the master of one Rusana.'

'Indeed?' I said. 'How is it with her? Did you love well?'

'Well, thank you. She was once yours?'

I nodded.

'What would be your attitude to repurchase?'

'Of Rusana?'

'Yes.'

'You are tired of her already?' I said. 'I'm astonished – poor Rusana.'

'Not tired. No man could be – whether at table or on the love bed. But she is a wearer of gold. She tried to conceal it as electrum, but, Sir, I am a metallurgist. I never intended to have a wearer of gold in my house.'

'I see,' I said. 'You don't mind owning women but you don't want to be owned by one?'

He grinned sheepishly. 'You wouldn't want it. I wear no collar. My mates would laugh at it.'

'Don't tell me,' I said. 'Rusana is getting jealous of your other slaves.'

'To the point of insult, not fighting yet,' said Faesto.

'And what do you want me to do about it?' I said.

'As yet nothing. This talk is preliminary. But in the event . . .'

'That you want to get rid of Rusana, will I buy her back?'

'Yes. For two hundred sidri. I paid five,' said Faesto.

I mentally looked up the trade-in price for Rusana's model in the Dealer's Manual.

'No,' I said.

'Why? She was yours and speaks kindly of you – when I ordered her to speak of past men.'

'Would you have the impertinence to make me an owner?' I said.

Faesto winced, and as nearly cringed as so large a man could, on whom a blow with anything lighter than a baseball bat or his own hammer would have made no impression.

'I do not know the customs of strangers,' said Faesto. 'I apologize. I realize that my sexual tastes are unpopular. And I see you too wear hidden gold.'

'Rusana was my companion,' I said, 'of her own choice. If she wants it, and only if she wants it, I will take her back for nothing.' And have her sacking Ayah and raising hell, I thought. 'I will also give you back the five hundred sidri' – I wonder who got them, I didn't; I'll check that with Thapsis. Ah well, gentlemen are born not made. I suppose the balance would rightly belong to Rosanna, who had sold her own property.

'You are generous and an honorable soldier,' said Faesto.

'You are generous and an honorable Smith of the Smiths,' I answered, hoping Ayah hadn't overheard the exchange from the duty room – the door was open.

'It may not be necessary,' said Faesto, rising and putting down the pipe. He looked a little blached. At the door he said, 'Mind she does not collar you. She wears gold.'

Ayah showed him out.

'I will not collar you,' she said. 'What does the Smith mean?'

'He was joking,' I told her.

She tossed her head. 'I do not wear gold – only a charm, for luck.'

'I know, Ayah. You're a sweetie, you're a woman without a possessive thought. Are the skins ready?'

'Yes, Sir.'

'Ah-ah,' I said.

'Yes, Eda.'

But she was quieter on them than usual.

7

'Craving the More, the More Enjoying'

I never in our entire sojourn ascertained the history of Adambara, and certain circumstances lead me to think that it may have had none, 'history' being a misnomer for their mode of existence. Losian has no word for it, the contrast being between *sti enpada*, 'that which is under our feet', and *aenpada*, 'not underfoot' – in other words, not now. Past and future exist as a single tense, and Losians add *aenpada* as a particle – at least in written Losian – to all sentences not in the present. More interesting, *sti aenpada* means also that which is divine, symbolic or abstract – Los and his Children, the Holy Cities of Commerce, Art and Generation, what goes on in the House of Enitharmon and the House of Play and all the elements of the Losian pleroma are *sti aenpada* – of the dream-time. So also is Our Side, the Losian place of Shades. Yet all the complex but invisible Losian technology is also *aenpada* – *aenpada tichan*, standing in opposition to practical skills which manipulate objects or natural forces – *enpada tichan*, lower or underfoot or material technology. Lastly *enpada* carries the implications, in many contexts, of 'lower', 'primitive', 'trivial' or 'superstitious'. Comprehension of what is and is not *enpada* and what is or is not *aenpada* seems to me the key to the comprehension of Losian civilization.

With this type of consideration in mind, and not having Rosanna currently to instruct me, I decided to call on the Adepts. There was no problem with the incognito, for the Adepts' House has a side door leading from the largest of Adambara's covered markets, the Losian equivalent of a department store, which, as I expected from what I was learning of Losian ways, opened spontaneously to the ring.

It was indeed a club and library, where in leather chairs like those of Thapsis, people of the most diverse kind were reading books, both scrolls and bound in the fashion of Our Side. Two Africans, the first black people I had seen in Adambara, were playing the Games of Adepts, but I could not by watching see in what way they overcame the paradox, simply that the pieces became fewer.

A young bare-breasted woman dressed as a Smith greeted me. Instead of 'You loved well?' she said, 'You know well?'

'Well,' I said.

'From what city?'

'From no city. From the Other Side,' I said.

She was totally undisturbed by this intelligence. 'By the door, or by your own powers?' she asked, almost casually.

'By the door. I do not know my powers.'

'Which of us does?' said the woman. 'But you could learn them here. I'm amazed at you Adepts from the Other Side. You overcome great difficulties which we do not face. It must be – without offense – like being an Adept in Verula.'

'More like the House of Play,' I told her, and she chuckled.

'I see you are half a Losian already. All our Adepts patronize the House of Play – your people are usually rather blue-nosed about it. But it is written "the Treasures of Heaven are not the Negation of Passions but the Realities of Intellect."'

'By an Other-Side Adept, of my nation,' I said.

'The asva bit me,' said the Adept. This is the Losian phrase for 'touché'. 'Of course it was. Make yourself comfortable. I see you have a ring and can read the books.'

'Do you have any chronicles of Adambara?' I asked.

'That is a complicated question, and as you know we answer questions only at initiation, when we also ask them. Were you initiated by a woman?'

'I was, it seems.'

'Great, capital – a pareunogenic Adept. Is she here?'

'Yes, but I don't know where – doing her thing as a slavegirl, but unfortunately she was envisaging it as an erotic game.'

'Which in Adambara it isn't. The Time of Choice is incredibly severe, even for Adepts: these fantasies! Virility for men, violation for women – we never outgrow ourselves. I don't imagine you expected promotion.' She was evidently vastly amused, as if the imbroglio was common. 'What a pity you had no House of Play!'

'We had a first-rate one in my apartment – she could have all the erotic slavegirl numbers she wanted, and I could be a male chauvinist – hyasa – without mischief. We simply didn't realize the door was taking notes.'

She hooted with laughter. 'I'm Hydaspa,' she said, shaking both my hands but with hands crossed.

'And I'm now Colonel of Asvin Eda,' I replied. 'Greetings, friend.'

'Did you mean that?' said Hydaspa, startled. 'Only an archimage calls an Adept "friend", but he calls her "fourfold friend", using our tessaract number.'

'No,' I said, 'Adept. I'm unfamiliar still with Losian.'

'Well, ask the lady to visit us, leaving her guard dog outside in the market,' said Hydaspa. 'He won't come in here anyway. And give her our love. Her tribulation won't be long – the Sons of Los are merciful to Adepts of our sex.'

Hydaspa told me much, which I knew, I found, already, but may not reveal. As I was about to go, she said, 'One more thing. Do you want to learn our game? It's siddhi, of course, a mere magic trick, but it's prestigious. Adepts use it as an introduction, and you might as well learn.'

'It's impossible,' I said, 'at a fundamental level.'

'On the contrary,' said Hydaspa, 'it's dead easy. You've learned too much topology and don't use your eyes.'

She showed me there and then the trick of the Game of Adepts, so childishly simple that only a mathematician could miss it. But the trick, being part of a professional communication, I naturally may not reveal either. It may be seen by any child who looks without preconception at a Möbius loop.

General Kari's only game was the Game of the Asvin, which he played well. I knew only the regular warrior's gambit – Asvin takes Asvin, Sun takes Asvin, Asvin to Tower two,

Asvin takes Asvin, Bull takes Suns and so on. I was amazed when after fifteen moves he resigned.

'That was luck, beginner's luck,' he said, 'so don't get above yourself.'

When I queried his resignation he showed me how I would inevitably mate in twelve.

'What do you know of Verula?' I asked, as he filled up with right-hand blach.

'Little as possible,' said Kari. 'Bloody lot of barbarian goons.'

'Have you ever been there?'

'Where in hell do you think I got this saber cut?'

'Potential enemies?'

'Everyone,' said Kari, 'is a potential enemy of the soldier. No, they aren't. They need us, or they couldn't play their silly games. We need them – finally.'

'Different style from ours?'

Kari put down the pipe. 'How would you like to live in a place where the punishment for every other bloody thing is death? Killing people is the local sport. Soldiers don't appreciate that. They know what death is. If I want to kill a man I go to the House of Play, knowing he'll get up and go home. They kill people for real. How would you like to live in a place where they veil women and call the love bed fornication? You can get two hundred lashes in Verula if a girl says yes once, and the chop if she says it a second time, and so can she – that is, if you're poor, and most of them are. The rich ones, who dole out the lashes and pass the sentences, spend their time scooting about in idiotic ironmongery and balling wretched slavegirls in brothels, but may the Four help any of the poor who copy them. How would you like to live in a place where they let people govern who *want* to govern? By the Four, I need some left-hand blach thinking about it.'

'Why did you go there?' I asked.

'Someone has to find out from time to time what the buggers are up to,' said Kari. 'Said I was a spy. Put me in the bloody arena as a show – cut my way out, and my asva brought me home, but collected this in the scrap. Bloody lot of gangsters.'

'Yet they're not potential enemies?'

'Everyone is. No, they're not. We'd blow them apart.'

'It sounds as if they have advanced weapons.'

'Advanced fiddlesticks. All they can do is kill. My asva can do that. How long do you think their society would stand up to a whiff of Adambara? They might rape the first three women they met, and kill some people, but mix the two cities and they'd be finished. Our House of Play would eat them for breakfast.'

'They'd close it on arrival.'

'Those horny bastards? Give me strength!'

I felt that he was by Our Side's experience optimistic, and possibly a little blached, but I did not like what I heard of our neighbors. Their love of bloodshed no doubt explained why so many Verulans had arrived on Our Side.

Not all my men were undersize – quite a few, mostly recruits, were ordinary Losians. The short contingent, however, were the élite – they are in fact plainsmen from Or-Cu, famous on Their Side for its wild herds of asvaya; Or-Cu men are the Losian cowboys, Gurkhas, Amerindians and Hungarians rolled into one, and being readily identifed by their build they get a certain deference as hard men. They traditionally come to Adambara: at the death of a father, when the asva herd is inherited, the younger brothers have a choice between herding for the eldest as subordinates and the Adambara mercenary service, and most choose the latter. It is their mission, I found, to knock practical soldiering into young Losians with military fantasies centering on asvaya, an interesting psychiatric trip.

Sergeant Takis answered my questions resignedly. I asked him how long asvaya live.

'A long time, Sir. A very long time.'

'Well, they presumably get old and die eventually.'

'I suppose so, Sir. Never saw a dead asva – unless it broke its neck or got killed fighting.'

I thought, you never see a dead donkey.

'How about the skins?' I asked.

'Very expensive, Sir. All the result of unfortunate accidents. I reckon they must die in the end, Sir, but they take themselves off and do it on the quiet. Pity, because the skins are the asva-master's perks. I'd be a rich man, Sir.'

'Maybe they know some Adept tricks,' I said.

'Very good, Sir – wouldn't put it past them. Now, tomorrow, Sir . . .'

Two days later we took battle training, and I experienced the confusion of an opposed asva charge for the first time. We fought with muzzled asvaya and wooden swords, but the engagement was hot enough to be realistic. I was covered with bruises, took several quite severe casualties among my squadron, and was clearly killed several times, not least when, in oblivion of Takis's warning, I followed a cut with my body and felt the muzzle of an oncoming asva brush my waist, with the razor teeth of a chalicothere inside it. I had no great relish for the prospect of training with blunted iron sabers and unmuzzled asvaya which I knew would come later.

I staggered back to my quarters to find Ayah and the bath. Instead I found a neat iron tube containing a small parchment which read, in Rosanna's writing, 'House of Play, Fourth Fire. Please. R.' That gave me exactly half an earth hour. I put on mufti and went out, aching and cursing.

Many were now coming and going at the House of Play. At the head of the steps were booths where one made payment of one iron mnu, the smallest coin – entertainment here is cheap. I passed through the foyer, which exactly resembled that of a cinema on Our Side, and where pulse rolled in vine-leaves was being sold from a counter. I surrendered my ticket to the bare-breasted girl at the curtain and stepped into darkness, looking for the seats and screen. Instead I was in a tiny booth, facing an aphrodisiac medium-power picture and an illuminated dial, where a hand tipped with a sun was running. Clearly this was a place of choice. I thought Rosanna-macho with all my aching imagination, and the hand reached its vertex. A curtain opened. There was another of those infernal doors, but plainer than the door which had started all this. I opened it resignedly. There was the familiar mental pause, and I was in another luminous crypt, wearing nothing but a well-padded leather jock-strap, which grossly exaggerated my potential, and holding a whip, which was never part of our scenario (Rosanna likes a peacock feather). Rosanna was fetchingly tied by her wrists and ankles to a pillar, looking alarmed but flushed.

'Oh, it's you,' she said.

'Do you want to play, or do you want to talk? I'd have thought you'd have had enough of this number,' I whispered. 'You could have done this at home.'

'Talk – both – anyhow I thought it would be you. Though it would have been fun if it hadn't been,' said Rosanna incorrigibly. 'Put that thing down and take me like this – so that we don't attract attention. They may be listening.'

'Silence, slave,' I said severely. 'None listens in the House of Play. You are at my mercy.'

'Pack it in, Edward,' said Rosanna. 'I came here to meet you: we don't have much time.'

'House of Play,' I said. 'Pleasure first, business afterwards.'

'You heard me,' said Rosanna: 'pack it in. I'm not in the mood. But take me too – without the charade.'

'You know you have to be stood on something,' I told her, 'and I hate uprights. Especially now. I'm aching all over. We rode in a mock battle.'

I got rid of the jock-strap and reduced the exaggeration – though not by much, because I had had Rosanna this way before. We closed, rather uncomfortably for me, but Rosanna closed her eyes and leaned hard on the cords which held her.

'How's it with Faesto?'

Gasps and a scream.

'How's it with Faesto?'

'I can't talk through an orgasm, you dolt. Fine. He's nice.'

'I know,' I said. 'He's been to see me.'

The slavegirl number evaporated instantly.

'He what?'

'He opened negotiations to sell you back. Says you wear gold.'

'Oh!' said Rosanna.

80

'You want that?'

'The beast!' said Rosanna. 'Mara's been at him. I'll kill her one of these days. What do they do to killers here? Impale them?'

'You never learn,' I said. 'No kicks, no masochism, just restitution and demotion to the caste of owners.'

'That,' said Rosanna, 'might not be so bad.'

A small silvery bell began to ring first very softly, then louder and louder until it was painful to listen.

'Time's up,' I told her. 'See you later. I haven't any small change in this costume.'

'Untie me,' said Rosanna, 'I'm going home. I'll come back here when I'm more together.'

I kissed her and went out by the way I had come, leaving Andromeda where she was. She had after all paid admission.

I was also pretty surprised at the Losians. Thapsis had built up his 'House of Play', but this whole thing had been porno, trivial and a bit embarrassing – not up to the worst kinky entertainment on earth. I made up my mind to tell Thapsis that we had better at home, that they had more Divine Imagination in a good Edwardian brothel, and that the Temple of Enitharmon was more like Rosanna's and my idea of what play was about. I reckoned the comeback would be that of course one found in the House of Play what one brought there, and so on, but knowing our usual form I didn't think we had brought this lot there. More likely Thapsis had been reading Our Side pornography and playing down to his visitors. Besides, although there had been reasons why it never took off – Rosanna had other things on her mind – we were finding some imaginative play of another kind going on in the general Losian world. Where this had fitted in, if it did, wasn't clear.

8

I Encounter Forms of War

'Did you love well?' said Thapsis.

'Very well. Ayah's a sweet girl, just as playful as Rosanna, and it's nice to play a different lot of games. Thanks for the tip. What this time?'

'Weapon training,' said Thapsis. 'But first, any questions?'

'A great many.'

'Good. I have one for you. You've been a colonel in our forces now for three quarters of a moon. What is your assessment of the military position of Adambara?'

'I'm not in a position,' I said. 'It clearly depends on the diplomatic situation. Everyone talks about Verula. Are the Verulans a danger?'

'The Verulans,' said Thapsis, 'are a danger to everyone including themselves.'

'How far away is Verula?'

'Seven hundred chalaya, give or take a chala or two. Which, on an asva, is under two days.'

'From Kari's account, and he's been there, they sound like a Fascist plutocracy with modern weapons, unless that's simply bluster.'

'I know,' said Thapsis, 'what you mean by modern weapons – Your Side modern. But Kari's quite right. He went on a mission there. He was doing fine too. But the trouble with him is he's as brave as an asva and as uncomplicated.'

'What happened?'

'He went disguised as an outlaw from Adambara. He sent two excellent reports. Then he saw a Verulan beating a woman, so he knocked him down with the flat of his saber. Even that would have passed in Verula, but instead of dragging her off by the hair, he stood there and said, "Can't have that sort of thing." And asked her if she was hurt. Of course, all hell broke loose, and finally he made a fighting retreat. Luckily his asva rendezvoused properly.'

'So he blew it by being a perfect gentleman?'

'A perfect idiot,' said Thapsis.

'But they have got technological weapons?'

'Oh yes, of a sort.'

'Firearms?'

'Naturally, but they're not regular armament.'

'Lasers, missiles, nukes?'

'Oh, yes.'

'I think,' said I, 'that you are being a little complacent. You told me they depend on you for components, but in my judgment that isn't enough. By now they must have stockpiles.'

'Let me ask you this,' said Thapsis. 'Are you alarmed that Norwegian Vikings with battle-axes might take over London?'

'Not particularly, except in Rag Week.'

'Or that Sioux with bows will occupy Kansas City?'

'That I'd like to see; but at least they'd need rifles.'

'The Verulans, unlike the Sioux, are barbarians, but like the old-time Sioux they have the technology of five hundred Four-Seasons ago.'

'Adambara has a very fine Iron Age army,' I said.

'Thanks to the work of our officers,' said Thapsis, 'but the defense of Adambara isn't, of course, entrusted to the army.'

'I'm glad to hear it.'

'In the event of trouble with Verula, the first step I would take would be to confine the asvin to barracks. I don't want anyone killed.'

'Thapsis,' I said, 'I am covered with bruises and saddlesore from soldiering. Three of my men had fractures in the last exercise and one is still in hospital. What in hell are we actually doing?'

'You,' said Thapsis, 'meaning our asvin, are defending Adambara against its most dangerous enemy. The most dangerous enemy of every civilization – the confusion between activity and aggression. Plus, of course, the wish to own and be owned.'

'In other words we're the location unit of the House of Play.'

'In a sense, yes. On Your Side you mix this into society. Here we siphon it off. And use it practically, of course. Police actions, hunting down dangerous beasts, providing men of self-reliance and sufficient violence to deal with Verulans without being killed. All useful missions. The House of Play copes mostly with the sexual side of the confusion, the virility-violation business. You cope with the hostility element. Which is why we don't issue real weapons to asvin.'

'Asvin get killed in our exercises,' I said.

'People on Your Side get killed in millions by play-therapy and in thousands by criminals,' said Thapsis. 'There were eight asvin killed in the last Four-Season.' (He used the tessaract, since seasons, though secular, are holy.) 'They were brave men.'

'Real weapons,' I said.

The word for 'real' was 'aenpada'.

'Aenpada,' said Thapsis. 'The range is outside.'

It was between high walls, and guarded by men of another force from my own, who nevertheless saluted me. Inside was a firing pit, and at various distances, covered targets.

'Number Three target and the fire-piece,' said Thapsis. The sergeant on duty brought the weapon. It was a Losian rifle, semi-automatic, a little short in the barrel for my taste.

'Careful with it,' said Thapsis.

'I'm used to firearms,' I told him.

'No, be careful of the weapon – it came from the Hall of Record; it's hundreds of years old,' said Thapsis severely. 'Number Three target.'

The sergeant pulled a cord and the cover fell from the target. It stood at easy range, a square composed of the same bright mosaic as the giant prescription outside the College of Physicians.

'Aim,' said Thapsis.

It was impossible to aim. By some neuro-optical effect, the target pushed the weapon away.

'Don't shut your eyes and blaze away!' said Thapsis, sensing my intention. 'We'll both be killed by the ricochets.'

'That,' I said, 'is a great magic trick. But it wouldn't work with a computer-aimed weapon.'

Thapsis smiled gravely. 'It would be unwise to fire a live computer-aimed weapon at Number Three target,' he said. 'Try this. It fires a wooden rocket.'

The sergeant pushed out a small cart, on which stood scanner, projector and controls. 'This will lock on a moving target, Sir,' he said. The target ran rapidly on its wire and hid behind a screen.

'Target,' said Thapsis.

It reappeared, scooting along.

'Fire!' said Thapsis.

I pressed the launch button. The wooden rocket, propelled by a spring, wobbled towards its target, trailing a guidance wire. After about twenty yards it circled smartly through 180 degrees, came straight back at us and scored a bulls-eye on the equipment.

'You could circuit that out,' I said.

'Oh yes,' said Thapsis, 'you could. They might even try. But we keep abreast, I hope.'

'Defense,' said Thapsis. 'That doesn't of course exhaust the subject.'

'No, you could write the enemy infantry a prescription too,' I said, thoughtfully.

'Precisely. Now as to offense.'

The sergeant passed me a perfectly ordinary bow and arrows.

'If you ever ride missions,' said Thapsis, 'you'll probably need one. All outlaws tend to carry bows.'

'I'd sooner have the rifle,' I said. 'I could be a wandering musician and carry a bhin-case.'

'Try a few rounds on Number One target,' said Thapsis.

Number One target was a conventional card. The bow was light and powerful but easy to draw. It was made apparently of Losian wrought iron, but springy, and it had a bright design just above the arrow-neck. I fired three arrows and missed each time.

'The technique,' said Thapsis, 'is this. You see the colored pattern? Right. At the top is a bead. Put the bead on the bulls-eye, then stop looking at the target and concentrate with all your mind on the center of the pattern. Fire! Nock, draw, fire! Nock, draw, fire!'

I had three golds.

'And Number Three target?' I said.

'Please yourself, but I'm going to take cover. You're an Adept already. If you meditate properly, you'll hit it. If you let your mind wander an instant one of us may get an arrow up his ear.'

'What does Verulan intelligence think about all this?' I asked.

'That it's a load of superstitious nonsense,' said Thapsis. 'They don't believe it, so they don't develop it.'

'But they must know about it.'

'On Your Side, do the R and D people know about – say – yoga?'

'I imagine they've heard of it. Some of them practice it – the Californian version.'

'So they consider constantly aenpada tichan?'

'The nearest they have got is photic drive with a strobe light to disperse crowds,' I said. 'But I don't put it past educated Fascists like the Verulan boss class.'

'How can aenpada tichan spring from enpada people?' said Thapsis. (The sense is, how can esoteric skills come from garbage people?)

'They could climb on your shoulders – these things are open to gross abuse. We call that sorcery,' I said.

'To develop aenpada astrat (transcendental weaponry) they would in the process of investigation have to become aenpada pursat' (literally: transcendental people in fours, a wholly Losian way of putting it).

'They can't get it by straight neurology plus human vivisection?'

'However they got it, they would by virtue of the style it implies have to alter their style, and in so doing they would lose interest in greed, murder and rape, which are the chief marks of the Verulan boss class individual. He is sick – an owner. He is of enpada pursai the most enpada.'

'They could pinch the things, I suppose,' I said.

'How often recently has the CIA stolen a Tibetan thangka?' said Thapsis. 'You don't steal things you regard as superstitious horse-shit.'

'They must have spies. All Fascist-type governments go in for spies.'

'They have spies. And the spies disappear regularly into the House of Play and the arms of our very pretty maidens and come out wiser men. So they stay here. One of them will teach you Verulan.' (This was unwelcome intelligence.) 'Once he's defected, a couple of good stiff tonics from our physicians do the rest.'

'I'd like to take some of those medical pictures home with me,' I said. 'On Our Side, as in Verula, we'd have use for them.'

'There are of course,' said Thapsis absent-mindedly, 'also pure radio frequency "targets" which can blind radar-linked computers. They'd interest you – but I'm afraid they're highly classified. This whole city, incidentally, is one. That explains some of our rather fussy public buildings, and our taste for reflecting surfaces.'

'Incidentally,' said Thapsis, 'the House of Play . . .?'

'Yes,' I said, 'we went there.'

'And?'

'Do you really want to know?' I said.

'I'd be interested. You remember, I didn't recommend it very strongly. Not for you.'

'Well, it was damn silly,' I said, 'utterly cheap and trivial. Kind of porno version. We have far better sex games at home. I thought Los stood for imagination. Even our movies are better than that.'

'Ahweel,' said Thapsis, 'I'm not all that surprised.'

'So why did you ask?'

'Well, it's important in a way. And I wondered how play within play would turn out.'

'Say again?'

'No matter. What did you expect, incidentally?'

'Something transcendental at least. It could be fantasy, but not like . . .'

'You went into the House of Play . . .' said Thapsis, interrupting.

'Yes, I told you once.'

'But are you sure,' said Thapsis, 'that you came out again?'

'Well, I'm here, aren't I?' I said.

'Because it can be difficult to tell. For Your Siders, I mean. I don't think that caper with Rosanna had anything to do with the House of Play. Except – well, like eating a sandwich in a dream. No taste. D'you follow?'

'No,' I said.

'Never mind, then,' said Thapsis. 'Let's get back to weaponry. Weapons as play.'

And he gave his psychiatric chuckle. There was no point in pushing play any further on this occasion. I settled down to learn.

The 'power pictures' of Adambara (*shaktu-citr'*: literally, 'spear-pictures'; *intru* = Yantra, 'tool, implement') are of course no more 'magical' or 'occult' than a clock. Similar artifacts exist in large numbers on Our Side – these, however, are almost entirely low-power, long time-constant alpha inducers; in other words, if one stares at them for minutes or hours in a state of undivided attention they facilitate cerebral alpha rhythms. Adambaran prescriptions are usually of this kind. The portable variety have to be stared at for prescribed periods each day; in the cancer ward at the infirmary, the prescription occupies an entire wall and all the patients face it, but even so the drive takes a couple of Losian weeks to reset the hypothalamus – power pictures, of course, are chiefly cortical in action, since the input is visual. People who use the Ageless Diagram (*agurh-intru*) cover all their walls and furniture with it. The small prescriptions given out to patients usually run at about the level of our own yogic productions, not more than 2 m/steiners m². (1 steiner = 1mV RMS at 9 hertz induced at 1 sec exposure and at 1m distance.) Others are used in pest control.

The more spectacular *intrut* are another matter – military, psychiatric, medical, they all depend basically on trapping and guiding the eye with an optical illusion and subjecting it to a complex photic drive, aimed at heterodyning control potentials in the nanovolt range, not hitting the gross electro-encephalogram. Power pictures can attack almost any cere-brally controlled process – they can induce aphasia, apraxia, acute confusion, schizophrenic thought disorder, mania or depression (and generally also control these when they occur as functional illnesses). They can trigger all manner of mental and physical states from sexual excitement to general anes-thesia. (The anesthetic picture is interesting – it is medium speed and has a segment missing, so that consciousness 'trips' as the eye scans it.) There is said to be a 'death picture', which causes heart arrest by vagal inhibition, but this is highly classified. The makers of these powerful objects safe-guard themselves with polarized or tinted goggles – in the case of high-energy objects, over 5 steiners/m^2, which are hazardous on long exposure even when unpowered, by working on separate transparencies which are assembled in a darkroom and covered immediately. Copying or exhibiting a dangerous or self-serving power picture is of course a serious offense in Adambara.

Background, character-forming, and learning-facilitating power pictures and low-power versions of the Ageless Dia-gram are features of all Adambaran decoration, from plates to wallpaper, and hang in every schoolroom. The cancer-therapy picture, which I have seen, contained two juxtaposed mandalas like the halves of an impaled coat of arms, one acting on cellular immunity control and the other on the sense of self-worth – this psychophysical two-pronged attack is typical of Adambaran therapeutics. Pest-control *intrut* hang in every garden or vegetable patch – they resemble colored decanter-stoppers, and are geared to the compound eyes of insects.

The small medical, educative or generally low-power dis-plays (*chhot' intrut*: all these objects take the tessaract – 'four-way pictures' – which reflects both their symmetry and Losian philosophy) are simply static arrays. The higher intensity, short time-constant objects of all applications are powered. A few are physically rotated behind grids to produce crawling moiré effects which draw in or eject the eye; these are nearly obsolete. Most modern high-powered objects, including all military applications, are made up either of glass fibers or of ceramic scales, some of which are solid-state photogenerators and can be strobed. The luminous flux is surprisingly low compared to a conventional strobe light, and the drive energy trifling. In objects such as the practice Number Three target, the flicker is subliminal: the neuro-output of a display in steiners bears, of course, no relation to drive energy. There are, in fact, unpowered static displays of alarming efficacy. The Bronze Age Greeks and Minoans appear to have discovered a static, cataleptic 'spear picture' of this kind. They called it the Gorgon's head.

9

Tyrant Men in Union Blasphemous

Soon after, as I sat in my quarters, a bird arrived through the open window and landed on my desk. It held out a taloned leg to me. This was a simurgh. It resembles a small greenish eagle, and it is the normal means of Adambaran official communication: in the anteroom of every important office is a perch with three or four hooded simurgh awaiting duty. When required, the bird is brought in, a message foil attached to its leg, the hood is removed, and it is set before a power picture consisting of a marked map of Adambara. Its reliability is high. Simurgh are fast and fierce enough to fly reconnaissance over Verulan cities and positions, carrying small cameralike devices; they are seldom detected, since flocks of wild simurgh frequent these cities to feed on trash, on the residues of Verula's carnivorous habits, and on the bodies of the executed – much like crows or kites in India.

The foil was written in code, transcribable however by my ring. It bore the message 'SPECIAL DUTY NOTIFY KARI REPORT ROTUNDA RETURN MESSAGE ACKNGD THAPSIS.' I marked it 'ROGER WILLCO EDA,' replaced it on the bird, and took her to the regimental simurgh room for programming.

'Yes,' said Kari, 'I've got one too.' I could smell simurgh – in Adambara they feed largely on hyasa meat and fish. 'It says you were wounded in the recent exercise – delayed concussion – and transfers you to the Infirmary. Go back to quarters and wait for the stretcher party.'

Half an hour later, attended by a solicitous Ayah, I was ceremonially carried out on a stretcher, put in a choreb cart, and removed – in through the Infirmary gates at the front; out in mufti, on foot, at the back.

'Do I hear my mission now?' I said to Thapsis.

'Not yet – no need to know at this stage. You're to be in a state of readiness.'

'For precisely what?' I asked him.

'To be absolutely honest, the details of the plan aren't worked out yet. We'll develop them with you. And any other persons involved. Today you're to see the armorer, and then I'll introduce you to your Verulan munshi – not safe to reply on your ring.'

'Mission to Verula, then?' I said.

'By deduction you may assume that.'

'Quarters during instruction?'

'Not in the asvin barracks anyway. The guest room here. You're supposed to be under medical observation. In about a week we'll put in a ringer, with his head in bandages. Can't be too careful.'

'That won't fool Takis,' I said.

'He's one of ours.'

'Still less Ayah.'

'Trooper Ayah will wait on you here. She was due for posting anyway.'

'Is she reliable?'

'Trooper Ayah's father was a general, who died in Verula on an undercover mission. Her mother's a ferry pilot and a squadron commander without assignment. She comes of the oldest military family in Adambara. Yes, she's reliable.'

'If I refuse?' I said.

'You won't. If you weren't going to jump, why should you come here and volunteer?'

The armorer was, when he arrived, a she – a pleasant technician about forty, bare-breasted as usual, for she was in mufti, and wearing the apron of the Smiths.

'Greetings, Colonel – did you love well?'

'Very well, and you, Smith?'

'Very well. Come downstairs, if you will, Sir, and look over the equipment.'

This was clearly a civilian, one of the Smith R and D people, and I appreciated the informality.

'Now,' she said, 'we think your cover should be as an

outlaw.' We had all three gone downstairs into one of the luminous vaults. On a long table, equipment had been laid out; bow, pack, battle-ax, lance, sword, two shields and other gear, including what seemed to be a silver toy umbrella, furled.

'The bow has a power sight,' said Riksasa the armorer. 'The sword and ax are standard issue. Try for heft and balance please. Now, let me demonstrate these. Pick it up, please.'

'This shield?' I asked, picking up the nearer one.

'Is that the blank?' said Thapsis nervously.

'Yes, Sir. And the other isn't armed,' said Riksasa. 'Don't worry.'

'Isn't it too beautiful and expensive for an outlaw?' I asked.

It was indeed beautiful. On it was a complex design of radiating leaves forming a golden sun within a narrow border. It was one of the finest pieces of metalwork I had seen, and the second was its twin.

'That's not a shield, it's an aegis,' said Thapsis, 'and don't point the thing at me.'

Riksasa laughed and moved the other shield to the end of the table out of harm's way. 'Now,' said Riksasa, 'mount it on your left arm. Like an ordinary targe – through the straps. Now, over here – stand in front of the bronze mirror on the wall, and present it.'

I did.

'Feel for the pin with your fingers, and the trigger with your thumb.'

I found them.

'Pull the pin and fire,' said Riksasa.

I did. The rays of the sun flew open with a click and disappeared into the rim. They constituted an iris, like a camera shutter, which opened exposing the polished metal of the shield underneath.

'Thumb off,' said Riksasa. The iris closed. 'Reinsert pin.'

The blank aegis was now at 'safe'.

'And the other, I take it, has a power picture on it?'

'It has,' said Riksasa, 'or rather it will have. At the moment we haven't taken off the screening paint to arm it.'

'Death diagram?'

'Certainly not. That's not an Adambaran habit. It induces various effects according to which hemisphere of the target is dominant – convulsions in most, terror in some,' said Thapsis.

'It's a crazy-making picture, in other words.'

'You could say so. Now,' said Riksasa, 'the mirror will remind you – don't arm it until you're positioned so that there are no reflecting surfaces, and don't point it at your friends. The range is about twenty yards and the angle about 100 degrees.'

'Does it work on asvaya?' I asked.

'Good question,' said Thapsis. 'Does it, armorer?'

'No, Sir, they don't have binocular vision.'

'Another question,' I said. 'This thing doubles as a shield, yes? Then if anybody hits it a clout with a weapon, the iris will either stick closed, or fire and refuse to shut.'

Riksasa looked annoyed, I thought. 'Stand clear, Sir,' she said.

She took the battle-ax and struck the aegis a Smith's blow. The ax shattered in all directions. The aegis was undented. She fired the mechanism and it opened.

'I made this,' said Riksasa, 'and you can rely on us down in the Smithy.'

'Pardon, Smith.'

'Granted,' said Riksasa, 'Colonel.'

'We'll get another ax from stores,' said Thapsis. 'As to the shield being too good for an outlaw, you stole it, of course. And your mount. They're putting Eastern markings on him – they'll be visible but the hair will have started to overgrow by D day.'

'I want the Tetrarch,' I said, 'my regular mount – the one that bolted.'

'You've got the Tetrarch,' said Thapsis, 'naturally.'

The pack contained rations, including dried meat, which the others viewed with disgust, pulses, a throwing knife, Adambaran compass, prisoner cords and an iron ring pierced with two holes.

'Silent horn,' said Thapsis, 'to rendezvous your mount. All

robbers use them. And in a tight spot, remember, when a trained asva hears that he'll go straight through a brick wall. The other hole is for signaling. For the Four's sake see you blow in the right hole.'

'And an unbroken asva?' I asked.

'He's getting his preparation while you get yours.'

That left the toy umbrella. I opened it gingerly. It formed a flat nine-inch silvery disc made of metal threads in a complex pattern.

'Code Name Window?' I asked.

'Roughly. Yes, it's a radar blinder. Use it coming back, or they'll get you by air strafing.'

'This I carry around?' I asked.

'We'll drill the ax handle without weakening it. It fits inside.'

'The other items are unfinished,' said Riksasa, 'but we'll have them shortly. Meanwhile, rendezvous at Third Fire and you can try the bow on our range.'

When she had left, we returned to Thapsis's office.

'I think,' I said, 'that you owe me some background at least.'

'Very well. This is a political briefing.' He took right-hand blach and passed some to me. 'Make yourself comfortable. Now you know,' said Thapsis, 'roughly what Verulan society is like. Rich technological pigs, the Elect, so called, living in a fortress; impoverished plebs, the Thorls, outside; general rule by terror plus deception.'

'Seems highly familiar.'

'That's why we picked an earthling. Now Verula has had eight governments which I can remember and two revolutions. In the last one, the Thorls got guns, looted the Palace City and shortened most of the bosses down by a head, under a fellow called Xarm. Made hamburgers of them and serve them right.'

'Then why . . .'

'Think, man. Verula is governed by people who *want* to govern.'

'So Xarm's revolutionaries are now guzzling away in the

Palace City, and there's a new slum population of Thorl's outside?' I said.

'Correct – or their sons are; it was a while back.'

'So freedom and democracy didn't exactly take in Verula.'

'Revolutions are made not by principles but by exasperation, and seeing the insolence of other people,' said Thapsis. 'Democracy, Verula-type, yes. Freedom, no.'

'Xarm still around?'

'No, he got impaled by his friends, and the simurghs ate him. I should add, the other force in Verula is the Church. At the revolution it was – reorganized – but it's back and doing its office.'

'Don't tell me,' I said. 'Xarm is now a God.'

'Precisely, an incarnation of the Unnameable One, the Great Selfhood.'

'Which, of course, he was.'

'Yes, Adept, I couldn't have put it better myself. Now don't laugh, but the democratic Verulans just held a democratic election. One of the democratic candidates was likely to win, so the other democratic candidate framed him on a charge of fornication, being an Adambaran agent and a friend of Losianism, and got *him* impaled, so then there was one. And naturally he was elected. What happened next was our mistake. We sent an agent to look the new man over. Like idiots we didn't send an Adambaran, because we thought in the atmosphere of anti-Losian hysteria that was going he'd never pass. We sent a Tharmian. And the Tharmian pulled one of those insane terrorist tricks which you on Your Side seem to love so much. He sent the new boss an armed crazy-making picture, and the new boss opened it, we think. Anyhow, in addition to being a thug, he's now crazy, and they got the Tharmian anyhow, so that was that. And a Verulan Caligula we didn't need.'

'I see that,' I said. 'He might make his asva consul. You say Adambarans would be recognized?'

'You have a foreign accent. Moreover any thug or murderer is welcome provided he professes undying anti-Losianism – so an outlaw is perfectly acceptable. Losians threaten their attitude and their property, and they're paranoid about our religion. It's also handy to create a diversion, and Losianism is the diversion.'

'What's this dictator fellow's name?' I asked.

'Sutun. It's not his name, but he's taken a name of the Unnameable. Any time now he'll be deified.'

'It becomes perfectly clear,' I said. 'I go to Verula, get an audience with Sutun to volunteer as one of his goons and give him anti-Losian information, for his ears only, split his skull with the ax and run. If they catch me, they repatriate me, on the end of a sharpened post.'

'That,' said Thapsis, 'is a typical earthly remark.'

'Send him and all his men the death diagram through the mail?'

'So is that,' said Thapsis.

'Hang a carcinogenic picture in his office as a token of my esteem?'

'Better,' said Thapsis, 'but it isn't on. It will kill his slaves.'

'Hang an uncrazy-making picture in his office . . .'

'Now you're talking like an Adambaran. But the only picture in Sutun's office is of Sutun, naturally.

'You know,' he said, after a pause, 'I often think the particular penchant on Your Side for revolutionary terrorism must come from Verulans who have passed over. It's so witless. You send the oppressors dozens of explosive bombs through the mail: the first one that goes off unmasks all the others. You cause indiscriminate explosions. Now and again you get one of the swine, and another swine replaces him.' (The word he used was *hyasa* – actually a lizard, but considered the most disgusting Losian animal.) 'If I were an earthling, which thank the Four I'm not, I'd at least send delayed-action weapons which don't unmask at once; also I'd use directed weapons – like planting plutonium buttons on all police uniforms – or simply interference with services . . .' His voice trailed off. 'Mind you, Adambarans oppose assassination as pointless, except as rough justice. But it's much less indiscriminate than your wars; those only kill the wrong people.'

'Some help with the spiritual logistics of this,' I said. 'I take it that, decent humanity apart, I don't just run around wasting Verulans?'

'You most certainly don't,' said Thapsis.

'Because if I do, they just turn up on earth?'

'Well,' said Thapsis, 'they're all there already, of course. As you are yourself.'

'Then look,' I said, 'if you're only causing paper casualties anyway, why don't you blow the whole whistling bunch of them to hell and back with a clear conscience and get them out of here? That would clean up *one* world.'

'Because,' said Thapsis wearily, 'we'd then have a Threefold World, not a Fourfold World, and we'd have to get them back again. The treatment for gout isn't to cut off your bloody leg.'

'But the treatment for cancer may be.'

'Only in your technology, and precisely because you haven't learned to apply the same principle. Whenever we get foreign Adepts we get the same problem – bright ideas and no basic sciences. If you still don't understand, ask Rosanna. And the answer to your question is no, you're not the Destroying Angel, if only because if you try any tricks *they'll* get *you*, and that I imagine you'd understand. Look, go and find the Smith, will you? She's been waiting half an hour.'

We had an hour's good shooting on the range. As we left, the Smith said briskly, 'That was very good. Now, I wondered, if you have time, may we have the pleasure of enjoying the love bed together?'

'Certainly,' I said, pleased to see that sauce for the gander was also sauce for the goose.

'Your place or mine?'

'Yours, please,' I said, thinking of Ayah.

'My name,' said the Smith, 'is Riksasa.' I was now either her slave or her colleague. Evidently it was the second.

In the event Thapsis relented, and I got the full briefing next day. It was what I expected – the targets were the profile and intentions of Sutun, the Verulan computer system, what it and he were up to, and if possible its programming, plus one which I didn't understand. This was apparently a crystal. I imagined it was concerned with, say, frequency control, and indeed the Verulans were planning to employ it in this fashion, generating what can most briefly be called 'bad vibrations', or there was the risk that they might. But at the same time it was a religious object, and could be looked into, like a crystal ball, which the Verulans apparently were unlikely to realize. I understood little of this, except that the Adambarans wanted it, and also that it was both small and indistinguishable from other crystals. Moreover Thapsis hadn't seen it and didn't know what it looked like. So any crystals in the Verulan strongroom would presumably have to come back with us. I hoped they didn't have more than an asva-load, or alternatively that there were U-Haul trucks in Verula. The rest of the mission made sense, however.

It took an hour to get through the general briefing, because Thapsis went on and on about his crystal. My mind wandered a little because of a disturbing session with my munshi. In the event he ended not trying to teach me Verulan, beyond a few words, but telling me in Losian about some Verulan customs. Since coming over he had guilt complexes sticking out all over him, and he was as vocal as a defected Communist. As on Our Side, Verula enforces a 'front' culture, for Thorls, and a 'back' culture, which is what people actually do, especially the Elect in their Palace City – like compulsory worship for Thorls and general scepticism and dissipation up top, rather as in Imperial Rome. Thus for Thorls reproduction is compulsory; fornication is capital, blach is strictly prohibited, and so on, though everyone practices both, and punishment is wholly arbitrary – this sounded familiar: the Elect, living a life of hectic, slave-tended, extravagant boredom, are into any intoxicant they fancy, including alcohol, which doesn't occur in Adambara, and into sex – but theirs is not the cool sex of Adambara but the hot sex of a porno movie, brutal, hostile and incapable of initiating anybody.

The idea of a boss class composed of drunken and insightless rapists was unpleasant but hardly strange; nor was the Verulan diet of choreb and anything on four legs, which shocked Adambarans, and converts, more than it did me.

There apparently were other horrors which the munshi was too embarrassed to discuss, but no doubt I would learn.

Thapsis realized I wasn't attending. He stopped, and went to the door of the office. 'He's as briefed as he will be: come in,' he said. 'We'd now better go over the detailed tactics.'

It was Rosanna and Faesto who entered. She had abandoned the flour sack and watchdog and was now in Minoan. Faesto was still the Smith, and he entered after, not before her.

'Hello,' said Rosanna. 'We're briefed. I hope you are.'

Blast-off was set for seven days' time

It was a trying time for everyone. Faesto, when we were not training, kept making things – jewelry, toys and the like – from wire. Rosanna and I sat about in my quarters. I even offered to play her at the Game of Adepts.

'But that's ridiculous,' she said, when I showed her the board.

'Quite ridiculous,' I said.

'It isn't even a game. A child could do it.' And she moved all her pieces to the other side. 'Now teach me cat's-cradle,' she said, 'the way the Losians do it, to make a long-life diagram.'

The last night we all spent in the Rotunda guest room, Ayah joining us on the love bed. Riksasa refused – not because of any squeamishness, I learned, but because in Adambara any tetrad is holy and should never be disrupted or augmented. Faesto seemed to have no problems in the worship of Enitharmon that I could detect; he finally fell asleep with Ayah.

'Did you understand about the crystal?' Rosanna said, in my ear.

'No. But if they want it, they get it. Go to sleep. We've got to be up in five hours.'

'Listen. It's important. I can explain.'

'It oscillates on some kind of spiritual frequency, doesn't it? Thapsis wants it for good medicine, Sutun wants it for bad medicine.'

'No. You don't understand.'

'Need I? Tell me tomorrow.'

Rosanna shook me gently. 'It's the only surviving hole in the Veil of Ulro. That's the lid which is on top of people. You look into the crystal, like a window, and see through the lid.'

'So you get a direct look into the implicate order?'

'Yes, right, right,' said Rosanna, 'but not *just* that. How *we* fit in, not just quantum logic.'

'How do you know?'

'Well, we've both more or less seen it,' said Rosanna, 'making love – and meditating. But it's still in two halves. The world-model bit doesn't click with the *us* part.'

'And it should?'

'Yes. Besides, I've read about it. It's been written up:

'"There is a Grain of Sand that Satan cannot find,
Nor can his Watch Fiends find it; 'tis translucent and has many
    Angles,
But he who finds it will find Oothoon's palace; for within
Opening into Beulah, every angle is a lovely heaven.
But should the Watch Fiends find it, they would call it Sin
And lay its Heavens & their inhabitants in blood of
    punishment."

'I think that's our crystal. You're like the Verulans – still thinging. They'll use it like a thing, in some kind of machine.'

'"The Mill, intricate, dreadful, and fill'd with cruel tortures"?'

'Yes, yes,' said Rosanna, 'now you're on course.'

'So that,' I said, 'is why tomorrow's caper is going to be worth it.'

10

The Mills, Intricate, Dreadful, Fill'd with Cruel Tortures

Torax the outlaw, alias Robin Hood, alias Colonel Eda, rode out of Adambara before dawn by the South Gate. Behind him were Friar Tuck, alias Faesto the Smith, and Maid Marian. We were headed for Verula.

On the previous evening, Riksasa had handed over the last of the weaponry. I had a set of slave chains, iron this time, but gold inlaid to copy the Verulan pattern. They had been fixed, Houdini-style, so that the wearer could remove and replace them. Faesto was dressed as an Eastern peasant-merchant, of the kind who sells choreb to the Verulan slaughtermen. Rosanna had the rich Minoan dress of an Adambaran lady, 'distressed' before she got it, so that it looked as if she had been dragged around somewhat. Round her neck was a large iron locket on a beautiful Losian chain. One side bore a sun, the other a moon. 'The triggers,' Riksasa had told her, 'are at the top. Use the moon side if you have to, the sun side only in total emergency – learn to tell them apart by feel, you won't get time to look – and remember what I told you about reflecting surfaces. The range is about ten feet, but the ricochet is really dangerous. Are you sure you can handle it?' Rosanna had said that she could. It was the nastiest booby trap I have seen. 'Only look in it yourself if at last you must,' Riksasa had said.

The plan was simple. Verula is surrounded by plains, despite the Mountain of the holy iconography, and the plain to windward is shrouded perpetually in fog, for the Verulans, despite their lack of Smithies, simply pump their effluent into the working-class quarter. At the edge of the fog we would kill the radar blinder and drop Faesto. I would chain Rosanna-Rusana-Maid Marian and ride into town as an anti-

Losian outlaw-fanatic with a slave to sell. Our assignment was twofold. We had to get a look at Sutun, which would not be hard, since interception of Verulan broadcasts made it clear that he liked personal appearances, and we would look for two things – the crystal, and if possible the print-out from the Verulan policy computers. If this turned out to be a black-bag operation, I would blow number two horn, and Faesto would take over, with a party of Losian technicians who would rendezvous with him separately, get us in, and out, and lock up. We would then, hopefully, split for home sharply. The only other piece of equipment not so far listed was a locket which I wore, this with one face, and a star to distinguish the live surface. It was a locket of invisibility. But here, compared with Our-Side mythology, Adambaran technology fell down. I tried it in a mirror. A tarnhelm it wasn't. What it did was not to make me invisible, but to generate a migraine-type aura of flashing zigzag lines which obscured me. I had asked Riksasa why I couldn't ride with it permanently open, like the Invisible Man, and she had been huffy and said that the effect fatigues quickly, and didn't I have a backside, as well as an asva with me? 'We're working,' she said, 'to improve it. This is Mark four already.' I'd as soon have waited for Mark five or six, but business was pressing.

Owing to the build of an asva it is hard to talk to the driver. Most of the conversation, which I could not hear, passed between Faesto and Rosanna, in pillow whispers. I felt she was taking her occupation too seriously. I passed back rations without stopping. We only once drew rein, to water the Tetrarch at a pool of greenish water. At dusk we bivouacked four hours. I stalked a hyasa, shot it with the bow and fed my mount, but did not fancy watching his meal. I got little sleep for the crunching of hyasa bones, but the other two slept in each other's arms peacefully enough. I rose before they did and checked the Tetrarch's harness. It included, stitched into the breaststrap, a piece of electronic equipment of Verulan manufacture, a mine exploder, modified in the Smithies to the frequency used in the Verulan barrier wall. I flipped it on, checked the green signal light, then off. We could go in following the choreb herds, by a

103

gate, but we should probably need this if our exit was unorthodox – in fact, our mission had been held up two days getting Verulan batteries to fit the thing.

As dawn rose, we were well on our way. I noticed that the desert became dirtier. There were hyasa bones, choreb bones, and later, junk vehicles of Verulan design, Verulan food containers – many of gold, which are environmentally foul because they never break down – and finally the skeleton of a man, with a simurgh perched on it. I could see mountains and brown haze ahead.

We kept going for several hours at the Tetrarch's steady pace. Then I asked Faesto how far we had to go.

'That's it,' he said, indicating the mountains. They were in fact towers, the Palace City, looking like the castle of the Tooth Fairy, and round their base rolled the dirt cloud of Verula. Already our eyes were beginning to smart. Yet from this distance I saw that the Palace City was beautiful. What was hidden was what maintained it. The towers, square or circular, were of glass, of artificial stone, of ceramic, studded with windows, linked by soaring metal ways, along which vehicles passed. On the largest, as we closed, I could see a blazing sun composed of gold leaf. Gradually, however, the air thickened, the Buckminster Fuller aspect of Verula disappeared, and we were into blinding smoky fog, at which the Tetrarch snorted and became unruly.

'Here,' said Faesto. 'Good luck – and for the sake of the Four, don't confuse number one with number two horn.' He slipped from the saddle and walked into the fog.

I halted, muzzled the Tetrarch on quick-release, and helped Rosanna forward, laid her face down across the saddlebow, clear of all weapons, and put on the Houdini chains.

'Comfortable?' I asked her.

'You could say so. But get on with it. I shall get sick like this, and this smog is as bad as Los Angeles.'

'Worse,' I said, for it was blinding.

Trotting forward we fell in with many hoofprints, choreb dung and finally herds of choreb, driven by surly looking Easterners, coughing as their beasts coughed. I heard the hum of a Verulan air patrol passing over. The Window umbrella was stowed already in the handle of my ax.

'Can you see?' I asked in a stage whisper.

'The ground,' said Rosanna. 'They had a better view from a Martian lander.'

I saw troops approaching. 'Struggle,' I said to Rosanna, and she did. I made a show of beating her with the flat of my sword, timing the performance to let them come level, and they roared with laughter.

'How much, outlaw?'

'Too dear for your kind.'

'Sell her to the Palace City,' yelled another. These, from their sun insignia were Sutun's police. A nice lot, I thought. Rosanna was obligingly screaming her head off, which increased their amusement. 'Sell her for our Lord's kitchen!' said another, and they were gone. I like Rosanna's cooking, but Sutun might not, and we were under strict orders excluding earthly tricks like poisoning him.

As an earthling, it only struck me then that they were mounted on rather ill-favored but terrestrial-looking horses.

The fog cleared a little toward the gates. There was an airfield where Verulan ships, shaped like automobile hubcovers with stubby wings, were taxiing for takeoff. I smelt their acrid exhaust. I also smelled Verula. The city itself stank.

Ahead of the gate, the track narrowed between barbed-wire fences. Outside these was a bare area, plowed in even furrows to show any footprint, and marked with real skulls set on posts, which are cheaper in Verula than manufactured signs. Beyond that a high pile of concertina wire lay outside a low-topped wall, running left and right as far as I could see. The gate was a simple earth frontier post, with a painted pole and guards, but I saw laser guns in the two watchtowers. Sutun's men manned it, and were engaged in trying to extract a bribe from a choreb driver. I felt for the Verulan coins I had been given, but the screaming and struggling Rosanna was evidently a passport, because they too roared with laughter and raised the pole. 'Nice work, outlaw,' they yelled. I slapped Rosanna with the sword-flat, then with my hand.

'If you can get it,' I yelled back.

At once I was rushed by the beggars. Piles of rags like moulted simurgh unwound from corners and held out hands: 'Mercy, rider! For the name of Xarm and Sutun! Alms, Elect!' They had every real or feigned disease in the textbook. I had been well trained in Verulan ways by my munshi. Instead of throwing the coins and getting them out of my way, I struck right and left with my saber-flat, reined the Tetrarch, and reached for the muzzle straps. The soldiers hooted, the beggars scattered. We were in Verula with a vengeance, and a verse from another place, another time, ran through my head:

'Now are we in, quoth Adam Bell,
    And that with little pain:
But Christ He knows who harrowed Hell
    How we shall come out again . . .'

The street was a flattened-out version of one of the back alleys of Calcutta or Rio, only dirtier. The substantial buildings had been decent but were old and subdivided – drying lines of rags no whiter for washing, screaming underfed children, graffiti and posters everywhere. The gaps between them, and every corner, including some roofs, were occupied by improvised, swarming huts built out of trash from the Palace City – cardboard, skins, corrugated gold sheets and flattened-out drums. Some larger drums constituted one-room homes. Stalls were everywhere, selling choreb meat, clothes and gaudy religious statues in gold and plastic of Xarm laying his hand on the head of a Mortal, presumably Sutun, before a sun disc. There were triptych plastic icon frames with the sun in the center and Xarm in benediction on the right, Sutun in uniform on the left. Starved-looking caniform chalicotheres picked around or fought over choreb offal, and all the time more choreb flocks filed in. They were headed for large sheds, where hides were visible in piles and blood ran out into the gutters. Music punctuated by oratory blared from horns on the poster-encrusted lamp posts. Gold-printed posters reading 'VOTE FOR A GOD – ELECT SUTUN' were relatively intact. Those bearing the name of

106

one Fuzo had been mostly obliterated with paint or filth. Among the stalls were long animal cages, like those of the Calcutta wild-beast market. A few contained battered hyasa. Most contained people of all ages and both sexes, chained and unchained, young and older. These were the cheaper slaves of Verula. Girls thrust out both arms, yelling 'Buy me, Elect,' hysterically, despairingly or as a matter of routine. Men stared sullenly. A horn blared behind me, and a flash-steam-propelled transporter and trailer of the two-deck variety lumbered up, forcing me over. It was clearly a stock transporter headed for the slaughterhouses which served the Palace City, but I heard no lowing and saw no choreb heads. Whatever was in it moaned or thumped on the sides – it was no Losian animal.

When we got into wider streets I checked under my breath with Rosanna that she could still take it.

'Go on,' was all she said, and started moaning and struggling appropriately once more.

There were stores here with glass windows. Overhead swooped a bright Verulan monorail, carrying the Elect above the mess and uproar of the ghetto to wherever they were going. The goods were universally, by Adambara standards, pretentious and badly made. There was not even a hand-made clay pot in sight. The first intersection was marked by a gigantic, and new, statue of the familiar Sutun, in uniform, giving benediction to the mess behind us, and one of his traffic police with white gloves, white topi and a stun gun, apparently conducting the orchestra of dissonance. Churches of Xarm and Sutun with the sun were frequent, and veiled women and badly-dressed artisans filed in and out of them, worship being apparently a continuous performance.

Beyond the next intersection stood a wooden platform with two statues. Fortunately it was on the side away from Rosanna's head, for I saw that they were recently impaled people, a man and a woman. The points of the stakes came out accurately at the side of the throat. Round each, after death, had been draped pieces of sacking concealing the women's breasts and the genitals of both. On the stakes below them were neat signs reading 'Fornicator' and 'Fornicatress.' Death had been recent, only a few hours before. The sickening odor of it, which was becoming evident over the symphony of Verulan stenches, did not come from them. It came from an official building ahead, the Palace of Equal Justice, as its facade proclaimed. The roof of this bore more impaled delinquents, like the statues on St Peter's, but in varying states of decomposition and surrounded by screaming simurgh. As I passed, I held out my arm, as per order on seeing a simurgh flock, and a bird, departing glutted from the roof, dropped on it. As unostentatiously as possible I bent back the corners of the message foil. I was now an unremarkable outlaw with his hawk. When the coast was clear, the bird, with a knowing look, took off again, and I knew that the tangle of antennae on top of the Palace City were not reading my primitive signal.

We were halted at the next intersection by the traffic jam round a better-class slave market. Here the wares were decently dressed; a girl, with the auctioneer behind her, was dancing furiously for potential buyers, while other slaves sat on benches. While we were stopped, a fat man in a gold-edged bathrobe came puffing up with a wax tablet and a bag. 'Two hundred,' he said.

'More,' I said. 'She goes to the Palace City.'

'I buy for the Palace City. I am Gulux.'

'And I'm Nellie of Mullingar,' I said, under my breath. 'Yes, Elect.' He was a Thorl, but it pays to call all police sergeants and all German waiters Herr Ober.

He tried to open Rosanna's mouth, and felt her buttocks. 'Three hundred,' he said. 'Lord Sutun feasts tonight to celebrate his deification.'

It struck me that a slave might get a close look at Sutun. But my radar said 'no,' and at that moment one of Sutun's police cracked a bullwhip over the crowd, and we got through, leaving Gulux shouting 'Three hundred fifty!' It seems he had been taken short.

11
The Last Child of Enitharmon

The inn, asvaya-lodge, or whatever else I may call it, was exactly where Thapsis had marked it. I parked and unmuzzled the Tetrarch, placed my tal in the machine, and saw a meager side of not over-fresh hyasa fall into the trough. The Tetrarch, luckily, was not particular. I took off his muzzle and put it in my pack. Unmuzzled he was also unstealable; I did not think any Verulan could hot-wire an unmuzzled war asva. I took off the more vital gear, loaded it onto Rosanna, chains and all, and dragged her as brutally as possible into the inn.

'Evening,' said the host. 'Slave pen's at the back. Here's your key.'

'She's quality, I'm not having her stolen.'

'Please yourself. Then chain her to the bed, and see she doesn't make a row.'

'That suits,' I said, grinning at him. 'I only got her yesterday, I rode all night and I've work to do.'

Mine host leered.

I snapped one of the four chain-bracelets round the heavy gold bed-post. Rosanna had one hand free, and the locket to protect my armament. I went down with mine host to dinner. It had taken all day in the turmoil of the ghetto to reach base, and both were famished, Rosanna as well as I, but there was no help.

'Feed her.'

'You feed her. No room service here.'

I was obliged to go.

He had few regulars, mostly Eastern herdsmen. Faesto was not among them, but I did not expect him. The choreb was good but the vegetables, after Losian food, foul. I ordered the colorless Verulan schnapps, took the bottle with me to the washroom, rinsed my mouth with it, emptied it down the drain and refilled with water. From the host I learned that Sutun would be deified at a public feast, three hundred thousand tals a plate, in three hours' time only, with audience, and proceeded to get drunk on ill-flavored Verulan water, keeping mine host's hand off the bottle. Finally I rose, with half a loaf and two choreb chops in a rag.

'For her,' I said. 'Room service.'

'Give her porridge. She's a slave, isn't she?'

'I want her sweet.'

'Love well,' said the host, a ghastly parody of the Losian greeting.

'And get stuck on a post? It's against the law,' I said.

He roared with laughter. 'You are indeed a stranger. That's for the simurgh.' He put his thumb to his nose.

'I saw two poor devils on pales today.'

'So she didn't pay off the police, and didn't fancy the station officer,' said the host, 'or she's a Losian. All these loose women are Losians. They're destroying this country's moral fiber.'

'Then they deserve what they get,' I said. 'I drink to that. And anyone who disturbs me, by Xarm I'll slit his face. Tell them I'm busy tonight and I won't answer the door.' And I staggered out.

Rosanna ate hungrily and quickly. 'Three hours,' I said.

'Enough.'

'Do you think you can really take this?'

'I'm tougher than you are, Colonel,' said Rosanna, 'and I also care. Let's get going.'

In half an hour a slightly inebriated robber and a raddled but traditionally veiled Verulan prostitute slipped out of the inn by the window. Tied with a slip knot, the Tetrarch came like a shadow, and I reloaded the gear. I took the arms, Rosanna the slave gear, for a quick change without returning to the inn. I left a heap of tals on the bed, rumpled it, and checked carefully. We wanted no warrants out.

The ghetto was streaming to Sutun's inauguration, expedited by some of his police. I left the Tetrarch unmuzzled in a public parking lot, relying on his talent for unarmed combat. He could well guard himself and my gear. I took only the sword and aegis.

We climbed steep cobbled alleys rising towards the Palace City, but, as we knew, there would be no entering it. The arena where the ceremony was to be is normally the site of Verula's gladiatorial shows – fights to the death, wild-beast killings, feedings of obnoxious persons or pro-Losians guilty of un-Verulan activities to asvaya and mass execution. Impalement is a matter of which the Verulans, Thorls as well as Elect, are connoisseurs, and they give bettable points to the execution squad, booing a crooked result, in which the point fails to reach the neck cleanly.

I had expected a colosseum. In fact, the top of the hill's shoulder, between Palace City and ghetto, had been hollowed like a volcanic crater. On that side were awning-covered upholstered seats for the Elect. On this, standing room behind treble bulletproof glass for Thorls. Tonight the arena was full of white-clothed tables laid with shining gold plates and flatware. At the end of the oval to our right stood the altar and benedictive image of Xarm, with two slaves chained head to knees beside it. Behind was the Sun Disc of Urizen. The stands of the Elect were backed by the scented residential streets, flowering trees and tower blocks of the Palace City, and these stands were filling already, as the shining monorail and the Verulan street vehicles delivered parties of the Elect in what I took to be the local evening dress – veils and naked bellies for women, white bathrobes and black sashes for men. I saw officers from all the anti-Losian world, escorted by their goon squads. We for our part were pushing through Thorls towards the glass, where Sutun's police stood, face to crowd, at five-yard intervals, arms folded, bullwhips in hand, stun guns on their backs. It took an hour for the stadium to fill. The synthetic music, of a sugary rather than a martial texture, blared out from loudspeakers, and all stood. It stopped. All knelt, except the police, and the Elect, who pray standing.

Behind the altar the procession was headed by the disc of the Rayed Sun, carried on a tall gold rod. Six singing castrati followed it, their squeaky voices relayed over the public address system, then assorted clergy of Xarm and then his priest. Behind the priest came a grotesque human figure. It was nearly as tall as a carnival giant, but of natural body, and walked with difficulty, evidently upon chopines, or stilt-shoes, at least two feet high. The face was both pink and wizened, but was coated with makeup. The hair was curly, and appeared to be a wig of gold threads. It carried a long property scepter. A vast devotional cheer went up, then a rhythmic chant, started in our sector by the police at a radio signal, of 'Sutun, tuus, Sutun, tuus' – Sutun, god, Sutun, god. Some Thorls wept openly with emotion. The Elect looked more like an enthusiastic party convention, but chanted vigorously.

The divine freak, assisted by clergy, got down off the chopines, which were removed offstage, and went to the altar, where he bowed three times. He then took from it a blunt gold scimitar and inefficiently, in several strokes, struck off the heads of the two kneeling slaves. He held up the scimitar. Applause rose from the stands. He bowed. Stage-hands in masks and costumes to match the black backdrop unostentatiously struck the two heads, leaving the bodies kneeling. The Lord Sutun, preceded by the sun on its pole, went to his place in the middle of the high table, stood before his seat, the sun stationed behind him, and with a broad sweep of the scimitar motioned his guests to join him. The gesture left an arc of decreasing bloodspots on the tablecloth. The Elect streamed to dinner, and the waiters scuttled out to serve choreb soup from gold containers.

It is dull to watch a meal when one has eaten, and frustrating to watch one when one has not. The Thorls, some at least of whom by their looks had not, shuffled a little; the police looked extra watchful, but nothing happened.

Two whole choreb on enormous salvers composed the second course. So far it was straight Salammbô-D. W. Griffith stuff, and it bored me, apart from the two revolting murders we had witnessed. Rosanna was white under her makeup and veil, but wholly together. We might have been on the love bed, or this indeed a bad movie. It was at the third course that Verula struck home.

There were three vast salvers this time, quite eight feet long, more than enough for a roast choreb. They were preceded by a Verulan maitre d', and a vast cheer went up. They came almost to the carving table before I saw that on each was a roast human body, rehabilitated with some kind of spaghetti for hair. The maitre d' was the man Gulux.

'Come on,' I said to Rosanna. 'I'm going to vomit.'

'Stay,' she said quietly. 'We have to hear what he says.'

'But this?'

'I knew,' said Rosanna. 'But I didn't tell you, or you'd have run. For Verulan Elect, it's the final and ultimate kick. And those are all women.'

I thought of the aegis. It would have been a gesture, but the range was too long, and there was glass ahead.

I looked for the next half hour at the towers of the Palace City. Rosanna watched the meal, and I felt her harden steadily. I will not recount Sutun's address. It would be impossible to do so, except verbatim, and it lasted an hour and a half, until he staggered and was helped out, terminating the occasion. It was delivered in a high artificial yell, rather like the yawn of an asva. Much was idiolalic or merely incoherent, some concerned the religion of Xarm, and appeared to affect the Thorls deeply, in the style of a camp meeting: like a camp preacher, Sutun drew breath between phrases with an audible yawp, and his punctuant was not 'Praise God, hallelujah!' but 'Sutun tuus!' at each repetition of which Thorl voices shouted 'Yes, Lord.' He would have done well on an evangelical radio. This stretch ended with a benediction. Then his face blackened and he launched into a shouting tirade in the Adolf Hitler manner aimed at Los, Losians, Losianism, the Losian traitors amongst us, incoherent and so far strictly for the simurgh. The last five minutes were, however, more important. He seemed to subside a little and his head to clear. He even spoke quietly.

'But this shall not continue,' said Sutun. 'Now that I am your god, and the incarnation of the divine Xarm, the time has come in our national history to remove the cancer, with

the courage of the soldier, the determination of the surgeon.'
(He stumbled over the word, but got it out at last.) 'Los shall
be destroyed. Within the next three suns, Adambara the city
of slavery and fornication will be renamed the city of Sutun.
The sun will rise over the Mountain. I call you now both
Thorls and Elect,' (there was an audible gasp) 'to the banner
of the Unnameable. In three suns' time we move.'

A howl of approbation went up from both sides of the
glass. And a lot more of like kind. It did not end, but slowly
sank in a chant of 'Sutun, tuus, Sutun, tuus.'

'Come on,' said Rosanna, 'before the streets fill.'

'Schizophrenic?' I said, when we reached the street.
'Blached?'

'Schizophrenic and blached. But the last part is bad.'

'So?'

'Finish the job and warn Thapsis.'

'Adambara's wide open,' I said. 'They think these folk are
barbarians, but the barbarians have got guns and probably
nuclear weapons.'

'It's not wide open,' said Rosanna. 'But it needs warning.
Hurry up.'

The Tetrarch in crowds is his own snowplow, and we got
him out of the parking lot before the better-off Thorls came
for their horses and chorebs. He whinnied reproachfully –
we had been three full hours watching and listening to the
bedizened lunatic of Verula.

'Gulux wanted to buy me,' said Rosanna. 'I could feel you
thinking about planting a slave on him, but I couldn't say to
you.

'The building,' said Rosanna, 'is the only one actually in
the perimeter. It has an unclimbable wall. Follow the city
wire.'

There was a road round the mined wire of the Palace City,
built for patrols before the radar screen was set up – Verulans
now trusted technology more than policemen, however, and
we had deployed Window. We stopped under an immense
wall of glassy tiles, the windowless side of a twenty-five
story tower. I sounded number two horn. There was nothing
in sight except a belated choreb herd, but the ring beeped

cheerfully back. The herd bleated and blundered up, driven by four Easterners. The last of these slipped under the Tetrarch and stood in the shadow.

'Go,' said Faesto.

Four wholly invisible men in black, velvet-textured, radar-blind jump suits, with blackened faces and Mickey Mouse hoods, came from among the choreb. Two took stations right and left. Their aegises were blackened and nonreflecting. Another took off a pack, aimed a weapon from it at the wall, and a white adhesive bolt streaked up, trailing a climbing line. He ran up it like a spider, his suit changing from black to white as he did so. There was a pause, a subdued red flash and the line fell back. 'He's in,' said Faesto.

'No,' said Rosanna.

The man placed his gloved hands against the wall, came down as though parachuted, landed, though it was from a full two hundred feet, and shook his head. 'Laser-proof,' he said. He was now black as the ink of a squid.

'Damnation,' said Faesto. And then, 'You two go in.'

'In how?'

'The other surface, man. Game of the Adepts.'

It was obvious – to anyone but a Verulan, or an earthling.

'And you?'

'Not an Adept. Why the hell do you think we brought you?'

'There will be alarms, and locks,' said Rosanna. And there and then she calmly, clearly and, as I thought, against all professional etiquette, taught the Game of Adepts to a blacksmith.

Faesto grinned in the dark at its simplicity.

'Should you have done that?' I whispered.

'I have three sisters to avenge,' said Rosanna concisely.

We were inside. It was a locked store, full of unpunched cards, tape reels and junk. It was the right building. Faesto ran his fingers over the lock, checked for alarms, and beckoned. 'Stairs,' he said, 'not the elevators. They make noise. We want the tenth floor.'

'Like this,' said Faesto, 'no laser holes. Better idea. They won't know what hit them.'

We took a deliberate two-minute breather. Faesto unlocked the stairway door, and approached another, in a lighted corridor, and to the right. He held up his hand and stepped back, unshipped the second climber's black backpack, took out alligator clips, then a knife, with which he slit the carpet. 'Crude,' he said. 'But there may be . . . yes, there it is.' He slipped on what seemed to be galoshes, performed a surprisingly agile handstand, and walked along the magnetic ceiling towards a grated ventilator, as if inverted progression was as normal to him as to a woodpecker. I saw why the pack had a waistband. Faesto, still upside down, opened it, took out a thin plastic screen, and slid it in front of the vent. 'Safe,' he said, vaulted down and went to work on the lock.

'Their pattern doesn't see you upside down,' he said, complacently. 'Haven't thought of it. Verulan thingers aren't smart.'

12
In Which We Find a Grain of Sand in Lambeth

However advanced one's technology, there are only a limited number of ways of performing digitally based computation. I do not know what the Verulan switch-unit is; it may or may not be a transistor. But for the purposes we had in mind, the Verulan equipment might have been built by IBM. Faesto checked that it was not booby-trapped. There was of course the question of devices against unauthorized operation, but people who could leave their machine without human guards in blind reliance on alarms were likely to be complacent, and the secrecy system was primitive. As I ran the tapes, I handed the sheets to Rosanna, while Faesto cursed over the safe. That had two alarm systems and four booby-traps in addition to an electronic lock.

'I've got the hang of it,' said Rosanna, in a relatively short time – how long we did not reckon, for Losians do not measure intervals less than One Fire. 'This stuff,' said Rosanna, 'is military deployment and targeting. It could have been pay checks, but it isn't. The Four are on our side. Now we know Sutun is in earnest as well as crazy.'

'Bugger it up for them, there's a good girl.'

So while Rosanna punched out a spurious program and Faesto worked, I stood guard with my aegis, listening for the inevitable footsteps which never came, and seeing the blind bright eyes on the clubs and offices of Verula's Palace City blazing uselessly into the night, and the smog rolling over the ghetto.

'Enough, I think,' said Rosanna, switching on the card scanner. She brought the folded printouts and the pile of cards. 'Get rid,' she said, and with Faesto's boring-laser I reduced them to a puff of smoke.

'Careful,' said Faesto over his shoulder, 'there may be fire detectors.'

We stood in total silence. The place was dead – the tape had stopped running. Then there was a click, and the Smith of the Smith's had done. 'Yours,' he said. He was sweating professionally.

The safe was smallish. It contained one box. In that was another, and in that a small square of plastic material, mounted on contacts. In the middle, between sprayed metal tracks, was what seemed to be a grain of sand.

'Is this it?'

She took it. I looked for crystal-sockets on the equipment.

'No,' said Rosanna, 'like this.' And she held the square to her eye, against the lights of the Palace City.

A full minute passed.

'Well?' I said.

Rosanna seemed transfigured. She handed me the square. 'You look,' she said. I did so, until Faesto took it from me and did the same. We did the only thing then possible, and all three embraced. There is no way of describing in plain what may be seen when the Veil of Ulro becomes for an instant pervious. The implicate is easy enough. The implicate with feeling is something else – which is why mystics don't talk much about it.

'Put it back,' said Rosanna.

'What about Thapsis?'

'They need it more.'

'What, these beasts?'

'Put back my revenge.'

She took from her dress the lipstick of a Verulan prostitute, and wrote in clear Losian characters on the small square 'Let Sutun look into the crystal.'

'Faesto?'

'I agree, Adepts. I take responsibility.' He closed the safe and armed the warning systems. 'Now, everyone out.'

At the ground floor each performed the Game of Adepts. The Tetrarch knelt. Rosanna changed into slave costume. The two aegismen saluted and blotted in darkness. The Tetrarch stood as one anxious to go.

'Mission over,' said Faesto. 'Now run like all hell.'

I thought of the safety of the four technicians in black, who had the hard part, staying outside. 'They'll make it,' said Faesto. 'They're all trained men. Don't stay stood there, Adept. Slave chain, please.'

Within less than a minute a robber, a peasant and a chained slavegirl were riding unremarkably on an asva into the smoke and general but decreasing pandemonium of the Verulan ghetto area; it was very late and the streets were clearing of all but police and garbage. Rosanna had a scarf tied round her face to make her look plausibly gagged. I slowly revved up the Tetrarch.

In doing so, and because I was preoccupied with our exit procedure, I made a trivial mistake. I went through a Verulan stop sign. One of Sutun's police stepped out, right hand raised, left hand aiming a stun gun. To complicate matters, the man was either blached or drunk. Laboriously, and standing directly in front of my mount, so that to move I must ride him down, he wrote a ticket.

'How much, Elect?' I asked him cheerfully.

'One hundred tals.'

I fished for them.

'Plus fifty tals for me, and half an hour with the lady.'

I fished for the fifty, laughing, and remarked that the lady didn't give trading stamps. He took the money and stood his ground – the son of a chalicothere was in earnest.

'Half an hour,' he said, 'and you get off lightly. The charge could be suspicion of intent to fornicate – I have reason to believe you two are not legally married.'

Torax the outlaw roared with robberly merriment and held up his shield to the officer in mock terror. At that moment I felt Faesto grip my shield arm and move it back. Behind the policeman's head was the glassy, tiled surface of the Popular Bank of Verula. 'Flat of your ax,' said the level voice of Faesto.

'Oh, all right, Elect,' I said to the swaying policeman.

I grumbled a bit, pulled out a knife and sawed at the ropes which attached Rosanna's slave chain to the saddle. I cursed it for blunt, pulled out the ax, holding it close to the head in as unthreatening a way as possible, sawed a bit with that, then, as the officer lowered his weapon in impatience, brought down the flat of it on his skull. Unfortunately, he fell in front of the Tetrarch's feet. Not thinking Verulan, I backed the animal to go round him. 'Look out!' yelled Rosanna through the scarf. She alone of us, being prone over the saddle could see to the rear. We had not noticed another policeman standing behind us, and behind a booth. He was armed with a stun gun also.

13

In Which the Horse is of More Value than the Man

I recovered with an almighty headache, on a cot, with a bag over my head. When the ringing in my ears failed to stop I realized that the place was full of the white noise which Verulan security uses to confuse prisoners. I had been handcuffed, and finger examination indicated that these were Verulan handcuffs, not Adambaran, and had consequently not been fixed. Both my rings were intact; the problem was that my hands were behind my back, and that was the wrong place for them.

Almost as soon as I moved, a level voice started to ask questions. I cursed, outlaw-style, to judge how near he was and how many of him there were, but no blow followed – in fact, the questioning was polite. The voice asked me if I knew where I was.

'Among a gang of murdering sons of tripehound bitches,' I replied. The voice simply repeated the question. There was still no movement and no blow. I was beginning to know my Verulans, and this one was either clever or well-trained. I cursed him, his mother and his genitalia in the name of the Unnameable – nothing happened. I suddenly realized that I was being interrogated not by one of Sutun's bunch, but by a teaching machine.

I knew my cover story was perfect. The program here would be by overlapping repetition, and if my head stopped aching, or even if it didn't, I knew I could beat it. The Verulan rough stuff would come next, and it would be decidedly unpleasant – then, probably, the soft man – drinks and job offer if I cooperate, then the machine, and so on. This initial stage might be a longish business, and I had a sore head and the white noise to contend with, but the sensory deprivation was gone, and replaced by professional interest. For the rest, I have played blindfold three-dimensional chess in a reasonably noisy room.

The game was, as I expected, interminable. We went through the program three times, I noted a patch of additional sound as the tape restarted, and could check my inference as to the pattern of questions. And after three runs it stopped.

It was when it stopped that the white noise and the bag became oppressive. I determined to sleep (it was probable I was alone in the cell) both to prepare for what was coming, and to see if the Verulans intended to let me. It was difficult, and the handcuffs were painful in most positions, but there was no shaking or startling, and I contrived to doze sufficiently to recuperate, and at one point to dream. I dreamed that I was playing the Game of Adepts, and that the problem of transferring one's handcuffed wrists from back to front when one could not pass them over the feet was a rider, as it were, to the main knack of that game. The conviction was intense. Waking with a start, I realized that that was true.

The question now was whether I was under surveillance. The white noise would obscure small personal sounds, the guard might be behind glass or there might be closed-circuit tele-observation, probably the last of these. Finally I decided to chance it, on the offchance that nobody watches a sleeping suspect continuously, particularly if there are other suspects to observe, and I performed the maneuver. My hands were now in front. I cautiously lifted the edge of the bag, saw an empty featureless cell, and noted where the camera was sited. Then I rolled sleepily away from it, hoping that the cell was not truly soundproof, blew a short toot on the asva horn and returned my hands to the rear position. Nothing untoward happened, but the ring gave a short beep. The faithful Trigger was in place, probably in the police stable, deprived of all my vital equipment, but at least he was in place. Moreover the call-attention signal had fired the release on his muzzle. Afterwards I realized the stupidity of Adepts. They would have to transfer my hands to the front to feed me, make me sign a confession, or something similar, and I had taken an unnecessary risk.

Next time I dozed I was indeed shaken, dragged to my feet, and the bag removed. I was dazzled. Two of Sutun's men were in the cell; one produced a key, pulled my hands to the front and replaced the cuffs. I was quick-marched down a passage, no sign of other cells, through doors, and into the usual room. There was a blind-covered, barred window in the wall behind them, too small to admit an asva; still, an outside wall.

'Name?'

'Torax.'

'Occupation?'

'Thief.'

'From whom do you steal, thief?'

'From the bloody Losians, who else?'

'What do you steal?'

'Anything I can – money, women, arms – anything those sons of bitches have got. I also knock down drunken cops.'

'Don't you know we impale thieves in Verula?'

'Not if they don't thieve here,' I said.

'And what are you doing here, if not thieving?'

'Selling plunder, what else?'

'You had Adambaran arms,' said the second officer. This one, I judged was the hard man.

'You bet,' I answered.

'From where?'

'From their owner.'

'Where is their owner?'

I grinned at him. 'He had a little accident. The simurghs ate him.'

'You are lying,' said the hard man. 'You are an Adambaran spy. Admit it.'

'Who, me? Not bloody true,' I said.

'Your accomplice has confessed.'

'What accomplice?'

'The woman,' said the officer.

'What woman? Her? She's a bloody liar – don't you listen

to a word she says. I was going to sell her for good money,
and she hates my guts.'

'Liar.'

'Well, you wouldn't blame her, would you? One day she's
the wife of a Losian party boss, as far as those horny hyasas
have wives, next day she's going to learn manners in Verula.'

'Liar.'

'Or end up as a chateaubriand.'

'You lie,' said the officer. 'You are an Adambaran officer.
It is written all over you. You have Losian equipment, you
use Losian expressions, you speak of matters . . .' He stood
up and came my way.

'Not yet,' said the soft man. 'Tell me without lies exactly
how you got her.'

'I took her in fair fight.'

'From whom?'

'I didn't ask his name, Sir. You see, we weren't
introduced.'

The soft man grinned; my mind said, 'Be careful.'

'What happened,' he asked, 'to his asva?'

I thought, Adambaran civilians don't ride asvaya: the
Tetrarch has Eastern markings. 'It bolted,' I said. 'My asva
kicked it.'

'The man,' said the officer, 'was a Losian civilian?'

'Ferry pilot,' I said, 'probably – he was in mufti.'

'And your asva?'

'I pinched him out East.'

'Who is the man with you?'

'Hitchhiker – a peasant who smells of chorebs.'

'The woman,' said the hard man 'says under torture that
you are a Losian spy, and she is your cover. You're lying.'
He resumed his march on me. The soft man this time said
nothing.

At that moment my ring gave a quiet beep, more felt than
heard, but much louder than in the cell.

'And you, you fat-faced frog, are the first man to call Torax
a liar without getting his face slit,' I replied. 'If I wasn't
chained, I'd turn your mother-sucking face round to point
backwards.'

'Hold him,' said the officer, and struck me several times. Then he stepped back, the guards released my arms and he said, 'That will teach you manners, Colonel.'

With the most natural gesture I could contrive, I raised my joined hands to my mouth as if to check all my teeth were still there and wipe the blood from my nose, and in doing so I blew long and loud on the silent horn, mark one.

'You will now tell the truth,' said the officer, 'or watch your accomplice impaled. Fetch her!'

'Give me a moment,' I said, dropping Torax. There was silence. The officer raised his glove again. I heard a distant crashing of glass and equipment. All heads turned, and then the outer wall came in bodily, and through the dust and rubble came the blazing eyes and peppery unmuzzled head of the Tetrarch, lips back, razor-teeth snapping. His jaws grabbed the two men at the table and flung them right and left, a heavy foot landed on the hard man and seemed to condense him like a closing concertina. Then the Tetrarch took one petrified guard, while I took the other, with the chain of the cuffs round his neck. The Tetrarch shook his man screaming to and fro; blood spattered over me, then throwing him down he tore him there and then. Not until he had finished did I go near him.

'Sit,' I said. He sat, munching horribly, and, providentially, the saddle and gear were intact. I had the task of searching, handcuffed, what was left of the guard for the cell keys. I found the bunch, after a nauseating grope among intestines, shook the beastliness off them, and ran back towards the cell, clumsily carrying the keys and the other guard's stun gun. It was a dead end, but the end wall struck hollow. I put down the weapon, examined the bunch of keys, found a magnetic key among them and looked for the slot. Time was passing horribly. Then I found it, low down, I put the key in, and the panel slid back.

There were indeed cells beyond. In the first was Faesto, his handcuffs neatly in his hand, waiting calmly. 'I didn't open the door,' he said. 'The lock's outside – there. That key, I think.' He pointed to the bunch. He was right.

'Where is she?'

'Next cell. She's all right. Here – hold out your wrists.'

Rosanna was all right, in that she was asleep, but she was bleeding and half-naked, and woke as I turned her like a tired child. 'A horrible dream,' she said. 'I'm aching.' Faesto worked on her wrists in turn. Neither then nor later did I ever ask her what had been done to her, nor what her dream had contained. Faesto picked her up, threw away the fetters and carried her out. 'Back to the Tetrarch,' I said. 'I'm doing a quick reconnaissance.'

It was well I did. There was a guard room at the end of the passage, away from the panel. The door was ajar, and through the crack I saw on the table my aegis and ax, laid out as exhibits. In a chair, before a radio transmitter and the surveillance monitors, a guard was asleep. I judged the distance, and was raising the stun gun when I saw that he was dead, and not only dead but dead staring as if strangled, and black in the face. In his hand was something which trailed a thin Losian iron chain. I shut my eyes, backed up to him, and, eyes still shut, unclenched his hand and fumbled Rosanna's locket until it closed. Then I threw it to the far corner and in a quick blink checked that the death picture in it was disarmed. I picked it up and rejoined the others, after hitting the radio a few times with my battle-ax. Faesto and Rosanna were up, the Tetrarch still munching on ribs and lungs, my place vacant.

'Up,' I said, and we went through the wrecked wall, and at a bound over the perimeter and into the street. There was no pursuit and no commotion as yet. We probably had about five minutes left before the Verulans took their finger out and were after us.

The guard outside fired his stun gun, not at me, but at the Tetrarch. The Tetrarch flinched, looked at the weapon with extreme disapproval, and in passing, gave the marksman a rear left-hook which sent him bodily through a sentry box and a closed wooden gate.

After two blocks I wheeled him off the boulevard, into the ghetto area. It was the way to the wall, and it was also an area where Sutun's police only venture in force. The Tetrarch splashed through garbage. We were behind the Palace of

Equal Justice, and I could smell the stench of the impaled. As luck would have it, on the next corner was a sandbagged post with two of Sutun's thugs in it. There was no stopping. I put the Tetrarch over it, not round it, and we were across the intersection and covered by buildings before they could fire. But I knew they would give the alarm.

The ghetto opened into wider, lit streets – mostly industrial. The towers shone behind us, and so quiet was Verula at this hour that there was a sound of revelry by night: we could even hear the blaring of their music and the uproar of screams and laughter which characterize the mobilization partying of the Elect. Derelicts were sleeping under walls; the slave cages were dark. Inside a parked meat transporter someone was weeping hysterically. We had about two more blocks to the wall. We rounded the corner. At about five hundred yards, there it was, wall, wire, lights. At about two hundred yards a Verulan police vehicle was drawn across the street. In front of it stood an officer and two men. Behind were drawn up two cordons of Sutun's troopers, weapons at the ready.

'No,' said Faesto, 'too much firepower.'

The Tetrarch could have cleared the roadblock or gone through it, but Faesto was perfectly right. I checked him to a slow trot, ostentatiously threw away my sword and raised my right hand in surrender, recalling Thapsis's injunction to think Adambaran. At twenty yards I halted. The officer and the two police came forward gingerly, covering us with stun guns. Behind I saw rifles, laser projectors, the Verulan lot. Then, giving the Adambaran war yell and feeling like Athene, for the first time in anger I raised my aegis.

14

In Terror of Those Starry Wheels

In tribute to the Verulan security forces, I will say that they managed to get off two rounds. Both of them missed. I have seen the effect of mortar and machine-gun fire on unprepared, undeployed troops. What I saw now was in a sense more horrible than blood or dismemberment, for a dead man, even when blown open, is in a sense no longer human. The Verulan guard, if they were human, remained so. For an interminable five seconds they froze. Then first one and then another fell in convulsions. The nearest to the aegis was the officer. He did not fall. Instead his face became distorted with terror, he clapped his hands to his eyes and rushed past us screaming 'No, no, no!' until his head hit a wall. I saw two men sitting on the ground, happily counting one another's fingers. Rosanna's mouth came open and she too hid her face.

'Good' said Faesto. 'Cease fire – quickly!'

I had overlooked a dim store window ahead. In it, as the iris shut and the strobes went out, I caught a minimal flash of a part of the dying aegis pattern, and felt an icy hand pass over my mind. Luckily it passed.

'Get the laser gun?' I said over my shoulder.

'No. *Go!*'

The wire and wall were ahead, not high, but wide. 'Remember, mines,' said Faesto. I jumped the Tetrarch over the gibbering, writhing, foaming cordon and the armored vehicle to avoid the risk that he might pick up a man to tear, halted him deliberately, and switched on the exploder – the green light came on. Faesto was quietly breaking out the silver Window umbrella, having reached over and helped himself to my battle-ax. The Tetrarch, with three up, was facing the jump of his career, and knew it, for he turned and looked at me, running up his motors. Then I slapped his side with the ankus, stuck in my spurs, and he began to move, steadily, counting his paces, faster and faster. The foul Verulan smog rolled in the minefield beyond the wall. A shot, then the green line of a laser-strike passed high over our heads. The Tetrarch gathered. For an awful moment I thought he had risen too late. One foot touched the coiled wire, and a mine went off below and behind us, and still he seemed to rise. Then I felt his underpart go down, his front claws make contact with soil. The barrier was behind, with about four feet to spare. In the rolling fog, as we entered it, mines exploded in orange columns and deafening noise, showering us with dirt, as the harness exploder discharged them. All that now remained of Verula was the Palace City, rising out of the fog, and incredibly beautiful, its feet of clay mercifully concealed in its own effluent.

We rode in silence through the smog cloud until it thinned and we were in the starry night of the Debatable Ground. After some time I passed back rations. Faesto woke the sleeping Rosanna and fed her – the Tetrarch was well baited and had no need of hyasa meat. A whispered conversation went on for sometime behind me, including some kisses. Slowly the dawn rose towards the Eastern Cities as we continued northwards – hyasa returned to their burrows, surrounded by the grooves of tailmarks, simurgh flew over in flocks headed for Verula, a few distant wild asvaya snorted, looked at the Tetrarch, and bounded away, while I prayed there would be no mares in heat. Still there was no pursuit. Time seemed to have stopped. We were beyond feeling tired.

About Fourth Fire we camped briefly. I did not muzzle the Tetrarch as he stood partriarchally over us, his tongue lolling. Faesto helped down the stiff and still almost speechless Rosanna. She held him, then myself. 'We're alive,' she said, and fell asleep again.

'For the moment,' said Faesto, 'we can congratulate ourselves when we get back. Don't lager here too long.'

'An hour?' I said.

'Less – our shadows will lengthen. That thing doesn't prevent a visual search.'

'We'll ride better for resting, and she's exhausted. She had more to take than we had.'

'And took it,' said Faesto. 'She can sleep riding. Every minute counts for Adambara. Let's mount now.'

We had hardly done so when I saw, low down, a Verulan ship which was methodically quartering the desert. The silver disc dipped behind a dune, then reappeared, flying a pattern. 'Everyone under the beast,' I said, unbelting.

'No,' said Faesto, 'too late.'

The ship was turning.

'He'll see our shadows. They're laser armed,' said Faesto, unruffled. 'Use the closed aegis – don't open the iris.'

I held it up and waited. The ship had seen us – dived, steadied on course, and I could see the gunner taking aim at a sitting pigeon. The golden aegis was an irresistible target – moreover a shield is not laser-proof, and scatters molten shrapnel as the beam pierces it. Nearer and nearer he came. Then the green line leaped out, not in a single pencil but in a dazzling V, its point at my aegis. The return limb touched the Verulan ship.

'You got him,' said Faesto. It careened off edgewise, trailing smoke, and crashed out of sight in a brilliant explosion. A black column rose from burning fuel. 'Infantry properly armed can always beat low-level strafing,' said Faesto, 'if they stand their ground. Watch in case there's an escort – he'll see the first man's smoke.'

There was something odd about Faesto now. The Smith of Adambara who sweated and suffered from premature ejaculation had either changed under stress, or never existed. Coolness under fire comes only with training. 'Why didn't you command this operation?' I said, over my shoulder.

'And blow my cover?' said Faesto. 'Ride, man, and be damned to you in Fours – that's an order.' I rode, like Paul Revere. The Tetrarch pounded along like his namesake – the locomotive, not the horse. I had a half-dream in which I held the regulator while Faesto the Smith fired the furnace, the rails stretched ahead and signal lights flew by. It was, of course, night. Ahead were three reds and a green, a junction. The lights, however, were real.

'Adambara,' said Faesto. 'Tally-ho!' The lights dimmed slowly as the dawn rose again. First the watch-masts rose, then the domes, then the shining wall. I heard a trumpet sounding the charge. The cavalry was coming. It came in a monstrous dust cloud, in fourfold column which split and wheeled to form on each side of us, General Kari at its head; at the rear, I noticed, two civilian technicians with outsized aegises. Thapsis was taking no chances under the walls. Now we had escort. The gates of Adambara opened and we rode through. At the barracks the escort wheeled and saluted, leaving the two technicians to ride with us to the Rotunda. I looked behind me. In the aftersaddle Rosanna was awake, staring in front of her. In front of her was an anxious, puzzled, competent Smith, wiping off his forehead with the back of his hand.

Thapsis asked two questions only. 'Sutun?'

'Deified yesterday. Mad as a hatter and dangerous with it.'

'The crystal?'

'I left it.'

Thapsis huffed impatiently. 'Too well guarded, I suppose. Ah well.'

'No,' I said, 'But I looked into the crystal. It would do better in Verula. It's our most powerful weapon.'

'I see.' He paused a moment.

Rosanna said, 'The decision was mine. Edward and I are both Adepts.'

Thapsis shot her a penetrating glance.

'But damn the crystal,' I said. 'The main thing is that Verula means war.'

'With us?'

'Yes, with you.'

'They try that periodically. A few Thorls sent to harrass . . . Are they arming the Elect?'

'Yes,' I said, 'they are. They aim to take over Adambara once and for all, in the name of Xarm and his divine reincarnation Sutun.'

'When?'

'For all I know they're on their way now. So for the sake of the Four, get moving.'

'He's right, Sir,' said Faesto. 'We've probably got about three hours. Full-scale attack, and they mean business.'

15
The Arrows of Intellect

The effect of this intelligence on Thapsis was not what I expected. He simply sighed deeply, as at a complex blunder by subordinates, and said in English: 'Jesus wept!' then in Losian: 'Simurgh-vala, tacho!'

The perch was wheeled in. Thapsis wrote four characters on each of a number of slips of the writing foil, each of the eaglelike creatures, unhooded, held out a taloned leg to receive its message and departed without ado, leaving falling feathers from their confinement. 'They know where to go,' said Thapsis. It was not five minutes before the most typical sound of Adambara on a working day, the underground boom of the Smithy, stopped. Faesto looked up. 'They never,' he said, 'in one hundred Four Seasons stopped before.' The fact had brought home to the Smith, it seemed, the gravity of the situation. I admired his act. Iron tubes were being sounded and horns blown. A simurgh arrived in a flurry of feathers, holding out his leg almost before it was stably perched. Thapsis took its message and stroked its neck, while it watched with a round, vigilant eye.

'You got us about an hour's start,' said Thapsis. 'A Verulan armored column has been sighted.'

'You're totally unprepared,' I said.

'On the contrary. We are armed to the rear teeth. But we needed that hour. It will save us some bad moments, a lot of rape and destruction. Come.'

The stairs to the top of the tower by the Rotunda were long and spiral and all four of us breathless at the top. Adambara seemed unchanged by the threat that hung over it. Then I noticed that stalls were closing, windows were closing. Also the College of Physicians had changed. A whole wall, which we could see above the houses, was no longer shining ceramic. It had rolled open like the doors of a scenery store, and vast canvases were being moved out – drawn no doubt by my asvaya. Choreb-drawn carts arrived, filled with white-tunic-wearing technicians, who proceeded to set up booths at every street corner and unload covered clay jars and what appeared to be large wooden printing blocks, like oversize cattle brands, set on rods. Most remarkable, I heard not only laughter but singing. This might have been Third Tasuranga, and Adambara in festival rather than facing the threat of bombardment and pillage. Three asvaya galloped past, ridden – for the first time I had ever seen them so – by artisans with hammers and crowbars, not asvin. 'They're going to unblock the West Gate,' said Rosanna, holding Faesto's hand on one side and mine on the other. 'And use those asvaya as bulldozers.'

Thapsis heaved a deep sigh of relief. 'Once that's open,' he said, 'we're safe. I owe this to you; we owe this to you. May Los and the Three bless you and unite in you.' For the first time I heard the ancient Losian for 'threefold', the triact, never normally spoken. Faesto made the sign of the Hammer, and we imitated him. Thapsis took his and my free hands so that we stood, as four, in a circle; the most solemn Losian act.

'No city under siege is safe,' said Thapsis, 'if you leave one of its gates walled up.'

'And you thought,' said Faesto, 'that we weren't ready. Well, I'm relieved to see that we are ready.'

Not an earth hour too soon, I thought. There was an ominous dust plume rising over the desert in the direction from which we had so recently come. We descended the stairs.

'Nukes,' I said, 'if you throw back their first attack?'

'Not a chance. They want our women and our Smithies. I'm glad – I'd hate to turn one of those back on them. They don't smell out the Elect.'

'They're probably pre-programmed.'

'Behind every program,' said Thapsis, 'was the mind of a programmer. We'd try to land them in desert.'

'Gas?'

'We're ready. We know what they have. Override cards have been prepared. They'll be at every street corner. And they're going up on buildings now, or should be.'

'Laser beams?'

'Our walls, you may have noticed, are nearly perfect mirrors for radiation. We needed just that hour, Colonel Eda. It will save many lives, a few here, many there. Now they will be destroyed only if they use their own weapons, by their own weapons. And for what they are about to receive,' said Thapsis, 'may the Four make them truly thankful. Verula was rotten ripe to die by its own hand. So be it.'

Faesto said little, as was his habit qua Smith, but he was clearly fretting to be at his post before the place of his craft. On the stairs Rosanna had to choose hands, and chose his. General Faesto of Adambaran security, I recalled, was a pareunogenic Adept, like it or not, though perhaps he hadn't realized the fact. Nor had I. Rosanna had been right to teach him the Game.

'What happens,' I said to Faesto, 'if they attack under smoke?'

'Could be tricky – but A and one, our air-pollution control was built with that in mind. It's got a two thousand per cent overkill for our industrial needs. So it wouldn't be easy – most smokes just fall to the ground like a lead balloon. B and two, the best way of getting blasted by one of those aegises is to look at it in an infrared sight. C and three, we've got other goodies if we had to use them. The eye isn't the only way into a Verulan's tiny mind.'

It struck me that this was the longest monologue I had ever heard Faesto deliver. In the course of saying ha, ha, among the trumpets, he sometimes let his craftsmanly manner waver.

Rosanna's mind was elsewhere. 'Will they change?' she said.

'Who knows?' said Thapsis. 'Not many things change people.'

'Do you know,' said Rosanna, 'what their biggest turn-on is? Do you know that a bunch of the Elect of both sexes pick up a Thorl girl, make a fuss of her, take her to see the Palace City, tell her they love her, ball her, then tell her they have a surprise for her and turn her over to the butchers while they watch; that's the surprise.'

Faesto held her hand and shook his head.

'I think we can reckon to stop those excesses,' said Thapsis. 'Changing people, however . . . Well, we shall have to see, and we shall see, pretty soon.'

'When we were running away, after the Tetrarch got us out, there was a girl crying and crying, inside a truck,' said Rosanna.

'I don't think,' said Thapsis, 'that there's going to be another Verulan banquet.'

'Can't you do something?' said Rosanna.

'Does you credit, my dear,' said Faesto. 'No thought about what they did to you, only what they might do to her. Pity we can't freeze Verula in its tracks somehow. What do you think, Sir? Could be a good military case for it if we've got the hardware mounted – their second strike will just about be mobilized, but it won't be out of Verula yet.'

'It does her credit,' said Thapsis, 'but we have to look at the larger strategy. That poor girl may be dead by now.'

'There are bound to be others,' said Rosanna.

'She'd only be moving to Our Side, Rosanna,' I said.

'I hope she likes it better,' said Rosanna.

'Don't we still have Dormouse operational?' said Faesto, after a pause.

At the bottom of the stairs, Thapsis stopped. 'You know,' he said, 'I think that's a good idea. It might meet both points – including the risk of a nuclear counterstrike. Sutun, after all, is deranged. He might just try it and kill everyone in Verula, Elect and Thorls. We can prevent them committing felo-de-se, at least. Simurgh-vala!'

A couple of minutes after the bird left, I heard a sound of the Other Side, unfamiliar in Adambara. Thapsis opened the door and went outside. We all followed him.

From inside the Smithy a huge disc was wobbling up,

raised by six conventional jets which streamed kerosene smoke, its navigation lights flashing cockily as if it were on civilian business. Then the jets rotated from lift to drive, the disc deployed a tail, like the tail of a kite, and it came our way, its motors bellowing, climbing and leaving a skein of smoke trails. As it galumphed over I saw that the enormous iris of its bomb-bay doors, painted outside in the Number Three target pattern, was closed, but spoiler targets, missile rejectors and anti-radar arrays were deploying out of pods every which way. The angle of climb was steep. In a few seconds military pandemonium broke out in the distant Verulan lines.

'Give them some instructive target practice. Better now than later,' said Faesto.

'It's unmanned anyhow,' said Thapsis. The firing stopped abruptly, as if the gunners had received an IFF code, or spotted a friendly.

'It wagged its tail at them in Verulan,' said Faesto.

'A flying aegis?'

'No, you could call it a mild sedative – sleepy-making. Code name Dormouse. It's many Four Seasons old; they may even hit it. I'd forgotten we had it until you spoke. Used it on outlaw bands. It was due for the Museum in the Hall of Record.' He turned back indoors.

'I hope Sutun doesn't take it for *our* preemptive strike and press the button,' I said.

'Vikings,' said Thapsis, 'or Redskins, or Yogis, don't *have* any advanced technology, remember? An antique Rube Goldberg contraption like that, the Elect will take for one of theirs. It about fits their size. They'll switch on the runway lights for it, I shouldn't wonder. And then – bingo! In it goes, under their radar, rooftop high.'

'When it's too late,' said Faesto.

'They won't all look hard at it,' I said.

'Enough will. Even the flicker off walls will make people indoors feel very, very sleepy. Do you know, that thing has the only mercury strobe tubes left in Adambara? A real museum piece.'

'Thank you, Thapsis,' said Rosanna.

'Ever think,' I said, 'of modulating a few moiré patterns onto the Verulan television time bases?'

'We did,' said Thapsis, 'and it was a mistake.'

'What happened?'

'Xarm's revolution. Only Thorls watch television. But we have the equipment set up in case of sudden and temporary.'

We reached the office and drew breath. There were no more warlike noises from the desert.

'Why us, Thapsis?' I said.

'Well, think. We needed people from Your Side, who are used to Verulans. We needed systems' experts. We needed them also to be Adepts or potential Adepts whom we could train, who had the necessary powers and would have some notion of what was going on. And we needed people unspoiled by the House of Play who could play method on the necessary roles. I'm sorry, but there was not even a short list.'

'You need not,' said Rosanna, 'be sorry.'

16

To Wash Off the Not-human

'Well,' said Thapsis, 'you completed your mission. You disobeyed explicit orders, but then you are an Adept, and that was to be expected. Also the lady was absolutely right. If this were a happier time, I'd suggest we went to dinner.'

'I'd better get back to duty,' I said.

'No,' said Thapsis, 'that is that. The asvin are confined to barracks.'

'Then give me a transfer,' I said. 'I'll go and help them set up the mandalas.'

'I told you,' said Thapsis, 'that is that. There is a possibility that there will be some casualties. Only a few. But you are a magnet for trouble. Also I don't want insubordinate Adepts running around. The next few days or weeks will be hairy. Did you let foreigners run around like riderless asvaya during your Battle of Britain? Report here at the next Fire for orders – I shall anyhow have someone for you to escort back with you.'

Along the top of the wall outside, the upper edges of the huge painted designs jigged as they were carried hurriedly to the wall of Bowmen.

'Won't those things blow your people's minds?' I said. 'They're not even covered.'

'Those,' said Thapsis, 'hang in every infant school in Adambara. The real stuff is already on the walls – covered. Or in transparencies for projection. It's safer to handle that way.'

'I won't say good-bye, Thapsis. I have a suspicion it's au revoir.' He inclined his head. 'Come on and help me pack,' I said to Rosanna.

'No,' said Rosanna.

'Say again?'

'You heard what I said, Edward – no. I'm not a Verulan. I'm not going to leave Faesto in the middle of a war. Not after what I went through in that awful place. He saved my life, you both saved . . . Anyhow, we're going to choose a collar. While there are still stalls open. And before he goes on duty.'

'And what about us?'

'There will be time for us,' said Rosanna, 'when I die. I'm an Adept, remember – implicate time stands still. I love you, Edward. See you after the funeral.'

Faesto gave me a desperate look and took both my hands. 'Blood brother,' he said, and gave the formal embrace of blood brothers who have shared a woman.

'Run split, scarper,' I whispered as he did so. 'There's still time. You can mix with the crowd.' Faesto shrugged and followed Rosanna out into the chaos of the street.

'Why not now?' I said to Thapsis.

'I told you, you will probably have someone to escort.'

'I'd like to cut it short, if Rosanna's determined to stay. I don't know, but I imagine none of this is in real time on Our Side, so she shouldn't be long, in spite of your physicians and the Ageless Diagram. And I'm not packing. I feel sure nothing will go through customs.'

'Wise,' said Thapsis. 'Anyhow the streets are almost impassable now.'

'But I would like to help in your struggle. To see the Verulans change step, or get their come-uppance. To see the Four united.'

'I appreciate that,' said Thapsis, 'but there is nothing useful you can do, beyond what you have done. And the Four, I think, are already united?'

'When, where?' I asked him.

His only answer was 'Wait in there, please.'

'There,' was a luminous-ceiled cell with a chair and a small window. It opened on a vista of streaming people, mandalas carried to the wall like Trade Union banners in a procession, the shining wall itself, the dust-cloud of the now advancing Verulan forces rising beyond like a conflagration. A Verulan

140

reconnaissance ship swept over and came back at rooftop
level, confident in the lack of ground fire. The cloud of dust
moved to obscure the sun. I heard screaming whinnies from
the asvaya stables. I hoped the Verulans would not enter
Adambara by night. As the short Losian twilight darkened, I
saw that I need not have worried. The mandalas of instruction were luminous, as if in black light, glowing more fiercely
as night came on: I imagined the glare of other more powerful
arms when these were unmasked. The people too were
naked now, men, women and children. Clothes lay in the
street. They lined up in orderly manner at booths, where
technicians, with large wooden stamps, impressed on their
bodies, front and back, the pattern of invulnerability. The
paints in their receptacles glowed in innumerable colors.
They moved to stations with the quiet undirected Losian
discipline, typical of an ungoverned people, serious but
laughing and singing still. I first saw, then heard, a rumor
run through them, and caught finally the words of it: 'They
are opening the West Gate!' and knew that Adambara was
now secure, facing a devoted enemy with all its gates barred
in complete openness, while the unpleasant dust cloud
advanced to meet the destruction of Verulan civilization, an
offense which had outlived its time. I caught the words of
the song: 'Satu joyat ev empada' – Right will prevail in real
time.

'Come on,' said Thapsis. 'I have work to do.' I had not
heard him enter. 'We shall have twenty thousand freaked-
out and very astonished prisoners to feed and house. I have
to mobilize every woman in Adambara. Here's your charge.'

My charge was a woman, veiled from crown to waist, so
that I could see nothing of her, and bound, wrists behind her
back, in the fashion of one who is to enter the presence of
Divinity, or who has come from it, in the House of Enitharmon. She seemed drugged also, with nepenthe perhaps.

'Neither you nor she may touch or address each other,'
said Thapsis. 'As an Adept, you know that.'

He turned to the side door.

'Follow me,' he said. Two men, of Thapsis's own force, fell
in behind, with the strained look of soldiers who are dis-

armed in a dangerous situation – wishing themselves, no doubt, naked and marked with the mandala signs of the civilians around them streaming to action stations.

We headed through the orderly confusion, inwards, towards the eye of Adambara. Halfway there was a whoosh outside the walls followed by a crash in the Verulan lines and a long orange conflagration. Thapsis shook his head. 'I was afraid of that,' he said. 'Probably they won't try another round.'

'Scare shot?'

'Yes, a guided missile, and they fired at a mandala. They must have got it back in the battery which fired it.' I pondered on the paradox, in the Losian army, of telling an incoming from an outgoing round, and wondered how quickly Verulan officers learn by aversion.

In the wall of the eye of Adambara is a gate so rarely opened that it takes two security men, using a dagger as lever, to turn its three keys. 'Enter the small building,' said Thapsis, 'and proceed as an Adept, recalling the Game of Adepts, which you now know. Good-bye, *friend*.' The greeting, in Losian, confirmed what I had suspected. Thapsis was indeed not an Adept. He was an archimage, who alone calls an Adept 'friend' in the Losian tessaract. I could not reply before the gate closed. I heard the locks turn. The holy ground was level unlit desert, tangled with desert plants. I picked my way, my prisoner following me – I would have carried her if I might touch her, but remembered my orders, even though she stumbled. There seemed to be no building. Then I saw light on a low ceramic dome, and realized that it stood underground. The dome was familiar. It belonged to the House of Play. We descended a long flight of steps, unswept from leaves and trash like the disused entrance of a subway station. The iron door of this tomblike edifice was ajar, and light came from within. It was not, as I had feared, a tomb, surrogate for the Door of Death, but only the luminous-ceiled crypt I knew; at its end another door, which I knew even better, and that door was locked. It did not respond to my ring. My prisoner stood like a statue, the maiden on the Eight of Swords. Then studying the form of the wrought handle I perceived suddenly from the Game of

142

Adepts how such locks function, and that they are keyless, and I opened it, motioned my prisoner through it, and stepped after her, closing it behind.

There was the expected suspension of thought. I was standing naked in bright moonlight. My prisoner was naked, still bound, still veiled. The room on earth was familiar; the clock, I noted, still wound and ticking. I untied her wrists and let fall the cord – it appeared to turn rapidly inside out, became a point, vanished. I removed the veil, and it crumpled on itself and disappeared like pipe smoke. The prisoner was Rosanna. Nor had any time passed.

BOOK TWO
A Grain of Sand

1

A Male Without a Female Counterpart

Rosanna left me after about a year. There was no manner of dispute between us – our shared experience was in its way a bond which we both felt to be indissoluble – but she had a career to further, the medical school to which she had been admitted was remote, and the parting, though painful, was more in the nature of an adjournment, which we might or might not choose to reconvene.

I recognized its imminence without much discussion between us. When the telegram came, I helped her pack, took custody of china and other possessions which she was not taking with her and drove her to the airport. We drank coffee, exchanged promises to write, her flight was called, we kissed and she gathered her effects.

'Call anytime you need me,' I said.

'I'll wire,' said Rosanna. 'It's cheaper, and you usually aren't in. Until then. I love you.'

It would be untrue to say that I did not miss her acutely, but we had had a year and several weeks in real time, and indeterminate and quite uncovenanted extra time on the other side of the carved door, and I had an equally sharp sense that the adjournment was temporary. Other lovers might worry about other attachments, but we each knew that the other would form these, as we always had done, without subtraction from our own. Beside that, it had been confirmed to us on the best authority during our previous adventure that she was a spontaneous Adept, and that I had been made one by virtue of sexual intercourse, Adepthood, like gonorrhea, being communicable but far more dignified, beside being apparently incurable, and to two such people anything might happen at any time.

The apartment nevertheless felt empty, and I had no woman. The first of these was tolerable, and the second better not addressed in too much haste. Accordingly, I got on with my work on the computer decipherment of Etruscan. To the languages in the computer lexicon I added Losian, the tongue we had acquired during our spiritual journey, smuggling it in as an invented 'hypothetical' language and getting some unmerited compliments from the linguistics team on my sense of humor. I still wore the electrum ring which had been provided on the other side of the door, but its ability to transdict spoken language was limited to the Other Side – as I found out in experiments with Finnish and Pakistani colleagues – and I could consider myself lucky it had come through customs at all. It was the only physical object other than our two selves which had. I thought of having it x-rayed to learn whether its basis was electronic or transcendental; it seemed to be an advanced kind of Intelligent Speech Prosthesis – but gave up the idea as being a little impertinent, and wore the thing as a reminder.

There was still that oppressive door, with its carved panels showing the Four Beasts and the Four Emblems, and its frame, the Tree, the Serpent and the Spinning Woman, with the primeval Couple over its lintel. It was unlocked now, though we still had no key, and we opened it repeatedly prior to Rosanna's departure. It led to the blind corridor which served as a suitcase store and sexual playroom, and in the last days of our cohabitation we went in and out on both accounts without any expectation of unusual consequences: they seemed unlikely and inappropriate. On my return from taking Rosanna to the airport I opened it again, half-expecting to find her inside, but found nothing beyond my own luggage and a few props which had entertained Rosanna when she performed her slavegirl number. The door would evidently not reactivate itself arbitrarily, which was a relief.

I wrote twice, and Rosanna twice – I about routine matters and my undying affection, she about her arrival; I in duplicate, one letter about not buying a used car without getting it inspected, and the other a set of sexual instructions, to be performed at a stated time, so that I knew what she was doing, and without the least deviation from script. This was to act as a long-range turn-on in case Rosanna was not otherwise occupied, and would, I knew, produce results (we had done it before – Rosanna called it mail-order orgasm) and pave the way for a repeat by telephone. She replied that it had worked – which was obvious from the letter, written shortly after it had stopped working. In her last paragraph she mentioned some striking new opportunity, without specifying what it was, and promised to be in touch with me about it shortly. After that, for a month, nothing happened.

And then I found, on my return from work, a yellow Western Union cablegram envelope: Rosanna was evidently abroad – I wondered with whom. The message read: 'NEED YOU EARLIEST EXPLAIN ALL MEETING I LOVE YOU ROSANNA.' I would have taken this for a flashback from the mail-order orgasm, and was beginning to rearrange my next week, when I realized this cable was peculiar. It had not been pushed under the front door of the apartment by the mailman, but under the carved door leading to the cupboard, so that it lay in quite the wrong part of the floor for a prosaic origin. Moreover the cupboard door was now locked, and presumably, if one might use the expression, armed.

I meditated for a considerable time on this, and laid my plans. I was willing, and since such extratemporal journeys do not score against real time there was no obstacle of a practical kind, but I needed my head together. This was going to take some spiritual preparation. I recalled the Time of Choice which succeeds passage through the activated door – on the last time we had been translated in the middle of a sexual fantasy which would have been quite jolly on this Side but had had some pretty hairy results on the Other Side, and I wanted a quiet life. If the bloody door was going to be so literal-minded, I'd do a great deal better to start in a suitably Adeptic state of grace, but even that had better not be overdone.

My first precaution was to discuss the previous experience with McPherson. He'd seen the door before we discovered its properties, and he'd obviously recognized them when we didn't. McPherson showed neither surprise nor contrition. He listened to the story with polite attention.

'Ahweel,' he said, 'it was my opinion, you will surely recall, that it is no ordinary door.'

'That's what you said last time,' I told him. 'I think it was a rotten trick not to make it crystal clear that we'd end up in Bedlam – we both might have been killed.'

'I think,' said McPherson, 'that there was upon your own showing verra little risk of that.'

'Well,' I said, 'do I open it or don't I, and will it work again?'

'I think on the whole,' said McPherson, 'that in your place I would with due consideration open it. With consideration, you mind I have said.'

'Mac,' I said, 'come off that infuriating Highland act and tell me what you bloody well think will happen. Any normal friend would punch your head. Come to think of it, how *did* you know?'

'You have had,' said McPherson, 'a verra typical shamanic experience, modified by your own culture. If I knew what might happen on another occasion I would tell you. For a start I would not myself be opening it in a mood of punching any heads, or there may well be ill of it. And I will be assuming that you ken how to open it, not having as you tell me the key?'

'Yes, I do. Now stop talking like a Greek oracle, and deliver, or I'll open the damn thing now and push you through it screaming.'

'I think you will not,' said McPherson. 'Will you stop havering, man, and listen without anger?'

'All right, I'm sorry. Remember I'm a thick-headed Anglo.'

'There is no need to apologize. I am assuming you are anxious to shamanize again. In your place I would open the door circumspectly, in a spirit of seeking more understanding of the phenomenon. All of your troubles come from the thick-headedness to which you refer, though that is not my own chosen word, you ken. You rushed at it, man, like a bull at a gate. You were lucky not to find yourself something worse than a comic book hero. You have had your play. This now is a privilege, and it is one I would in your place be taking seriously – if you are an Adept, think like one, and not like a fule.'

'I agree.'

'I spoke plainly because you asked me to speak plainly.'

'Keep it up,' I said. 'Do you think Rosanna's there?'

'It would seem from her message verra probable.'

'What about you coming with me?'

McPherson considered weightily. 'I think on the whole,' he said, 'that I will not. You see, I have no need of any doors of that kind. And now, if you will permit me, I have a class.' And off he went. McPherson had the infuriating ability to turn any ticking-off one gave him for not posting warnings on spiritual booby-traps into a rebuke on the ticker-off. I sat down and thought hard.

At midnight I was still thinking and the door, when I tried it cautiously, still locked. I removed my clothes, put myself as well as I might in a state of spiritual grace, trying to forget that Rosanna was no less a physical and accessible woman on that side than on this, performed the Game of the Adepts, and opened the door in its keyless mode. I passed into darkness and fell over a case. I was in the cupboard. I retraced my steps and closed the door. At two A.M. I repeated the maneuver. The result was the same. I went to bed baffled. There was clearly something wrong.

It must have been at three that I woke again. I must have been dreaming, for I found myself arguing aloud with the spiritual emanation of McPherson, and shouting, 'All I want is to understand!' The room was moonlit, as on the occasion when Rosanna and I had first opened the door. Waking, I knew for a certainty that the door was now activated. Indeed, there was no need of any Game of the Adepts, for when I tried it, it was not locked. I went in.

2

I Become What I Was Doing

The interval of suspended thought must have been brief, for I heard the door close, though I had not myself closed it.

I was standing in a wood at dawn. It was warm, for the wood was tropical, and the light was yellow behind small and a few larger trees. It was sufficient to see that I had emerged, in fact, from one such larger tree, in the bole of which the door had been situated. Its inner surface was covered in bark, and as I watched, the line of its closure was being effaced, as if by a zip-fastener. Before I could have touched it, the bark had become entire and quite doorless, so that was clearly that.

I inspected myself with a good deal of apprehension for evidences of the warrior number. I need not have worried. I had no arms or insignia. In fact, I was wearing what appeared to be a long ochre-colored dressing gown. Something which tickled my left shoulder and passed under my right arm turned out to be a well-worn cord, of the kind which a Hindu receives at his initiation. Attached to my girdle was a very clean, empty, brass bowl. Propped against the now wholly doorless tree was a kind of scepter or spear ending not, as I had expected from the rest of my costume, in a trident, but in a weathercock-like emblem bearing on its four tips the Sun, Moon, Star and Mountain of the fourfold holy Losian world. I was evidently a begging monk, or something like it in a Losian religious order. I'd asked for it – and got it.

This in itself raised problems in my mind. It is one thing to be in command of an unfamiliar regiment, regiments differing chiefly in their armament, and that with the technology of their parent society – monks were another matter. It would be an unfortunate experience to be turned into an earthly

Franciscan, even for a devout Catholic, if he did not know the proper deportment of the Franciscan Rule. But a Catholic so transformed would at least have some idea what was expected of him – I had none. There were practical matters. Did I belong to a community, or was I a self-contained ecclesiastical unit? Was there a refectory or did I have to solicit alms? The present location looked an unpromising site to take up a collection. Then there was the matter of chastity – in the Losian world I did not think this a likely condition of membership, but on my last visit I had heard mention of chaste Adepts, and I might possibly have downplayed Rosanna's accessibility too much. Last time, a macho hero: this time a prickless ecclesiastical wonder. The Time of Choice could be horribly literal-minded. I'd have to wear it now, however. On the economic side, the monk I most resembled was a Hindu sannyasin of the Daśanami order – role playing from cues had worked all right when I found myself a colonel of asvin, so I decided to start with this scenario and improvise as needed, sticking to all the details – not more than three nights in any one house, begging bowl, gifts taken with the right hand, and so on – hoping I met no co-religionists, and reading back on topics such as chastity by common sense, as any stranger would do in an unfamiliar culture. I also had enough confidence in the door to reckon that it supplied all the necessary props for any role it imposed, and that if I had to beg, begging would be feasible. What I now needed, then, was a village.

There were, among the trees and bushes, some rudimentary beginnings of a track, and I followed it, pushing aside large leaves, and then, as it widened, walking in the middle of it and trying to see where it led.

The forest had no bird song, as in temperate woods, but a whole repertoire of percussive cries from birds and insects, and birds of many kinds were moving about. Some resembled parrots with long green metallic quetzal-style tails, and there were flocks of doves, together with the simurgh, the small eagle which in the Losian cities serves as a message-carrier. I had gone about a mile with increasing confidence when, rounding a large tree, whose roots came out of the ground like gray walls, I came almost face to face with a predator. It was shaped like an enormous whitish ferret, large as a mountain lion, with a long ill-feathered tail, red eyes, and the needle ferret teeth scaled up almost to mountain lion size. It was tearing a carcass, probably of a small wild pig, and it came round with a hiss of annoyance to match the general meanness of its appearance. It occurred to me that the soldierly option, which at least had an issue of sword and shield built into it, might have been the less hazardous, and prepared for repatriation. The weathercock trident had very limited defensive or offensive possibilities. But the creature, in the act of making a rush, underwent a sudden and totally unexplained change of heart, as though struck on the snout, or pulled bodily back by the tail. Its aggression went out like a light, it backed a few paces, and began an extraordinary salaaming display, as if to a mate. Then it turned in its length and vanished, leaving me with its kill.

Only a few hundred yards on I found the village. Its first evidence was a series of rough, hand-tilled fields, chiefly of what appeared to be pineapples, then a long clearing with a row of huts so primitive that at first I took them for brushpiles. There were smoking ashes in a communal firepit, but not a soul was in sight. Apart from the pit and huts, not an artifact of any kind – not a spear, not a pot, not a mat – was to be seen, and not a soul was moving, nor were there any dogs, pigs or poultry. It was a Stone Age place, or more primitive than that, and the lack of children or people at this hour, early as it was, was uncanny. It did not seem to be the work of a culture which would recognize, let alone feed, a monk. But there was no help for it. According to plan I beat on my bowl, sat myself with my back to a tree, placed the bowl before me, and adopted a posture of absorbed meditation. Not a soul moved.

An hour later they had still not moved. I am a poor meditator, and had had a sleepless night, and when meditation passed into a doze I only realized that it had done so when I woke with a start. The scenario had evidently worked, for I was surrounded by a silent, respectful circle, who had come for my darśan. I looked at my bowl and could not see it. It had disappeared under what seemed to be a harvest festival – pineapples, mangoes, bananas and fruits like a large scarlet pear, unfamiliar on the Other Side. There was even a pumpkin. Beyond it my still-sleepy eyes fell on the ring of villagers. All, adults, children and babes at breast, were improbably clad, in the growing tropical heat, with black Eskimo fur suits. These were not people but chimpanzees, or creatures very like them, sitting in a respectful and expressive silence.

The opening of my eyes must have been noted, for there was an audible gasp of devout expectation. Then a large adult rose and approached the pile of fruit, topping it with the largest pineapple I had ever seen. He was an old male, gray about the face, and he placed his hands over his eyes and bowed.

'Bless you, my son,' I said in Losian, using the fourfold number of holy invocation. 'The Fourfold be with you. Did you love well?' The venerable elder rose, pointed at me, described a halo about his head, pointed at the sun and held up all his fingers. Then he joined his hands in the conventional Christian gesture of prayer.

'You – saint – many suns – pray,' I said to myself. The animal was talking deaf and dumb language.

'I am the Adept you have long prayed for?' I said in Losian. He nodded vigorously. I mustered my recollections of Washoe, the Ameslan-talking chimp, and awaited the next address.

'Huge – flapping-wings – chew – trample – pineapple – you – wallop.'

He made it more difficult by jumping up and down, and by hamming up his gestures as no deaf human would do, but he made up in emphasis what he lacked in clarity. The circle joined in with the jumped equivalent of 'Yes Lord, Hallelujah!'

'A great bird is destroying your crops?' I hazarded.

'Shake head: huge – all fours – snarl – flap-flap – you – wallop.'

155

'A huge flying quadruped?'

'Yes – You – prayed – many suns – wallop – command – go away.'

'Wallop – command – go away,' echoed the circle.

'A flying four-footed mean-minded monster is eating your crops, and you've prayed a long time for an Adept to drive it away?' I had a feeling that the translation was getting garbled, and my ring was unfortunately serviceable only on spoken and some written communications, but the circle was in no doubt. It broke up and rolled on the ground, embracing and hailing me as a deliverer.

'You – sky – command – here – thanks,' signaled the Archichimp, overcome with emotion. God sent me to deliver them, I said to myself, from a monster, and wished devoutly for my squadron of asvin, who were monster proof at all reasonable odds.

'Good morning, Adept,' said a voice. 'You know well?' A boy and a girl, human this time and in the ordinary Losian dress – tunic and trousers for him, frontless Minoan bodice for her, were standing outside the rejoicing ring of villagers, on my right, where I had not seen them approach, and thoroughly enjoying the proceedings. 'I see you've met our villagers,' said the boy.

'Thank the Four for language,' I said. 'You can tell me what this is all about.'

'You seem to be doing pretty well on your own,' said the girl.

'Who are you?' I asked.

'We're their communications officers,' she said. 'I'm Erin and he's Tari. What good Losian you speak.'

'I'm delighted,' I said, 'to see you. Did you love well?'

'Very well, thank you.'

'How did you know I was a . . . foreigner?'

'We knew you were coming. We asked for an Other-Side Adept with special knowledge.'

'And they want me,' I said, 'to get rid of a mean flying four-footed monster which is eating their pineapples?'

'That's what they say. They usually know what they want.'

'What sort of monster?' I asked.

'We haven't seen it,' said Tari.

'Couldn't you have sent for troops?' I asked. 'Why me?'

'You don't send troops to help the Klars,' said Erin. 'Bloodshed would mean years of guilt and ritual pollution. They don't even kill caterpillars. You sound like an Other-Side Adept – you really have to respect these people's customs: if this thing's an animal and you kill it, you'll disrupt their whole way of life, and anyhow it probably isn't, and spirit monsters are swordproof.'

The Archichimp was jumping up and down and beating on the ground in an agony of suspense during this conference. Erin spoke rapidly to him in sign language. Evidently she confirmed that I would oblige, for the rejoicings broke out afresh.

'Good,' said Erin, 'that's settled.'

'I have no experience with real monsters,' I said, 'or for that matter with spirit monsters. Can't you send to Adambara for an aegis and frighten it away?'

'There's a pest-control mandala on its way,' said Erin, 'but it'll take weeks in this country. They want quick results.'

'Maybe I saw the monster,' I said. 'There was a mean-looking giant weasel up the track – I nearly trod on it. Luckily it ran.'

Tari and Erin looked at each other. 'That,' said Erin, 'was a verra. It feeds on Klars. If you can deal with one of those, Adept, you need have no fear. It would have killed either of us on the spot.' They looked badly frightened.

'You won't be able to stay here,' said Tari, 'and a Klar hut isn't too comfortable. Let them escort you through the village, give them darśan till sundown, then we'll take you to our camp. You can stay with us. There's another girl with us, so the tetrad will be complete. May we have the honor of worshipping Enitharmon with you?'

'Oh yes,' said Erin, 'it'd be such fun to share love with an Adept, if you wish to join us. Let me help carry your fruit.'

And so, bearing my staff, flanked by the two youngsters carrying offerings, followed by the crowd of devotees, and blessing each hut as I passed, we moved off in procession.

As for me, my fears that the door had taken me too literally were at rest.

3

The Terrors of Entuthon and a Reunion

The four of us, Tari, Erin, myself and an ethnoprimatologist and veterinarian called Eli (her name was Elynittria, the first Losian I had met who bore the name of a holy Emanation) lay on the love bed next morning, ate fruit and held a counsel of war.

'The only thing the Klars know,' said Erin, 'is that this thing flies through the air, shakes the ground when it walks, and drinks at the holy pool.'

'Anybody actually see it?'

'One Klar did. He says it has four heads, fifteen eyes, and tried to kick him. But he was frightened out of his wits and the creature gets bigger and weirder every time around.'

'The holy pool,' said Eli, prettily eating one of the red pears and letting juice run down her slim chest, 'does sound a bit as if it were a spirit.'

'Any Losian animal it could be?'

'We don't think so. The Klars are poets – their whole world is full of magical things we can't see. Los himself speaks to them, as he does to children – they are his innocent children.'

'How big?' I asked.

'Three times as big as an asva.'

'And the holy pool?'

'It's a green-water drinking pool. The Klars go there in parties for fear of meeting a verra. You'd better just sit there and see what happens.'

'I'll wait,' I said, 'for that aegis.'

'You can't. Not if it's eating their crops. They rely on you.'

'Spirits don't eat crops.'

'If I know Klars, their spirits might. The crops will just fail for lack of the proper rites in tending them. So we don't have much time.'

'I'll do my best, then,' I said.

Erin put her arms round me. 'Thank you, Adept,' she said.

'You care a lot about the Klars,' I said, kissing her.

'We love them,' said Tari. 'They're the only holy people left. They live in Eden, even in this time. They are Adepts in their own right, innocent Adepts. They see through the Veil of Ulro and can live with the vision. I sometimes think that in them the Four are in constant harmony. That's how it will be with man one day.' It needed no ritual for us all to take hands, for the act seemed to spring naturally from what had been said.

'When?' I asked, 'do I start?'

'Tonight won't be too soon,' said Eli. 'I'm afraid what any delay will do to the villagers.'

'I take it I'd better go alone, then,' I said. 'If we send a bloody regiment we'll scare the thing away. What about verras and any other nasty creatures?'

'We've got scare lockets,' said Erin. 'We left them off yesterday but that was foolish. We won't do that again.'

'Will they work on whatever this is?'

'There's no knowing. On a verra, yes, but they're mean and jump you, and they move like a flash, so unless you're invulnerable you mustn't relax an instant.'

'Any other vermin?' I asked.

'There's a big hyasa which is nasty, but it's slow, and you'd hear it coming. We haven't tried the locket on it, but if that fails, hit it on the nose. They're cowardly things and usually they only take children.'

'Klar children?'

'Yes – there are no others here.'

'Where's here?' I asked. 'I came in a hurry and forgot my map.'

'The Forest of Entuthon Benython. Where Los and Enitharmon first desired each other,' said Eli. 'That's why it was so good to worship Her here.'

'Are we far from Adambara?' I asked.

'Far. It's in the desert plain. These are the foothills of the Mountain.'

'Do you have news of them?' I asked. 'When I was last there, they were at war with Verula.'

They were around me like children. 'You were there? You saw it? When the Adept from Your Side rode from Verula to warn the people?'

'I saw some of it,' I said.

'They set his statue in the square before the Palace of Records,' said Erin, 'riding on his great asva with his female Emanation before him. Some think he was the spirit of Milton, and Ololon his consort.'

'And the Verulans?' I asked.

'They are stunned. It will take generations. All our brothers and sisters are enlisted to teach them, but the ways of Los aren't their ways. Many kill themselves in remorse, and it will take much love to unwrite the iron books.'

'What happened to old Sutun?' I asked.

'He was one who killed himself. It is thought that he looked in the crystal,' said Tari. 'So his slaves said when we freed them. But he cast it from him and it is lost once more – one grain of sand among many grains. Maybe there are more. I would love to look in it.'

'So would we all,' said Erin.

There was an appalling hullabaloo going on in the Klar village. 'They have reason to be glad,' said Eli. 'It's you whom they praise today.'

At midday we scouted the pool, Tari going first, the girls next, I following, watching sharply even by day for verras couched on the branches overhead.

We came suddenly on it, a round, weeded green eye in dense undergrowth. Reeds flanked it and marched into it; beetles gyrated on its green surface.

They found a place for me under a rock which overhung enough to prevent a rear attack by verras or the unknown beast itself. Eli unrolled a cloth and laid out a number of bitten sticks and smooth stones.

'The Klars sent you these,' she said. 'It's their strongest medicine. They want to be a part of this operation, not just to be defended by us. Touch all of them, please. I'll tell them you blessed their medicine and it gave you strength.'

'We'll go back quietly now,' said Tari, 'and come back at dusk to place you.'

Who else, I thought, was it who waited for a winged four-footed beast beside a pool? It was Perseus, who waited at Hippocrene for Pegasus, the horse of inspiration and lyrical poetry. No such luck for me, I fear.

And so at dusk they gave me the locket as reinsurance, placed me and left. I watched, listened and heard innumerable night creatures, but there was no monster.

'Better luck next time,' said Tari in the morning. 'You get some sleep. We have to try every night.'

The second night Eli, who had been my consort by day, watched with me under the rock. We heard noises, branches cracking. Then a buck came and drank. He was the only visitor, silent as a shadow. Next day I spent with Erin, then tried again, alone. Eli, though she did not show it, had been terrified, and I did not want the responsibility of protecting a second person.

Night fell quickly, the pool darkened, stars and sounds came out. I watched their points of light, the Losian constellations, rotate slowly about a foreign pole. A moon came up, like a fingernail, not enough to light the still water. The buck returned and departed. Dawn was just rising, a lemon-colored light behind the reeds, when I heard, or rather felt, a sound. It was a vibration rather than a tread, but so heavy that it startled me to full attention. Something made a giant leap and its landing shook the whole forest. Then the reeds parted and I faced an enormous, squirrellike head, a long neck, stout clawed forelegs, and knew I had seen, not others like them, but these same things before. I whistled. There was a startled snort, and a snarling whinny, which changed at once to a question. I whistled again. He crashed and splashed through the pool, emerged dripping, and then, as if on his parade ground in Adambara, knelt in the water for me to mount. His saddle and accoutrements were gone, but I mounted the spotted hide and he rose to his full height. I was up once more, and the Tetrarch, whinnying with recognition, moved off, bulldozing his way through the lower growth, thoughtfully avoiding branches, and apparently as pleased and as astonished as I. I was now a monk mounted upon an asva, neither friar nor warrior but a hybrid.

There was not time to say good-bye to my friends or to the gentle Klars. My mount knew where he was going. After some minutes or longer, while I let him go, as I must having no rein, he paused in a clearing and very deliberately knelt. I stayed in place. He whinnied, stood, and knelt again, trying to overcome my obtuseness. I was to dismount. I did so. Leaving me to use my eyes in the rising light, the Tetrarch reared and began to claw down leaves and graze on them. I had never seen him eat leaves before.

There was something hanging from one of the larger branches which I could not reach. I called him, mounted, and from his back I was able to detach it. It was his harness, the girths broken, and all but the ankus lost from his gear. I set about mending it while he fed, saddled him, and mounted again; then I wheeled him back toward the pool, and we thundered through the camp, finding it deserted, then on to the village. The Losian youngsters were there, surrounded by waiting Klars who fled in terror.

'Tally-ho!' I bawled, as the Tetrarch loped down the village street. I heard Losian laughter, cheers, a voice crying 'It's an asva!' Then the village was behind, and the Tetrarch, shoveling on coal, was off at his steady pace along the track. Far behind I heard an awe-struck voice, the voice of Erin: 'Holy Four, it's he – it's the Great Adept! I've slept with the spirit of Milton.'

I did not return to disabuse her, nor yet to meditate on the paradise of the Klars regained.

4

Beggars Rags and Lame Philosophy

It was a couple of hours after full daylight when we left the village. The Tetrarch had fallen at once into his steady thirty-five miles an hour. He was surefooted and considerate, or else his own head, coming higher far than his rider's, made him avoid branches, for he moved on forest tracks as fast as in level desert which was his home. I wondered how he had escaped from the barracks and wandered there, yet the rendezvous lay somehow in the logic of the Losian world, and I could not question him. About noon he smelt water, veered off the track and drank at another green pool, pausing considerately a few minutes later under a tree laden with the red pears, of which we both partook. Then he returned to the track. By afternoon it had grown to a boreen. We passed a few Klar villages, then the forest ended for a space and we entered a plain of elephant grass through which he sailed like a ship. Once we flushed a covey of huge storklike birds, and once a verra flashed out, almost under our feet. The vigilant Tetrarch grabbed and kicked at the same time, but it eluded his teeth, which would have snapped it in half, and fled for its life. Before us we could now see the Mountain, a conical mass topped in snow and cloud, rising like Kilimanjaro out of a dark belt of forest, and then we were among trees, first outposts and then groves, and presently woodland again. The air grew colder and the boreen turned to a road. It was paved with stone blocks, and marked, I noticed, every chala by a stone pillar, mossy and carved with the Four Emblems upon its face.

It was at the end of a long straight vista of this Roman-like causeway that I saw the first human figure since leaving the camp. It was that of a beggar, by its tattered appearance, and it was thumbing a ride.

I slowed the Tetrarch, in two minds about taking on a hitchhiker. The figure saw my indecision and emphasized its gesture by shouting, 'Holy Adept, for the charity of the Four!' In my character as a monk, I reined the Tetrarch and knelt him. The beggar scrambled up behind me. I would have preferred him in front. He might be armed, and the Tetrarch had assumed his friendly intentions from the fact that I had taken him aboard, and could in any case not get at him. Any unarmed combat would have to be by me.

Moreover one cannot really ask a beggar if he loved well, and my fund of appropriate small talk was at that moment low. 'May the Four bless you,' I said. 'Where are you going?'

'Where are you going,' said the beggar, and then added, 'fourfold friend.'

'Thapsis,' I said, 'You son of a gun – you organized this.'

Thapsis was chuckling. 'I suppose you could say so,' he said. 'I thought the beggar's rags would take you in. If you weren't so good an Adept I'd have had to walk to the city.'

'What city?' I said.

'The Foursquare City,' said Thapsis, as if that settled it. 'Well, I'm glad you made a better entry than last time. You've learned a lot, I see. No macho trip – a respectable sannyasin who has renounced all that nonsense. Now he wants understanding, not play-therapy. That's fine – just as it should be.'

'You found my play-therapy useful once,' I said. 'I gather that in Adambara there's a statue to a certain colonel of asvin. One of the Losian girls up-country with the Klars thinks she shared the love bed with the spirit of Milton.'

Thapsis hooted with laughter. 'Well, fourfold friend, she might be right at that. But you're no puritan. You need no Ololon to mourn and rebuke you for being too square to know your own strength.'

'Where's Rosanna?' I said. 'I came here because she sent for me, not to please you.'

'In the city. We'll be there by morning, if we ride all night. You can find her, and I'll find a good inn. You're an asvin and can sleep riding, but this is the first time I've been on one of these brutes.'

'What are you doing out of Adambara, anyway?' I asked.

'Posted,' said Thapsis. 'We are, you know, from time to time.'

'And Rosanna was right about the crystal. Sutun did look in it, and hanged himself like Judas, I hear.'

'She was, and he did. It's little gain, I fear, for the Unnameable is also unkillable,' said Thapsis, 'and not, as you now probably understand, really evil.'

'Sutun not evil?' I said.

'Sutun was evil, for in him opacity was combined with knowledge – I mean knowledge of the wrong kind, the kind that measures but does not feel . . . Actually those delightful Klar villagers have more knowledge than he had, with all his ironmongery, but it's seeing-knowledge, not knowing-knowledge, you understand.'

'I don't,' I said, 'or at least not when I'm driving.'

'Never mind,' said Thapsis. 'Milton himself got bogged down in knowing-knowledge. Rosanna will show you what Ololon showed him. But don't be surprised if even in the Foursquare City, the Measurer has his place. The place due to limitation. That's why his eternal name is Urizen – he is bounded by reason. But he is still one of the Four – without him, the tessaract cannot be spoken. Whoops!' The Tetrarch, mistrusting a stone bridge over a rushing stream, decided on his own initiative to jump it. Thapsis clung grimly on. 'You see the example,' he said. 'Until now I knew about riding on an asva. Now I'm riding on one. That's seeing-knowledge.'

I was tired. The Tetrarch stopped beneath another tree laden with other fruits. As darkness fell, Thapsis was talking, more to himself than to me, chiefly about the book of Cornelius Agrippa, in which he shows that all knowing-knowledge is not only useless but actively harmful. It struck me that Thapsis's phenomenological empiricism was over-done. If the astounding weaponry of Adambara wasn't knowing-knowledge, it was a striking imitation of it, but being, as Thapsis said, an asvin, I slept finally in the saddle, letting him talk. Eventually so did he, and continued to sleep after I had woken to find the Tetrarch scaling a rising stretch of causeway which wound among pines.

Not much after dawn he slowed. I had expected more fruit, but this time it was a small hostelry with smoking chimney and asva-troughs of running water, hollowed out of the clear Losian onyx. We dismounted, stiff from riding. A boy, quite unafraid of an unmuzzled war asva which could have swallowed him whole, led the Tetrarch to a trough filled with pineapples, which he chumped with as much relish as ever he showed for hyasa meat. Two girls in Losian bodices led us in giggling, undressed us with undisguised distaste for Thapsis's beggar outfit, put us in a Losian onyx bath and rubbed our backs, dried us still giggling, brought us clean Losian dress of a reassuringly unmonastic type and breakfast of the small yellow pancakes and curried vegetables with choreb-milk dahi and dahl. I was at home again in a country more my own than that which I had left, and in beginning to know its ways, I felt that this was seeing-knowledge, and therefore free of opacity and the errors of the Unnameable.

5

In Which Objects of Perception Seem to Vary

The inn, at the sign of Beulah's Daughters, stood by itself. It was built of mossy stone, its rooms cool and ceiled with the light-giving Losian wax-stone; there were reed screens round its patios for shade, and the whole place, at midday, was bathed in green light from leaves far larger than any I had seen in our own rain forests. It was cooler here by night and at early morning than in the lower forest, but still hot and humid by day. Later wind sprang up, and Entuthon Beny-thon sounded like a distant river. Thapsis and I rested in preparation, then stayed the night, though the Tetrarch in his stable seemed to be expressing the opinion that we had been there long enough. The city would be for tomorrow.

I asked Thapsis who lived there.

'Adepts,' he replied.

'What, all of them?'

'Certainly.'

'Including cooks, plumbers and general support staff?'

'Naturally. If they weren't Adepts of one or another kind they wouldn't be let in. Don't imagine, however,' he went on, 'that a city consisting entirely of Adepts is problem free. An Adept is simply someone who recognizes that there are two sorts of knowledge, and puts seeing-knowledge first.'

'Have they all had what we call "mystical experiences"?' I asked.

'You mean straight quantum-logic perception?'

'Well, yes.'

'Oh, no – some don't need any violent exercise to take the point. But it wouldn't make society any more problem-free if they had had. In my experience, if you are a stinker before you have a mystical experience, you remain a stinker after

167

you had it – that was the opinion of a very astute yogi from Your Side, and I heartily agree.'

'Say again about Adepts – ' I said, 'we're people who see things others don't?'

'Certainly not – we're people who don't see things other folks think they do, when in fact they didn't see them at all, only inferred or heard about them. It's non-Adepts who think up things in the abstract and then call them visions. What shape is the earth?'

'I beg your pardon?'

'What shape is the earth?' said Thapsis.

'You mean, phenomenally – or is this another koan?'

'Just in terms of straight human experience.'

'Round, of course.'

'Spherical?'

'It's supposed to be an oblate spheroid.'

'I take it,' said Thapsis, 'you're not an astronaut, so that's purely skull-knowledge on your part. Now, what shape is it to you?'

'Flat,' I said, 'with the sky coming down to meet it about twenty miles away.'

'So the earth you know is flat?'

'Unless I'm building a very long freeway or flying a Great Circle course, yes.'

'In which case it becomes a curved surface, because you are now seeing a curved surface. In other words, when you do these things it changes its shape. As to the oblate spheroid, only astronauts see that, and when they do, they think it's a mystical experience and get badly upset by it – though they've only seen what they were taught in school. Now if you *were* the earth, you'd experience what it looks like to itself, and that would be a roundness with you inside.'

I refrained from trying to intuit the earth's possible self-image.

'It doesn't take a mystical experience to see any of that,' Thapsis went on: 'the reason it helps is that what you call "mystical experience" is simply the turning-off of selfness, so that you and the earth don't have a perceptual customs barrier between you, and that can help a lot. But you don't need any neurological tricks to see the point that since we do normally experience self, what we see goes in through it, and when we express what we see it goes out the same way, and it pays duty in each direction. If you open the customs barrier, so that you feel non-distinct from everything, it doesn't help classification, but it does an awful lot for empathy.'

'Thapsis,' I said, 'is this the general level of discourse in the Foursquare City? Because if it is, I'm going to talk exclusively to Rosanna and the Tetrarch. I'm beginning to wish for the Adambaran cavalry service again. I used to think the small talk at Lawrence Berkeley Lab was heavy going.'

'Not any more than conversation in London turns on the fact that twice one are two. A city of Adepts doesn't need to lecture one another on elementary fact.'

'I think,' I said, 'I'm going to take Rosanna back to see the Klars. Sign language at least cuts down on transcendental philosophy.'

'I hate to tell you,' said Thapsis, 'but the Klars are on the same trip. Not having speech they don't have to have half their brain mark time while what they see goes through a logic program. So they don't have a constant déjà vu between the two halves. And accordingly they don't have our illusion that there's a little man called "self" sitting inside cogitating and therefore being. You'd find human philosophers a much softer option.'

'Incidentally, Thapsis,' I said, 'do you have any idea how long the present operation will last?'

'Does it matter?' said Thapsis.

'No, I suppose it doesn't – since time here doesn't score in real time.'

'Right, it doesn't. Once you break through as an Adept, you can spend a whole life here, if you want, at right angles to real time. It doubles the time you have to acquire wisdom – most people from Your Side are obsessed with life span, and think of it as extra longevity, but that trivializes it, as I'm sure you agree. And it's bad physics.'

'I can come here,' I said, 'only if you activate that door.'

'Nonsense,' said Thapsis. 'Come when you like. You know how to open it.'

'Twice,' I said, 'I opened it and nothing happened.'

'Well, did you expect it to? On a play-therapy trip, yes, but you'd outgrown toys. You came for enlightenment, right? Then surely you know that every Zen novice gets refused twice before he is let in. The door was simply reinforcing your Time of Choice scenario.' He poured out more herb tea and passed me the yellow chapatis. 'In any case, you don't *need* the door.'

'Don't need the door?'

'Of course not. The door was simply a prop to show you how to get here the first few times. If you shut your eyes and perform the Game of Adepts on that sit-in self of yours, instead of on a door, you can move either way, any time. I know an Adept who comes here regularly for a few weeks while he's riding a Rapid Transit Authority bus in Los Angeles. He still gets to work on time. Keep the door as a conversation piece and open it when you want to take out a suitcase.

'I take it,' said Thapsis, 'that you're planning to go back together when you've finished here?'

'I hope so,' I said. 'That depends on Rosanna, of course.'

'Of course. Though you realize this visit will score slightly against real time if you do, because you came separately from different places – after all, your bodies have to be in place. Unless, of course, you'd rather return to your room, and Rosanna to where she was when she came – I believe she was traveling.'

'In which case she might decide to go somewhere else,' I said.

'Then it'll be simpler to give her time to reach your place and let herself in. Three hours should be plenty. You won't notice anything.'

I settled for three hours – it seemed very little to surrender in view of the advantages.

'You'll be credited, of course,' said Thapsis 'against future visits – next time you come, you'll each be three hours younger in Losian time, naturally.'

'Naturally. I wish,' I said, 'I could take the Tetrarch.'

'In the nature of asvaya, you can't,' said Thapsis. 'He has work to do here – and you'd look a charlie, if I may say so,

170

riding an asva in Edinburgh. But he's on twenty-four-hour call if you need him on future visits. An asva like him is a highly personalized mount. He'll be in place.'

'Like a rental car?'

'More or less,' said Thapsis. 'We try harder, you know, especially with visiting Adepts who have deserved so well of us.'

Thapsis was unusually communicative, and seemed worth pumping. 'I still don't understand how time here scores against real time,' I said.

'Normally it doesn't,' said Thapsis, 'though there are exceptions – overlaps if you like.'

'Let me get this right. To be Here, we have to be alive There, so that we have a brain to conduct the operation?'

'Right,' said Thapsis, 'but there is a gray area. It arises from what we call "Terminal Transfer". Some Adepts, who really know what they are about, perform the Game and come here practically at the moment of real time death: it's risky timing it, but it can in fact be done. In that case they're marooned here for a Losian lifetime – which presumably is real time instantaneous, since some have been here years, and I never saw anyone called in because his earth brain died on him meanwhile. The oddest effect is that you quite often meet Adepts here who died in real time before you came – it's called Swedenborg's Anomaly. Obviously it can be made use of.'

'And when they've done their number here?' I asked.

'Presumably they go back and finish dying in real time, and that's that. This isn't a place you come when you die – you need to be alive to come here. Some of them believe they will reincarnate somewhere, but that sounds like biological hogwash to me: I don't care much for disembodied intelligences. Doesn't bother me much anyhow – implicate reality's timeless – but we all like the explicate sort: yours and ours. Of course if you die *here* and stay alive *there* you can come back via a Losian rebirth, but that's not a paradox – the neurological continuity is all on Your Side. Only traffic exception seems to be for This-Side suicides. They don't "reincarnate", but some get a nasty experience of having to rerun their whole earth lives to the same point, and they may get out of time-synch doing it. It's a very odd effect.'

'So everyone here has a real-time counterpart there?' I said.

'Nice question,' said Thapsis. 'Wish I knew. I don't know where pure Losians, like those girls here for instance, who never left the village, fit in. But Goddamit, you have to have a neurological base *somewhere*. And after all, there are at least twice as many available selves as there are people alive on Your Side, allowing one male self and one female self for each human being: probably a lot more, if you read Jung. I'm only a neurologist by training.'

'Last question – you're assuming real time is the objective state?' I said. 'Aren't both explicates equally real? Or is this an Everett-Wheeler-Graham model?'

'You are taking your sannyasa seriously,' said Thapsis. 'I'm assuming nothing. Objective just means what the self reads as not-self, and which appears consistent. If you want to write a book on phenomenological ontology, do, but I'm not about to do your Ph.D. thesis for you. The palaver is finished – what a hell of a time and place to talk neuropsychology! Go and get some practical enlightenment from one of our nice giggling hostesses if you're still hungry. I'm taking a snooze.'

Flies buzzed, the Tetrarch stamped and chewed on his pineapples, Thapsis slept in a wicker chair. Between the stems of the reed fence I could see streaks of the road. It was a strange highway, immensely solid – for the paving was in two-foot blocks of solid cyclopean stone – but singularly unfrequented. A few Losian pedestrians passed, a single choreb cart delivered loaves at the front door. The road itself was mossy, as an unused railroad track loses its swordlike shine of traffic. It was an immemorial road, robust for that reason, and not by reason of being often traversed. As Thapsis started to snore, I heard the Tetrarch move and whinny – his indication of attention – and then a rumble as of an approaching train and the rattle of claws on stone, and two squadrons of my asvin, my former comrades, swept past, necks towering, guidons fluttering. The Tetrarch whinnied not at them but at me. Evidently my sloth was beyond his comprehension. The cavalcade woke Thapsis with a snort.

'Eh? Oh yes,' said Thapsis, 'I know about them. A party of verras killed a Losian boy about ten miles from here. The unfortunate lad went hunting on his own, it seems. We have a few verras everywhere, but a pack's too many, and the cavalry will hunt them down. If they bring back a pelt you can have that for your love bed – it's softer than asva hide.' And he went back to sleep.

We set off early. There was mist, and rain had fallen during the night – the moss on the great stones of the road appeared freshly grown. The two girls brought our breakfast, the Tetrarch was brought out; he seemed preoccupied – evidently he was still thinking about the cavalry. We mounted and set off, and in a couple of minutes the Daughters of Beulah was out of sight. Where they sprang from, I do not know, for there were no obvious habitations, but gradually the road became peopled with travelers, chiefly on foot, a few on choreb, a diverse assemblage who had the air of scattered Canterbury pilgrims, all bound for the city. The surrounding country of the forest grew rockier and the road climbed. The pedestrians left the road to mount a wide stair leading from it, made of the same mossy stone, and we were alone again, ascending steadily.

Approached from this side, the Foursquare City has no prospect. One sees it only on reaching it. Turning a corner we faced a high, carved and mossy arch, of a piece with the flanking rocks. In the road before it were two verras, twice the size of the young specimen I had encountered, arching and hissing at our approach. The Tetrarch's interest in the journey returned at the prospect. I could feel him deciding which he would take with his teeth, and which with his rearward mule-kick. He began to progress cornerwise.

'Hold him in,' said Thapsis, placidly. 'He'll do them a mischief and we shall have to pay for them.'

I saw that like the lions in Christians' path, they were chained. I patted down the Tetrarch and steered him protesting between two hissing predatory heads. After we were through the arch, and into the winding cutting beyond it, he turned around and gave me a look of deep reproach, as if I had prevented a display of asvan kung fu which he would have enjoyed, for his eye said, 'Spoil sport.'

There was another arch, with buildings on it, but it and they were hung with ferns and moss and seemed also part of the rocks on which they were built, then more buildings of similar aspect, and then the road emerged into a cobbled square among them, the outlet from which was a large carriage-entry. In front of this and to its left, on my right, side, was a small table, at which sat an extremely handsome young bearded black man, the duty officer of the gate of Adepts.

'Hello!' he shouted. 'Well met. You know well?'

'Well, Adept,' I shouted back.

'Down with you then,' said the black officer. 'Breakfast's ready. We knew you were coming about now. Where did you stay, or have you ridden all night?'

'At Beulah's Daughters,' said Thapsis.

'Great,' said the officer, 'that's where I go at weekends for fishing. You've probably had a good breakfast but you won't mind another. We'll take care of that chap.' He indicated the Tetrarch, who was led off resignedly towards a pile of pineapples by an elderly soldier.

We entered the archway, and passed through a door leading off it, into a room with a laid breakfast table and half-a-dozen Losian officers, men and women, all of whom stood to greet us. The black officer seated us, took the table head, said 'To the Four – may they unite in this food,' and we fell to.

'We do appreciate this,' said the black officer. 'I hear you came specially – my wife and I would have loved to have you both as house guests, but in view of the short notice we couldn't get things ready in time. I'm sorry – she was very anxious to meet you, and so of course am I.'

'And I'm afraid he's under orders,' said Thapsis. 'He has to go straight to the College of Adepts – you and Mrs Olowende can have him later on. When he gets back.'

'Back,' I said, 'from what?'

'Your assignment.'

'What assignment?'

'Ssh!' said Thapsis.

'If this is going to be another . . .'

'No,' said Thapsis, 'it isn't. Rosanna is commanding this operation. No heroics. Simply research, I gather. More herb tea?'

The other Adepts plied me with questions about the Other Side – some had been there, some not. They were like Muscovites asking a visitor about England – why we lead our children about on leashes like dogs, and whether it snows a lot in winter – except that theirs were more penetrating questions and uninhibited by political considerations: things like the number of academic departments devoted to Fourfold Knowledge, and why we needed to import yogic Hinduism when we didn't recognize our own greatest Adept as a religious teacher. Of these I struck out on three and ran one. When we had done, the others excused themselves, shaking both hands with us in the Losian style, and left us with Adept Olowende. 'That was a good breakfast,' he said. 'Now the formalities. No problem, but we all have to go through it.' And he led me out of the breakfast room, where young Losians were clearing the tables, all, boys and girls, wearing the Hindu-style shoulder cord of an apprentice Adept, into a side office.

'Now,' said Olowende, 'let's play a few rounds of the Game.'

The board was already set on the table. I played him, winning one game to his one, with two drawn, and an error game when a piece fell from the metal path. 'Weak magnet,' said Olowende, and threw the piece in the wastepaper basket. 'Call that an error and try one more.

'Fine,' he said. 'It's more enjoyable than filling out papers. Now for the real stuff.'

And he produced another board, with two Möbius loops set in such a manner that only one who knew the device of the Game of Adepts would indeed recognize that they were, for the purposes of that Game, at right angles, and possessed for those purposes not one but four surfaces. The idea I know

175

is difficult, but I cannot be more precise without professional indiscretion. Olowende watched me closely. I started to grin as I saw how the thing worked, and so did he.

'That's terrific,' I said. 'I wish I could show it to the head of mathematics. It would blow his mind.'

'We don't need to play,' said Olowende. 'You're passed in, Adept.'

'Let's play,' I said. 'I want to see it with my own eyes.'

We did, and Olowende won. But as scrutineer of Adepts in Foursquare City he'd done it often before.

'In Nigeria, where I come from,' said Olowende, 'I saw an old Yoruba countryman do that trick with grass strips and thorns. It's sacred to the Trickster, Eshu-Elegba.'

'One day,' I said, 'I'll try it in the *Scientific American*: for Adepts only.'

'You see,' said Thapsis, 'Anglos don't have *all* the technology.'

And we all three went out in an arms-around shoulders position. With no fourth person present we couldn't make the appropriate Losian gesture of solidarity, but the sentiment was obvious, and I decided that I liked being an Adept. 'Walk on in,' said Olowende. 'It's not far.'

'How about the Tetrarch?'

'He's checking in at the best hotel. Send a simurgh if you need him, but give me a bit of notice.'

We shook hands all round, and Thapsis and I were in the paved mossy streets of the Foursquare City. Ten minutes or a quarter of an hour later, in the guest rooms of the College of Adepts, I was on the love bed with Rosanna.

6

A Gate Between the Thighs Opening Into Beulah

For two hours no business other than our own was transacted between us.

Sexual intercourse on earth is the nearest we come to the Losian world – indeed, as Thapsis once pointed out, four, not two, are present: man' woman, man-in-woman, and woman-in-man. And again, the Losian tessaract itself is remade – Imagination, Intellect, Feeling and Sensation – Urthona, who is Los, Urizen, Luvah and Tharmas. Possibly for these reasons, or because here we were more fully at home than on Our Side, sex between us seemed always doubly effective in Los's world. For the first while at our reunion it was furious, then remarkably tender, and then Rosanna asked me when the ravishing would begin and we played that through too. Evidently Adepthood had not reformed her.

Afterwards, full of this entirely empirical Fourfold Knowledge, which ought on its face to meet all of Thapsis's philosophical tests, we lay side-by-side and held hands, feet touching, and stared into the glowing wax-stone ceiling.

'I missed you,' I said.

'Yes, yes.'

'What is it this time? Thapsis says you are in command of the operation. What operation?'

'There are two. One's mine, and one is his. I don't know what his is going to be, but he promised no more violence, so I believe him.'

'And yours?' I asked.

'You heard what happened? Did Thapsis brief you?'

'You mean after we went back – in Verula?'

'Yes.'

'Thapsis didn't brief me, but I heard from a girl up-country. You were right, it seems. Sutun looked in the crystal and killed himself, there's a statue of us in Adambara, they think I'm the spirit of Milton and you're his anima, who tried to cure him of Puritan theology, and there's a task force of Adambaran missionaries recivilizing any Verulans who are reclaimable.'

'They're trying to love them back into human shape,' said Rosanna.

'They might have done better to love them back into ape shape,' I said. 'Give me apes any day.' And I told her about the Klars.

'That's beautiful,' said Rosanna.

'And I got the Tetrarch back. He was their monster. Apparently he was just waiting for me, in place. This is an odd trip for coincidences.'

'No, it isn't,' said Rosanna. 'Of course he would be waiting. He's simply a part of your earth self.'

'Not you too, girl or you go back to being a colonel's slavegirl.'

'Why do you always have to be flip about what we've learned?' said Rosanna. 'You know it's true. And I was right about the crystal.'

'Yes,' I said, 'you were.'

'And now it's lost again. Sutun threw it away.'

'There may be others. Do we need it?' I asked.

'I don't think we do,' said Rosanna. 'The other gate is here – ' she put her hand between her half-open thighs – 'or one like it. But that passes over – the crystal is there all the time. Like a record, or a statement.'

'Sutun had sex too,' I said, 'and made a sadistic pig of himself.'

'Yes,' said Rosanna. 'It's like our door. If you go through it halfway ready you can become an Adept, or it helps, but for a garbage person it leads into a junk-cupboard. I've had sex with those too, and it's simply demeaning. But the crystal isn't . . . ambiguous. Even that horrible psychopath couldn't miss the point.'

'You're the Adept, Rosanna,' I said. 'I didn't realize its

importance. I was thinking just quantum physics. Is it what the Catholic mystics call the Beatific Vision?'

'It's what Gerontius saw when he said, "Take me away," and asked to become an Adept in Purgatory,' said Rosanna. 'But if you tack on Christian crime-and-punishment stuff you'll get Miltonized, like the Losian girl told you. This doesn't happen after you're dead, but while you're still alive to experience it. What Gerontius had was a dream. Dead people don't dream. And we,' said Rosanna, 'are going to find it.'

'Back to Verula?'

'No. It isn't in Verula. Thapsis knows that for certain. I don't know how. It came here, to the Mountain, somehow. Thapsis may know that it homes, in some way. I'm not going back to Verula ever. Not even to see them change.'

'I take your point,' I said. 'It would be a bit like West Germany a few years back, where you just couldn't meet anyone who had ever been a Nazi. How do we set about the search and recovery program?'

'We have to work that out now,' said Rosanna. 'Thapsis has some kind of search equipment. But we'd only need that if the people who have it haven't found out what it is. If they've looked in it, even accidentally, we'll know – it changes people.'

'Did it change us, or Faesto? We all three looked in it.'

'Silly,' said Rosanna, 'of course it did. Aren't we different people? And we were halfway there already.'

'And Faesto?' I asked. I rather wondered when he'd surface. Rosanna had more than liked him, and I rather expected to be told he was here, and about to join us.

'He's in Verula, heading the reclaim operation,' said Rosanna. 'You needn't worry.'

'I don't,' I said. 'He's my blood brother and we could go shares – in the other mode of enlightenment. We did before.'

'Yes,' said Rosanna, 'that was nice.'

After a while she said, 'This time I think you understand.'

'Yes, I think I do.' I put an arm round her. 'So that's our next assignment. You've no idea what Thapsis is up to?'

'Except it's about the crystal. When we get it. But it's of that order. There won't be more nightmares, only dreams.'

'I don't know about that,' I said. 'This isn't exactly paradise, even for illuminate apes.' And I told her about the verras in the forest of Entuthon Benython.

'I thought the one I met alone greeted me because I was an Adept,' I said, 'or at least I wondered. But there are two tame ones here at the city gate, or as tame as those beasts ever get, and they'd have eaten me Adept or no Adept, if they hadn't been chained up.'

'But then,' said Rosanna, 'you weren't an Adept. You were a colonel in mufti on a war asva.'

'They kill Klars,' I said, 'and sometimes Losians. I don't know how far down in phylogeny Adepthood goes. All I'm saying is that there are dangers here.'

'Beasts,' said Rosanna, 'aren't really dangers. The fox provides for himself, but God provides for the lion. I'm more scared of foxes, aren't you?'

I thought that in a city of Adepts she had a point. Adepthood, according to Thapsis, did not always go with moral excellence. Presumably there might be bad Adepts – wizards, in other words, rather than sages. Rosanna agreed emphatically. According to her, even the crystal wasn't a cure for sorcery, nor could it reform the sorcerer. 'If he knows that already, and still can't see,' she said, 'he'd be part of the Great Selfhood in spite of the crystal. Sutun wasn't. But I think the Great Selfhood was in him.'

'What's this place like?' I asked her.

'Extraordinary,' said Rosanna. 'A bit like Adambara crossed with Cambridge. I like it – so far.'

'Any Temple of Enitharmon?'

'Yes, it's beautiful. I've been. This time I worshipped in the Inner Circle.'

'Last time it was too like a sexual game?'

'Yes. Not this time. Well, it was both – but holy,' said Rosanna, 'and not just a kick. But I like kicks too – I haven't changed.'

'I noticed that,' I said. 'Any House of Play?'

'A huge one. Some Adepts spend half their time there.

Including some very advanced ones – they call it a sadhana, but I think they just enjoy it like we do.'

'When did you get here,' I asked, 'and how?'

'I don't know in real time. A couple of weeks in This-Side time. And Thapsis sent a taxi for me.'

'Now you're being flippant,' I said.

'No,' said Rosanna, 'I'm not. He sent a taxi. It took me to a house. I went in, there was the Change, and a black Adept met me and took me through the Game of Adepts, and I was here.'

'That would be Olowende,' I said. 'He passed me in too – he's a great chap.'

'He's also,' said Rosanna, 'a great Adept.'

There was a knock – another bodiced Losian housekeeper with another Losian meal. 'Knowing, you loved well?' she said. I liked the combined Adeptic and common greeting – it was appropriate.

'Well,' we answered.

'You're both beautiful,' said the housekeeper. 'Call for anything you want. The bath is ready.' So we took it, ate and drew breath.

It had been a more wonderful arrival than I could have believed possible, and in spite of our tasks, or because of them, our peace was more total than at any time since Rosanna and I first came together.

7

In Which Every House is Fourfold

The simurgh arrived punctually after breakfast. It brought around its leg a tidy map of the city, with the address of the Senate House, and a request to meet Thapsis there at the Second Fire. Rosanna was in the bath – we had heard rain during the night, but it was now bright again. I was back in Losian clothes, for Adepts have no characteristic dress and, in fact, avoid any badge of recognition other than the greeting and the knowledge of their Game. There was virtually no street noise, though earlier on there had been a bizarre sound of someone chanting rather untunefully in Sanskrit – presumably at his morning exercises. There were no Losian books in our room – Rosanna had told me that we were, in fact, over the library of the College, but she did not appear to have borrowed anything. On the other hand she had managed somehow to bring the collected poems of William Blake through customs in a normal, Other-Side, printed edition. The wall hangings were very low power mandalas – two of general instruction, one a Tibetan-type alpha-wave inducer, and one, which we could roll down over the window at night, probably a sleep-inducing pattern. This was semitransparent, so that moonlight or street lighting would activate it if the occupants of the room were having difficulty in settling down for the night. Apart from that there was the love bed and the usual Losian furniture, right-hand, tobacco-style, but no left-hand, intoxicant, blach and no flask of nepenthe. Evidently we were now no longer in need of such support devices.

There was no square and no mounted statue outside our window, as there had been in Adambara, only one of the smaller streets of the city. The whole place was mossier, damper and less Mediterranean in appearance than Adam-bara – no stalls, fewer tradespeople and children, no asvin or parades and no bustle. It was, as Rosanna remarked, more like Cambridge, and it swarmed with whole-time Adepts who would have looked fully appropriate in gowns and squares – Losians, Africans, Orientals, all of these in Losian dress or ochre robes: a few, whom I took to be Americans, were incongruously wearing Hawaiian shirts with Losian white pajama-trousers. There were even a few Losian-dressed Anglo-Saxons who looked visibly uncomfortable in the clothes they were wearing, and who gave me an equally uncomfortable sensation that they were probably British. Adepts were clearly of all kinds, and as I had feared on the journey, some of them had intellectual argument as their main activity. Others, who looked more like my inner picture of the genuine article, were more impressive – a young, bearded Orthodox monk, for example, who walked alone, argued with nobody and had an air of inner joy which seemed to surround him. The majority, however, were what I had feared – professional intellectuals, who had somehow acquired enough experiential knowledge to get past Olow-ende and the admission test. Among the crowd, which appeared soon after breakfast, swarmed for a while, then thinned to extinction probably into various institutions of study, all the most interesting characters were non-Euro-peans, who seemed to be here naturally, and were often going against the general stream of Adeptic movement – women, too, who slightly outnumbered men, and seemed equally uninvolved in the academic side of the operation.

When Rosanna was ready we went into the street and set out to find the Senate House. Thapsis's map had been extremely explicit, and the Foursquare City is easy for the stranger: at each street corner is a luminous wax-stone bollard or post, with one of the Four Emblems at the top, to indicate the compass quarter, and below that one of the Four Beasts, for the compass square within the quarter, plus a sign of the zodiac corresponding to the postal code – we were looking for Sun-Eagle-Aquarius, and found it without any trouble. The shops here, we noted, were not craft shops, as in the

City of the Smith, and they combined handmade pottery and ironwork from Adambara with high-earth-technology goods from Verula. The Adeptic culture clearly drew on all kinds of skills as it needed them, without any ideological biases.

Thapsis appeared to have moved his office bodily from Adambara, for it was exactly the same.

'Did you love well?' he said. 'I see you did. Well, you've seen the city.'

I told him it looked painfully like any university city, and seemed to be full of precisely the knowledge-seekers I had feared.

'They'll get over it,' said Thapsis: 'most of those are apprentices anyhow. You wouldn't discount Tantric Hinduism because Kathmandu is full of hippies, would you? Those aren't the Adepts you'll work with. The genuine ones are chiefly shopkeepers or peasants who came here by their own unaided efforts. But let's get to work – we have business.'

'We have to find the crystal again,' I said.

'Yes,' said Thapsis, 'that was the project which the lady chose. I take it you now see the point of it? Because if you don't, say so.'

'I think he understands,' said Rosanna.

'You know it isn't in Verula?' I said. 'I was told Sutun threw it away.'

'He did,' said Thapsis, 'and as it was free again, the wind blew it away. We found the mounting the Verulans had put on it. Naturally, it wouldn't remain there in the plain.'

'So how did it get here, if you think it isn't in Verula? Another Losian coincidence?'

'The same kind of Losian coincidence,' said Thapsis, 'which rendezvoused your asva when you came here. But it almost certainly wouldn't be in the city – there are people here who would know immediately if it were.'

'So what is the area of search?' I said.

'Wide. The Mountain, the whole of Entuthon Benython and the badlands the other side of the city. You can take it from me that it's somewhere in this general area.'

'Any way we can home on it?' I asked. 'You say some Adepts would know if it were here – vibrations, dousing?'

'You're off course, Edward,' said Rosanna. Thapsis was looking patient and waiting for me to finish. 'Let me tell you. I was thinking, Thapsis, isn't there a moment in time, in each day, which corresponds to the crystal, just as the crystal is a grain of sand among grains?'

'Yes,' said Thapsis, 'there is. You don't, I see, need me to instruct you. I'd forgotten about that – it's a brilliant idea. We'll see what the others think about that when they get here. The first meeting is set for after lunch.'

'What resources have we?' I asked.

'Anything you want, which we have got, you can call on. If it takes a regiment of asvin, you can have asvin. If it takes electronics, we've got Verulan technicians. But I don't think we can do this by saturation. It clearly isn't the kind of task. You're going to have to stop tackling it on Other-Side lines. She knows that. Just listen to what she says, and don't be clever all at once. Your skills may come in later.'

'It alters people,' said Rosanna.

'Yes, unless they have the vision it contains already.'

'So either it's still unrecognized,' said Rosanna, 'or fully enlightened people have it, or it's found by less enlightened people and we shall see the change in them.'

'That,' said Thapsis, 'seems a better approach than magic or hardware.'

I was becoming out of my depth. There was something a little unreal about this entire project. Who was behind it was not clear. Thapsis had referred to it as Rosanna's project – compared with the depth of his concern that Sutun and the Verulans should not have the crystal in their possession, his present interest seemed a little perfunctory – moreover if he knew where it was, or was likely to be, it seemed odd to make us stage a treasure hunt. I had the feeling that we were earning brownie points in some obscure way. Rosanna, on the other hand, appeared to know exactly what she was doing, and if she wanted the thing as a personal source of enlightenment, I had no objection, provided the search did not involve any more quasi-military operations.

Thapsis had on his wall what I took for another mandala,

but soon perceived to be a map of the city, marked with a stick-on red arrow inscribed, 'You are Here'. 'Here' was on one side of a largish paved square containing a fountain and a rank of choreb-drawn rickshaws, which constituted the normal taxi service for Adepts. Near the end of the preceding discussion, clocks began to strike (an unusual sound in a Losian city, where time was normally marked far more nonchalantly by Fires) and Adepts of all shapes and sizes began to issue from the three ranges of buildings which completed the square. Class was evidently coming out.

'Yes,' said Thapsis, 'those are the three colleges. You can do the tour of them later if you want, but I don't think you'll learn much.'

'Why not four?' I asked him.

'Good point. Why do you ask?'

'Four spiritual senses, four ways to knowledge?' I said.

'Tell him, Rosanna,' said Thapsis.

'Abstract intellect, sensation, passion and imagination,' said Rosanna.

'So?'

'Well, you can't teach imagination. The other three sadhanas you can teach.'

'Genuine Losians don't go to Adept-school because they don't need to?'

'Right,' said Thapsis. 'We get all kinds of Adepts here.'

'So you send them to the kind of experience they know about?'

'No – the kind they don't know about. The naturals, who just find themselves here, are short on abstract intellect. They go to the Solar College and get jnana yoga – Bacon, Locke, Heisenberg, you name it. Mostly very talented Adepts from skull-free cultures – Eskimos, Bushmen, South American shamans. The square Adepts who thought it all out and give discursive explanations and talk quantum logic need to learn to do it with feeling – they get bhaktī next door: it can be Krishna consciousness or devotion to the Sacred Heart, whatever they can take culturally. And the bloody ascetics, who are the bane of my life, but who get here by sheer unpleasantness, we send to the Tharmians, to learn they have bodies to enjoy. It's a kind of orthopedic exercise, developing limbs which have atrophied. Ideally they end as Losians, with all four spiritual limbs the same length. So if you want any of these experiences, by all means have them. I don't think the lady needs them, but you yourself might get something from the devotional trip – you seem all right on brains and on sensuality, but you're still a little inclined to be flippant. You won't find the major Adepts in the schools, however – most of them are around the city doing useful work: shopkeepers, plumbers, choreb drivers and the Faculty. You never see people like Olowende in a place of Higher Learning – he'd sooner go fishing, or play you at four-dimensional Adepthood.'

'Look, Thapsis,' I said, 'come clean. Is this crystal thing important, or is it simply a training run for Adepts? I think I'm entitled to know. Last time we went after it, several people got killed, Rosanna was badly knocked about, and the whole thing was bloody unpleasant. If finding the crystal matters, that's one thing – if it's simply a part of our spiritual education, say so.'

'You have my assurance,' said Thapsis, 'that it is important. If it also gives you new awarenesses, that only shows that it was a valid experience.'

'But from what you said, you obviously know where the thing is.'

'I don't.'

'Does anyone?'

'There's one Adept who quite possibly does – we'll talk about that in a minute, when we get to planning – but you'd have to find him, which won't be easy: he's a solitary and never comes near the city – can't stand Adepts, and I don't blame him.'

'How does he know? ESP or something?'

'More likely something. I never met an Adept, other than a quack, who believed in ESP,' said Thapsis. 'That's Your-Side term for any visit over here which gets aborted. No use for finding anything – we aren't fortune-telling Romanies.'

'So now we have a missing Adept as well as a missing crystal.'

'Look,' said Thapsis, 'I understand your suspicion. You're not being manipulated.'

'Like hell we aren't,' I said.

'Perhaps you'll believe me when I tell you,' said Thapsis, 'that this is something only you and Rosanna can do.'

'And I volunteered to do it,' said Rosanna, 'so stop bitching about it, Edward. You could trust me, if you don't trust him.'

I told her that I trusted her implicitly in anything which was not just a sexual caper.

'Which this isn't – ' said Rosanna, 'and you never objected to sexual capers either, so far as I ever saw.'

'Am I allowed to ask how you know the thing really is in this area, not in Verula?' I said. 'You avoided that one when I asked you.'

'I didn't,' said Thapsis. 'It's perfectly true that the crystal turns up where it is needed – exactly as your asva did.'

'Then why isn't it on your table now?'

'Because it has to be looked for,' said Rosanna. 'Now shut up, Edward, and let's get on looking for it.'

The Faculty Committee (which is what it was, though nobody called it that) convened after lunch. There were three practical members, beside ourselves: a Losian Adept called Sarvas whose job was to brief us on the search terrain; a girl technician called Clia from the Smithy in Adambara, carrying a large obstetric-looking bag; and a tall, handsome, earnest young man whom I took at first glance for a senatorial candidate. He had the slightly unreal, varnished look which marks out the office seeker on any political platform. On Our Side he would have had the stuck-down blow wave, the Dior tie and the smile from the nose down. Here in the Losian world he had the monastic equivalent, the ochre robe and girdle, but the charisma was like bad aftershave lotion. He made me think of the ghost of John F. Kennedy in fancy dress. Rosanna spotted it at once.

'Ugh!' she said under her breath.

Clearly, however, he was not ugh to Thapsis, who gave him the archimagial embrace. 'Greetings, fourfold friends,' said the candidate for office.

'Greetings,' I said. 'You loved well?'

'Actually not – my sadhana now is chaste. I knew well.'

'Thank goodness,' whispered Rosanna, 'I was afraid he'd want to share. He turns me off, Edward.'

'Me too,' I whispered back.

'This,' said Thapsis, 'is Chorim. He is my closest assistant and my Tanist.'

'He means,' said Rosanna, 'the man who's going to succeed him. Oh, no!'

I don't know why our radar picked on Chorim, for he went out of his way to be agreeable. Possibly that was the reason. He treated us, despite his archimagial standing, with great and apparently genuine respect. We settled at the table, and had no sooner done so than the door opened and a couple of senior Adepts came in, so we all stood again. They were a very wizened and knowing old man of Australian race, who was introduced as Tjurip, and who touched faces instead of shaking hands, and a Tibetan lama in a yellow robe, an agreeable young man called Chonpa. They had the air of senior partners in a law firm dropping in on juniors during a troublesome case.

'This is the crystal project,' said Thapsis, 'and these are our two earth friends.'

'Aren't we all earth friends?' said Chonpa.

'What was that?' said Tjurip.

'The crystal project,' said Thapsis, 'of which I told you, fourfold friend.'

'Oh, ah, that,' said Tjurip, 'can't imagine why you want it. But the best of luck.'

'And our very sincere gratitude,' said Chonpa, and they left. My suspicions deepened. Tjurip, for my money, knew more about Adepthood than the entire Foursquare City rolled into one.

'We have no time to lose,' said Chorim. 'Now, let us begin. Sarvas, friend, please brief our two Adepts; you alone of us have traveled all the country around the city.'

Sarvas unrolled a contour map and hung it on an easel. The city was a round blob the size of a dime, on the flank of a mountain range. 'This side is Entuthon Benython,' said

189

Sarvas, 'and this is the road you came in by. All forest, much the same, not many roads, but on asva-back it's all passable.'

'Is that all Klar country?' I asked him.

'Mostly. There are some Losian villages. And an asvin post *here*. That's the only one in the area, but you'll have a simurgh with you if you want to contact them.'

'Hazards?' I asked.

'Verras – but on asva-back you should be safe. If you camp near your animal, he'll keep them off. And there are big hyasas in the grass plain, but they're rarely a problem – except that asvaya are inclined to hunt them and wander off.'

'Not mine,' I said. 'He's taken to pineapples.'

'Don't believe it,' said Sarvas. 'They never lose a taste for lizard meat. Now this is the problem area, *here*. You probably didn't realize it, coming in from Entuthon, but the city's on a cliff edge facing northward, and the badlands start at the bottom of the cliff. There's a road down into the desert, *here*, but it finishes at Tartara, about twenty chalas into the valley, and after that you're on your own. Beyond that there are three more valleys, with ridges between, each higher than the last, getting more and more volcanic, and then the Mountain. The lake's in the third valley, *here*. I haven't been there.'

'The Lake of Udan-Adan?' said Rosanna.

'Yes.'

'Which means Not-Being?'

'Yes. Said to be bottomless. Anyhow it's a place to avoid.'

'The whole area is a place to avoid,' said Chorim.

'So that,' I said 'is why you're all avoiding it and sending us.'

'You needn't go as far as the lake unless you have to,' said Thapsis blandly, 'and certainly not beyond it. After that it's the Mountain, and there's no point in going there – nothing but ice.'

'The search area,' said Sarvas, 'really narrows down to the lower two valleys.'

'Great,' I said. 'Hazards?'

'They're chiefly obvious – after all, it's volcanic country. Some of the vegetation's nasty.'

'Animals?'

'A few verras. The Salamandrine Cities are in the second valley – we can't map them, as they move about from year to year, but they're harmless, apparently, and you'll be on an asva.'

'Beautiful,' I said. 'Now, procedure. Do we pick up every pebble smaller than five millimeters and squint into it?'

'No, Eda,' said Chorim, 'we will equip you. Clia will show you next how you will proceed. Probably the crystal is not in this accursed country. But we know that Agrippa lives there, and if you can meet him, or rather if he chooses to meet you, your task will be easier and much time will be saved.'

'He's the one who doesn't like Adepts?'

'Yes. Only Tjurip has talked with him. He has spoken with every great Adept, I think,' said Chorim.

'If he doesn't like Adepts he'll hide – or set the dog on us,' I said.

'He may hide. But if he wishes to be found, you'll find him.'

'That's promising.'

'We think that he will wish to do so,' said Thapsis, 'but nobody can be certain. He's a very temperamental chap. So don't hunt for him. Do your search procedure, and if he doesn't show in a week, go on in a Great Circle course through Entuthon, and return here.'

'Clia?' said Chorim.

The Losian girl opened up the obstetric bag and started taking out gear. 'We don't have much,' she said. 'I wish we had more. Compass, power-sight bow, standard asvin arms; you won't need an aegis, for there aren't any human enemies – scare lockets for verras: mind you don't look in them yourselves, and follow the usual rules about reflecting surfaces. I gather you're familiar with Losian armament. I'll arm these when you set out. Now, for search equipment we do have this.'

'This' was a round, transparent mandala like a stained-glass window, about a foot across.

'You have to treat it carefully,' said Clia, 'and always keep it in its case. It's rather fragile. Now Rusana knows that there's only one time of day when you can use this. It's the moment when the sun touches the horizon. Luckily you've got a good horizon westward in all the valleys. Altitude doesn't matter, it depends on the light. If you look through the mandala then, it will pick up the crystal as a bright spot, up to twenty miles off if it's clear. All the rest is dead time, so you'll have to plan your sighting points well ahead. In the forest, I'm afraid, it won't work unless you're on top of it. You'll have to go by behavioral cues.'

'In people?'

'Yes, and animals. Birds can see it – they seem to have mandala vision. If you see them congregating on the ground at sunset, go and investigate. Send your simurgh up – he's trained to fetch you, and we have a mandala spectacle-hood which boosts his discrimination of active crystals. As to people, there may be word of a vision or a religious revival.'

'Klars?' I asked.

'Probably will treat it as normal and pay it honor as another magical stone. They, good people, are perpetually enlightened, so if they look in it, they will see only what they already know and understand. They won't be changed.'

'I wish we could share their vision,' said Chorim.

'Never mind, if you get the crystal, you will,' said Thapsis. I bet under my breath that he wouldn't, and saw Rosanna on the same wavelength.

The rest of the meeting was line-plotting, water-holes and ration logistics. Rosanna and I went back to the college in a choreb rickshaw.

'That man,' said Rosanna, 'gives me the creeps. But I don't know why.'

'I have a thought that he's the reason for our little excursion,' I said. 'Thapsis said we have two projects. I think he's the second. If he's Thapsis's successor, I'm sorry for future Losian Adepts. We may be part of his education. That crystal is strong medicine, as Sutun found out. Let's try the library.'

On the love bed, Rosanna and I went through a stack of literature, most of it on those infernal scrolls, which are fine in a synagogue, where there is a proper desk for them and they are open at the correct place, but impossible to skip through when one wants information. There was nothing in the subject index catalog under crystal except a card saying 'See *Stone, Philosopher's.*' Stone, Philosopher's, produced a budget of stuff, ranging from a treatise in Chinese by Wei P'o-Yang to a ten-volume alchemical chemistry. Rosanna and I shared out the references, put on our rings, and set to work.

'It confers longevity and changes lead into gold,' said Rosanna, 'and it's made by the Great Operation in which a King and a Queen are united.'

'Makes sense,' I said. 'You said this morning that it was a piece of congealed orgasm. Can you make out if they're talking about an object, or an idea, or both.'

'Both,' said Rosanna.

'And you can make this object-idea by mixing up yoga and primitive chemistry. Might be simpler than looking for a natural specimen. Do you figure from this that there's one of them or a lot of them?'

'There's a picture here,' said Rosanna, 'of the alchemist walking through a landscape with the Stone lying about everywhere in blocks, only he doesn't realize it.'

'I have the feeling,' I said, 'that Thapsis is having us on, and the damn crystal will turn out to be an Edifying Experience and not a thing at all.'

'Don't be silly,' said Rosanna. 'You've actually looked into it.'

'I'd forgotten.'

'But not what you saw in it.'

'No,' I said, putting a hand on her, 'but I'm used to seeing that.'

'Not now,' she said, firmly, moving my hand off her pubis. 'Work first. And it says here what an Adept is.'

'What?'

'Lapidem philosopharum adeptus – someone who has got hold of the Philosopher's Stone.'

'But none of these Adepts has,' I said.

'Perhaps,' said Rosanna, 'that's why they want it. In that case we two, and Faesto, are the only real Adepts around.'

'And Sutun, of course, though he's not around any more.'

'Yes, him too. Go on searching.'

'All these books,' I said, 'take it literally and talk about cooking up mercury and vitriol in a pelican and rectifying the distillate. The only useful thing they discovered was Glauber's salts.'

I was down to the last book – this one, providentially, printed. It was in Latin, and the frontispiece showed a bearded young man with a distinct twinkle in his eye – rather like the Serbian monk whose enlightenment distinguished him from the crowd of would-be philosophers. 'Listen to this,' I said: ' "It would be tedious to recite all the idiotic mysteries of alchemical art – the silly riddles concerning the green lion, the running deer, the flying eagle, the dancing fool, the dragon swallowing his own tail, the puffed toad, the crow's head, that which is blacker than black and a load of similar rubbish: as to the blessed Philosopher's Stone, it is of substance neither quite fiery nor altogether earthy, nor yet of air, neither blunt nor sharp, softish, or at least not very hard, and to be construed in a wide sense – rather as Thucydides defines a good woman as one about whom there is not much to be said, of good or of ill. Alchemists, forsooth, in their pursuit of easy riches and instant enlightenment, run in the face of God's commandment, that in the sweat of our brow should we eat bread." '

'So?' said Rosanna.

'Only,' I said, 'that that's our missing Adept, Agrippa. You remember *Struwwelpeter*? The Great Agrippa who dipped the boys in his inkpot for jeering at a black boy?'

'Oh, wow,' said Rosanna, 'I hadn't realized. No wonder he doesn't like phoney Adepts. He was the man who wrote a treatise on the excellence and preeminence of woman. I hope we meet him. I have a feeling he'd be good for Chorim.'

We took the literature back next day – it had got us nowhere – and took a choreb rickshaw, on Thapsis's advice, to the top of the city, near the north or Losian gate, to look over the walls into the search area where we were to go. The rickshaw could not cover the last quarter-mile, which was set in steps like some of the escaliers de Montmartre, and like

Montmartre, was filled with stalls containing more Adeptic books, over which the would-be-enlightened haggled with stallholders. The alley climbed to the wall itself and became a gallery below its parapet, and we were able to look over. The city was indeed on a cliff edge. It fell about six hundred feet, with the road descending from the Losian gate terraced into its face. The valley below was a great swept area of reddish sand and bushes, with the thread of track running into it as far as a cluster of distant buildings which seemed themselves to be boulders, the outpost station at Tartara. Then the reddish opposite wall of the valley rose into a truly horrific tangle of ochre rock points, crags and pinnacles, above which rose one large black-streaked mesa in the form of a vast chair, and beyond that again the snowy cone of the Mountain. It was indeed a country to avoid.

'Look,' said Rosanna, 'that's Satan's Throne.' I could see dead trees on its lower cliffs, each as large as a giant redwood, but at this distance thin as hairs, like an ill-shaven chin.

'Why should he want to live there?' said Rosanna.

'No Adepts,' I said. 'Have you got the mandala? It'll be sundown in a few minutes.'

Indeed, the disc of the sun was approaching the dunes at the far western end of the valley, the Mountain was becoming less blue and the crags redder. Skeins of simurgh were coming along the middle distance to roost below us on the cliffs. Rosanna unwrapped the disc and held it up, and it ignited like a church window. A couple of stray Adepts watched our experiment with interest. The sun touched the ground, becoming oval as if compressed by a foot, and the light quality changed. 'Now,' I said. Rosanna scanned slowly along the horrific landscape, bonier and more forbidding than ever as the shadows of everything from bushes to the pimple of the settlement at Tartara lengthened into streaks.

'Nothing,' she said. 'I thought I saw a spark, but there's nothing.'

The Mountain turned steadily to pink sugar, and the valley filled up with a rushing shadow, leaving us in reddish light on the edge of a totally obscure abyss.

'We shall have to go across to the next range,' said Rosanna, firmly. 'We'd better go back now – it's getting chilly already, and the rickshaw's been standing an hour. Have you got plenty of money.

It is difficult to say how one recognizes such things, but within two minutes of reentering our room at the college we were both aware that small objects had been displaced. Nothing was missing, but somebody had been turning over our drum, as the police say. I wondered precisely who and precisely why.

8

Cogs to Fit the Cogs of the Adverse Wheel

Next day Rosanna went for further briefing, and I went on a visit of obligation to the Tetrarch. He was under one of the large stone arches outside the gate where Olowende had his assessment office, munching on pineapple still, and very well groomed. Evidently they were taking care of him. He seemed pleased to see me, but a little resentful over the lack of action – in fact, he did not even stand up when I appeared. A resting asva kneels with his front legs and half stands with his rear (they rarely lie down when in health). I was attempting to make my excuses to his forward end when I noticed, below his belly, a pair of polished black asvin boots.

'By God, you make a fool of that beast,' said a voice.

'General Kari! What are you doing here, Sir?'

'Same as yourself. Always turn up when there's trouble – one thing we two have in common. Come and smoke blach.' He took my arm and we went down a stepped path, that which pedestrian Adepts used to bypass the two guardian verras in the lower road. 'There's a good asvin inn down here,' said Kari, 'and I don't talk business in front of an asva. Didn't ever get a chance to say what a cracking good show you put up in Verula, Colonel.'

'Sir!'

'Don't sir me, we're not in the bloody messroom. Didn't get a chance to say it before – they had us confined to barracks until the fun was over, and by then you'd been posted back home.'

The asvin inn was a clean little place, with reed screens and scrubbed tables and sawdust on the stone floors. We were alone in its small leafy courtyard except for the waitress.

Kari ordered blach and sherbet, and put his boots on the table, laying his sword alongside them.

'Trouble?' I said.

'Yes. Talk quietly. Trouble – Verulans.'

'I thought they'd seen the light,' I said.

'Like hell Verulans have seen the light. I'd have let some light into a few more of 'em,' said Kari. 'Butter wouldn't melt in their mouths, and my fool superiors believe 'em.'

'So you reckon we shall have another deified goon before long?'

'Oh no, not in Verula,' said Kari. 'They're having too much fun in the House of Play. It's the ones on the loose who worry me. They're the old guard, the people who ran that freak who killed himself. I got some grudging orders to patrol the forest and turn them in, and we got a few of them, but the others . . .'

Kari sprang up with the agility of an asvin in training, stood silent on a table and looked over the fence. 'All clear,' he said. 'The others are coming here.'

'To storm the place?' I asked.

'Nothing so crass. They're in already. And I can't go after them. They're converts, and these idiots Adepts are teaching them loving kindness – never could stand Adepts, saving your presence: a lot of pompous idiots.'

'But only Adepts can get in,' I said.

'So what?' said Kari. 'They learn a couple of magic tricks and they're Adepts. I can't go in, except in uniform, and there they sit grinning.'

'I see your point,' I said. 'Tell Thapsis – or I will.'

'He knows,' said Kari. 'Told me it was all in order, that we have to train some Verulans if we don't want a repeat performance, and he's keeping a personal eye on them. But I don't like it. Do you?'

'No,' I said, 'I don't. We had some people called Nazis on Our Side, and we were supposed to reform those. I take your point.'

'Good,' said Kari, 'I thought you would. Now you're on the inside, you're a bloody Adept yourself – wouldn't have had you in the regiment if I'd known, but never mind, you're a decent Adept – and you could keep an eye on them.'

'I couldn't,' I said. 'I'm under marching orders for another of Thapsis's missions.'

'Damn,' said Kari, 'I might have known it. But do what you can.'

'I will, General,' I said.

'And either rendezvous here or send me a simurgh if you find out anything.'

'Are they armed?' I said.

'No arms allowed in the city, except under special conditions, and on the occasions they have us in for guard duty. But that proves nothing.'

'They could have guns?'

'They could, but I doubt it – we swept Verula with magnetic detectors. Unless of course they got out before we got in, or had an arms dump somewhere.'

'What exactly are they supposed to be doing?'

'Some Adept number – part of their change of heart.'

'Under whom? Thapsis?'

'No – his side-kick.'

'Not Chorim?' I said.

'That's the chap. Earnest young man who fancies himself. Thapsis is grooming him to take over – I think he must be crazy, for the fellow's got as much sense as a choreb.'

'He reminds me more,' I said, 'of a verra in choreb clothing.'

'You know him?'

'Yes,' I said, 'and I've seen people like him on Our Side. In fact, we usually put them in office.'

'That,' said Kari, 'is bad.'

'In fact,' I said, 'on a totally unsupported hunch, I think it might be good for national security if Chorim met with an accident.'

'No earth tricks allowed,' said Kari, 'but you're probably right. Meanwhile, don't let him know you saw me, or *you'll* meet with an accident. What's your mission, if you know? I have clearance.'

'The crystal again.'

'Oh, no,' said Kari. 'Why the hell do I have to serve under raving lunatics? Is the lady with you?'

'Rosanna?'

'Your śakti,' said Kari, 'the one who foxed the Verulans – a very brave and courageous lady.'

'Yes, she's in charge of this operation.'

'Good,' said Kari. 'So there's one person with some sense. Wish I had more women officers. But you don't want her to get into any more tight corners – one scrap with Verulans is enough for a woman.'

'I think,' I said, 'she's safe. If Chorim's what I think he is, he fancies her. He says he's on a chastity trip, as part of his Adept exercises, but he got an erection talking to her and had to hold a map over it.'

'What do you reckon is the form?' said Kari.

'I don't know. How's this?' I said. 'Chorim is to succeed Thapsis as GOC Adepts, he's getting impatient, he wants this crystal thing because it has Adept prestige and might give him power, he knows that for some reason only Rosanna and I can find it: he fancies her as his śakti, and he could easily do without me. Somebody turned over our room last night while we were out.'

'I don't like it,' said Kari.

'And as a second line, he's collecting Verulan Adepts around him.'

'I like it even less. Come on back to the Tetrarch,' said Kari, 'and act a little blached. Don't want to be seen talking to soldiers.'

He paid for our refreshments, and we went out, slapping each other on the back and tottering a little. We remounted the green mossy steps. Alongside them was a ramp for handcarts, and up this a handcart filled with hay was being at that moment pushed by a hairy individual who leaned his back to it and propelled it by putting his feet into tread holes on the ramp. As it passed us, a wheel came off the cart and it keeled over. Hay landed on top of us.

'Clumsy idiot!' said Kari.

The hairy individual made no attempt to survey the

damage or argue with us. He split and ran, disappearing down the steps three at a time and into the forest.

'Huh?' said Kari. Then, sotto voce, 'Hold everything.' He looked left and right, saw nobody and started to pull the hay apart. In a few moments he emerged covered with it, hugging a flat round leather object. 'I thought as much,' said Kari. He opened the leather case. In it was a sun-faced Adambaran aegis.

'Go back,' said Kari, 'and say nothing. I'm keeping this.' And he was off down the steps.

I found this interview worrying. It was difficult to see how I could keep an eye on Chorim, avoid scaring Rosanna and do my boy-scout assignment simultaneously. With three hours to spend, I reentered the city and went in search of enlightenment, in case that helped. I did not fancy either the House of Play or the worship of Enitharmon without Rosanna. Thapsis had suggested that devotional experience might make me more serious, and in order to see what he was talking about, I went to the collegiate square and entered the College of Luvah, where it was cultivated. I had to hand over my shoes to a young woman who asked me if I were saved, assured her that I was, and found myself in a pleasant courtyard surrounded by seminar rooms and ending in what was manifestly a chapel. The sounds from the flanking rooms were familiar enough: the chanting of monastic worship, the singing of revivalists and other charismatic sounds, ranging in tradition from Sanskrit samkirtan to Pocomaniac dancing and Chasidic singing. Some doors had judas-ports in them which enabled me to view the worship without disturbing it. I opened that of a room full of revivalists singing incongruously, 'Pull for the shore, sailor,' joined unawares in the hymn, when a stentorian voice shouted, 'Don't sing it, Brother, if you don't mean it!' I shut the door hastily. None of these exercises were for me. The Chapel was another matter – how, given the sectarian zeal of all such charismatics, could they worship together, or even agree on an object of devotion? I had seen them process together in the streets, carrying an image which was veiled, so that it would represent no specific deity, but could be identified with each. Probably the Chapel worked on the same principle.

It was high, beautiful, dark, empty of worshippers and loaded with incense. Baroque spiral columns supported the roof. There was an organ and a gallery for singers. Lamps filled with oil or butter burned on tall brass stands. There were no flanking images, either of saints or deities, but in the focal point of worship stood a huge, cylindrical, red alabaster lamp, unhistoriated, uncarved and devoid of all iconography. I sat in a vacant pew and contemplated it.

I recall how for me, as a child, the immediate effect of divine worship was to make patterns appear in the structure of church woodwork and the nonfigurative portions of church windows. I suddenly saw that this was true of the alabaster lamp. There were veinings on it suggestive of a figure, though it was not a defined figure. At one moment it was Our Lady and the Divine Child, but it could equally be the Savior showing the Sacred Heart, or, in the indefinition of its patterning, the Lord Krishna playing on his flute. If one rejected the figuration which it seemed to hold, its seven points made it into a large menorah. The cracks traced a Koranic text in Kufic script. I saw the Losian skill in imagination and ambiguity fully expressed here. The devotees worshipped what they saw in it, and saw in it what preoccupied them – it was a highly sophisticated and unique religious device.

Outside, the faithful were making up their daily procession, singing, playing on tambourines and calling me to join them. A few sadhana doors were still closed – I opened one, of which the judas was closed, and saw kneeling figures before images of Krishna and Radha. The next door had no judas. I opened it slightly. It was emphatically the wrong door. On a dais, Chorim sat in yogic meditation, facing about twenty meditating novices. In spite of his glazed expression of devout preoccupation, I was pretty sure he had seen me. All the novices, dressed in what looked like judo shirts, were Verulans, and these were the bathrobe national dress of Verula. I shut the door.

I got back to the college before Rosanna, shortly after

sundown, and put down the blach and groceries I had bought. It was stuffy, and I opened the window. There was no need to turn on lights, for the glow of the wax-stone is continual – one learns to sleep with it. As I turned from the window, not fully dark-adapted, someone or something said, 'Whod!'

I reflected on the meaning of the word. 'Whod!' again. Then 'Whod!' followed by a tinkling of glass, and a vase fell. I recognized the noise and dropped flat, but the archer was not trying a fourth shot. I went down, after a few minutes, to the concierge's desk and asked for a simurgh.

When Rosanna arrived I showed her the three arrows and came clean about the day's transactions.

'Yes,' said Rosanna, 'you're right. I thought exactly the same.'

'I didn't want to scare you,' I said.

'I'm in no danger,' said Rosanna. 'I didn't want to scare you.'

It was no more than two hours later, and we were on the love bed awaiting dinner, when I heard the familiar sound of spurs. Rosanna pulled the furs over her. Someone thumped on the door. Nudity is acceptable in a Losian home. I opened it, and confronted two lance corporals of asvin in half-battle-dress, without spears. They were the short men of Or-Cu, my old command. I returned their salutes as well as a nude colonel can.

'Sir! General Kari presents his compliments. You are entitled to a colonel's guard.'

'Thank you, Lance Corporal. Carry on.'

From that moment on, there were two asvin posted one on each side of my door day and night, like two stone images, which only came to life when I emerged, and followed me, or stood at ease, as directed. Though not arrow-proof, they were reassuring to us both.

I reclosed the door and returned to the furs. 'I thought you said no violence,' I told Rosanna.

'I thought so, too,' she said, laying the arrows out in a row.

9

In Which We Prepare a Journey

Thapsis was infuriatingly complacent.

'Oh dear,' he said, 'what a terrible business! You must have been recognized. Some Verulan who still carries a grudge. There's a bad apple in every barrel – I'll get Chorim to see if he can find out who did it. Did you ask for the guard?'

'No,' I said, 'that was pure coincidence. I ran into Kari at the asva stable, and he insisted. I'm a colonel to him, and you know what a stickler he is for regimental tradition.'

'I must say, I'd rather not have troops in the city – non-Adept troops, when it isn't a festival. It seems to strike the wrong note. Still, in view of that unfortunate episode with the arrows, it may be a happy coincidence.'

'Thapsis,' I said, 'your act would just possibly be worth it if it took anyone in. All three of us know damn well what is going on. So why fool yourself?'

'I want to show you something a little more in your own line,' said Thapsis, at the top of his voice. 'Come and see our computer room. You've had enough devotion.'

The room was across the passage, well equipped with Verulan computers, and as noisy as hell, for fifteen Adepts were punching cards, and an outlet was pouring out sheets of printout.

'Now talk,' said Thapsis. 'There's enough noise in here to be safe.'

I told him my scenario.

'I might have guessed you Other-Siders would get the picture,' said Thapsis. 'Intrigue is your specialty.'

'Is Chorim strong?' I asked.

'I'm hanging on by the skin of my teeth,' said Thapsis. 'If

you come running to me and he thinks I believe you, there will be a little archimage born in Manchester or Polynesia. Remember, I'm harmless because I'm naïve – if Chorim realizes he's been rumbled, I'm a dead Adept.'

'How do we play it?' said Rosanna. 'He wants me as his śakti.'

'Play along if we have to,' said Thapsis.

'I think you don't understand,' said Rosanna. 'Faesto, yes; even being raped by that filthy Verulan storm trooper, yes; but Chorim no – he's unclean.'

'I don't think you need go to those lengths,' said Thapsis. 'The chaste trip cover will last for a while.'

'And if Edward gets repatriated, I'm leaving, if I have to stab myself.'

'Don't,' said Thapsis. 'He'll be in his eighties before you grow up to be nubile if you return in that manner. Suicides have to start from scratch – it's karma, you know: always a problem.'

'You didn't tell me that,' said Rosanna, 'when you gave me a death locket to take to Verula and told me to use it if I had to. If Edward gets killed, I'll marry Chorim and murder him,' said Rosanna, with determination.

'He won't, he won't,' said Thapsis. 'Edward is never out of surveillance. That's why I didn't want those two idiotic soldiers in full view. My people can keep an eye on him.'

'Then tell them to get their finger out and fire last night's detail,' I said.

'I already have,' said Thapsis. 'The Verulan got on the roof. They could have caught him, but then there would have been explanations.'

'And the crystal number is simply part of the power play?' I said.

'Not simply, not simply. We do indeed need it. But as it gives enlightenment to good Adepts, it's a natural trap for the Chorims of this world. Do it my way, like a good chap. There are more pitfalls in my way than you know.'

'You seem to be making them, with your genius for complication,' I said. 'I know you can't simply knock him on the head. But he could have an Adeptic accident. There are two tame verras down the road – one of those could get loose in Chorim's quarters. Or my old friend the Tetrarch could pay me a visit and happen to tread on him . . .'

'And if you make any attempt to take matters into your own hands,' said Thapsis, 'you could find yourself back in your apartment with a splitting headache and no prospect of ever coming near this city again. Who's archimage here, you or I? Come on back up, we've been long enough, and don't say a word.'

We went back. 'I'm very impressed with your Tanist Chorim,' I bellowed, for the tape. 'Do you think he would teach me his sadhana? A sadhana of chastity would be a new experience.' Thapsis scowled and muttered something about not over-egging the pudding, and Rosanna kicked me.

'Nice pickle you got us into,' I said, as we set off home. Two asvin tramped methodically ten paces to the rear.

'Just do as he says. Concentrate on our piece of the action,' said Rosanna, 'and quit playing soldiers. I thought we were over that. We have work to do, remember?'

'Yes,' I said, 'and you're going to enlighten me again tonight.'

'I'm not,' said Rosanna. 'I'm starting a period. And I've got backache. And I don't know the Losian for tampax. Men have it all their own way, I sometimes think.'

'The sadhana of chastity is a blasted nuisance,' I said.

'Then masturbate,' said Rosanna. 'I want to think, not service you.'

The lunar dependency of Rosanna's hormones made no difference to her efficiency. It was she, not I, who studied maps, plotted our scan points, arranged the stores and gave the instructions. I was to be the asva driver and armaments officer, and that only. It was emphatically her operation.

Thapsis wanted us out of the city as soon as possible – probably before Chorim got up to tricks against me. Rosanna spent a whole morning with him and came back wearing a locket. Presumably she insisted on it, in case Chorim decided chastity had had a long enough run. Chorim himself was all pre-election attentiveness. I spent a morning with him in which he told me four times how grateful he was for our courage and how much the crystal meant to his spiritual development. I complimented him on his missionary zeal in reclaiming Verulans, and fully appreciated how much the crystal would facilitate that noble task. How much we took one another in, I don't know.

'My chaste sadhana is for them, of course,' he said. 'I have to begin with something they understand. They were brought up to a religion of self-punishment. I have to start somewhere with them.'

'Wouldn't some shock therapy in the House of Play do the trick?' I asked.

'Oh, no. We have to temper the wind to the shorn choreb,' Chorim replied, and began a rambling warning to me about the poisonous vegetation in the badlands, which I didn't follow. He even had a botany book full of evil-looking plants, which I would have avoided merely from their appearance. I offered to take him on a training ride on the Tetrarch, hoping for a chance to get that noble beast some unarmed combat, but he wouldn't bite. Chorim was afraid of asvaya, I learned. That might prove useful.

We made, finally, the usual dawn start. I heard the Tetrarch's footfalls as he was led protesting past our bedroom and on towards the Losian gate. Rosanna was dressed – I was dressing, in my colonel's uniform once more, which I had found laid out for me.

'All ready?' I asked her.

'All ready. Good-bye, room.'

It was cold and damp, and nobody much was about. The two asvin stumped along behind carrying the asva gear – ankus, sword, ax and pack. Inside the closed gate a small party was waiting. The Tetrarch whinnied when he saw me and flexed his muscles, giving the elderly asva-groom a hard time. We began to equip him. Clia handed over the special equipment and put a hooded simurgh on my wrist. 'Check your asva horn,' she said, and kissed me on both cheeks. The supervision and farewell party stood to one side – Thapsis, Chorim and old Tjurip, who didn't seem to feel the cold, and quietly handed me a package wrapped in bark.

'You've got it all perfectly clear?' said Chorim.

'Yes,' said Rosanna.

'Good hunting then,' said Thapsis. 'Mount.' We did so. The two asvin got the gates open. Mist was coming up the cliff and the opened gate let it in. We moved off. Tjurip wasn't attending – he was trying to pull some object out of his loincloth, looking like Gandhi-ji with a bad gnat bite.

'Tjurip!' said Chorim sharply, 'wish the Adepts well!'

'Oh, ah,' said Tjurip, and made a sudden quick move. Something whizzed overhead, and a Verulan archer fell from a tree and over the wall. We heard his yell as the valley swallowed him. Tjurip stuck his boomerang back in his belt. The Tetrarch needed no urging. We were into the mist, descending what seemed to be the back stairs of Hell.

10
Of Snares, Traps, Wheels, Pitfalls and Dire Mills

We came out under the rising mist, which lay over us like a lid. The track was steep and rutted – it was as well we entered the clear when we did, for we met a wagon laden with firewood and drawn by six choreb, creaking its way up to the city. The Tetrarch elbowed past it and continued down. I made no attempt to rein him, for I knew his sure-footedness, and I wanted to be out of sniper range. Once in the plain, the terrain had the advantage that nobody could stalk us unnoticed. Verulans, who are brave enough in mistreating slaves, or anyone else at a disadvantage, have the reputation for cowardice which usually goes with such a style, and would not have much stomach for a pursuit into the badlands.

When we reached the desert floor, the mist was rising off the buildings of the Foursquare City, and a cloud was forming above it, for it is this escarpment which traps the rains which water Entuthon, denying them to the desert to windward. Satan's Throne stood covered with reddish fissures, the two gendarmes which compose its back surrounded by rising clouds of mist. The plain was featureless here, marked with wood gatherers' tracks and studded with the dead desert trees which they gather. The road ran ahead between marker stones. Tartara, when we reached it, had a small insalubrious square and a ring of houses, bothies and an inn, all of which seemed to have fallen by accident from the cliff rather than to have been erected by hand. We went round it, not through it – it was a natural site for ambush. But nobody save a few wild-looking residents was in evidence, and a couple of tethered choreb outside the shebeen.

The houses backed on decrepit yards, some containing carts, others rusted Verulan mechanical vehicles.

Beyond Tartara there is no road, and we rode by compass bearing toward the fissure in the ridges below Satan's Throne which marks the pass. The last waterhole was an unhealthy looking tank about a mile beyond Tartara, fouled with choreb dung, but the Tetrarch was not particular, and topped up his reservoirs. He could go now a week without drinking, if he must, though so long a dry period was unlikely. We ate in the saddle, passing forward the last sack of pineapples for him to chew, and pressed on steadily. I looked back for any pursuers, but nobody was behind us.

The land sloped up to the fissure, strewn with tilelike rocks, as though buildings had been demolished here, and we entered the winding canyon, passing into cold shadows. Simurgh flew up from its sides, and the stones under the Tetrarch's feet set echoes rattling. In places the rocks almost met overhead. This was a dry water-carved gorge. I wondered if sudden thunder on Satan's Throne would fill it with a flash flood, but there was no sign of driftwood. It was an eerie place. I saw a single half-grown verra, high on the cliff, looking down at us from a lair. The desert verra are few, and this one, a couple of hundred feet over our heads, showed little interest in our passage. By early afternoon the gorge was widening and steepening into the dry valley which it drained. Satan's Throne rose directly above us in monstrous cliffs and clouds of wheeling simurgh.

The tilelike rocks were being replaced with rough piles of black, solidified material like petrified mud, and the sand underfoot became black. The valley wound, and we could not see far ahead, each bluff revealing more lava and more black sand. The Tetrarch had to mount lava piles which obstructed its floor. Rosanna was listening. 'Do you hear something?' she said. Her hearing is the sharper, but I heard it presently, a sound like a monstrous sigh. It recurred, regular as a foghorn, at minute-and-a-half intervals. Round the next corner the ground began to steam. Between the fungus-shaped fans of lava was a hot, bubbling pool. The Tetrarch showed no discomfort, however, but loped ahead, jumping obstacles and scaling lava slopes. The sigh grew louder, and uncomfortable on the ears. Round the next corner we came to an array of the hot pools, some steaming, some bubbling, fringed with tufa and salts, like a child's sand game played with hot water and rock. The Tetrarch had to thread his way. At the next sigh, which was deafening, I saw the top of a plume of water and steam rising over a collection of vast stone spheres, petrified bubbles in lava which had solidified but never burst. One, which was broken open, emitted a long plume of smoke. I steered away from the geyser to the less volcanic side of the valley. The hot-water garden was behind us. The Tetrarch was headed for a smooth area like a landing strip which promised easier going. It was only when we were nearly upon it that I spotted its shining macadam surface, and the skeleton of a choreb, entire and fixed upright close to its edge. I reined him hard. It was a tar pool, and in it he would have stuck fast, like other prehistoric animals before him. Not all hazards were obvious to that intelligent beast. We flanked it – tar adhered to his pads, making him fidget. The air was full of the odor of road making. The geyser sighed behind us.

'It's an unpleasant place,' said Rosanna, 'but incredibly beautiful.' And so it was, from the red rocks to the fans of lava and the steaming hot-water basins. We left it behind us as we climbed, and the sigh of the geyser was muted by rocks.

The volcanic cup widened into another valley, level desert, of which the further side, almost hidden in dust, appeared to be a jagged line of rocks like those through which we had passed. There was a huge dark area in the cliff to our left, a cave portal, under the arch of which more simurgh were screaming – as large as a railway station roof, and running into darkness. We saw no reason to explore it. It was not a likely place for our crystal, and could easily harbor cave verras. We left it behind and entered the plain. The rocks on its far side were to be our first siting point. We had made good time, and there was no pursuit.

The volcanism of the Losian badlands is in fact confined to this one slit-crater, and the popular legend of a land of perpetual fire and smoke surrounding Satan's Throne has little basis in fact. From the high desert, the Throne itself is an eroded volcanic plug, no longer seatlike, and flanked with high screes of ash ejected before the solid column hardened. The plain before us was much like that below the city, but the vegetation had changed. There were distorted, apparently dead, trees, garnished with huge thorns, a few scalelike leaves being the only sign of inner life. Among these were tall whiplike growths resembling reeds or ocotillo, planted like inverted octopods, arms upward. The mottled green stems seemed to have a perpetual breeze in them, though we felt none, for they moved and rustled incessantly. In places they formed groves, through which the Tetrarch pushed. In other places there were drifts of tall thistles, or bramblelike tangles of a spiny vine like animated barbed wire, which he avoided or jumped when he came to them.

We reached the rocks an hour before sunset and camped beside a clump of the reedlike plants, whose twelve-foot canes sprang from a kind of bole like a congealed chunk of tar. The Tetrarch showed interest in them, but I tethered him on the side towards any possible pursuit. We scaled the rocks and took our siting. The sun bulged and sank, the Throne became angry red, but Rosanna, scanning with the mandala, saw only one spark, a long way off to westward, which went out as soon as she took its bearing.

'I don't think that was a positive,' she said. 'It's cold here. Shall we light a fire?'

'Better not,' I told her – we were only a day's asva ride from the city, and I mistrusted Chorim enough to want our first camp to be unmarked. Smoke would be visible from the other side of the range, and might be distinguishable from the steam of the volcanic ground. We ate, but did not unroll the love bed, sleeping instead on the ground in asvin blankets, under the lee of the patch of whispering canes.

Something woke me. It was still wholly dark. The sound was repeated. It was a chacla, the Losian coyote, and a long way off. The Tetrarch whiffled a question, then resumed his rest. As I turned, I noticed two things – first, that something was missing; and second, that something, inserted into the blanket, was tickling my ankle. The tall canes of our screening clump had gone. I held up the piece of Losian firestone which served us as a lamp. The tall rods had been replaced by prostrate cables, crossing the ground, and all pointing in our direction. Two of the longest had reached me. It was one of these which was tickling my ankle. I withdrew the ankle, and it adhered. I pulled it off. Where it had touched me, I saw a line of blood drops appear. The second cane was within inches of my ear. Another was clinging to Rosanna's hand. Those which had not reached us were undulating at their tips, and approaching as I watched. I woke Rosanna, pulled the cane from her wrist, and saw blood drops there too. It was an unpleasant awakening, and a still less encouraging introduction to Losian desert vegetation. I moved our sleeping place to a spot distant from any of the cane-clumps, and with my sword severed most of the wriggling tips. Dark stains ran from those which had touched us. I hope the plant had not been long in undetected action. Neither of us slept again. At morning, when I brought the Tetrarch over, he studied the canes, now erect again, and proceeded with relish to eat the entire gruesome plant, leaving only the bole. We breakfasted in chilly mist and moved on as soon as the sun rose.

Within two hours it was warm again. The blood canes were all round us, swaying with their own inward motion. I could find no pass through the next intervallary range, but there was a scaleable saddle, which the Tetrarch mounted without much trouble. Satan's Throne, in this light, shone silver with the crystalline gneiss in its veins. Simurgh passed, and some larger birds which I could not identify. At one point we came on an assemblage of simurgh gathered on the ground, in a small clear space among rocks. Our hopes rose, but reaching them they scattered. The object of attention had been the picked skeleton of a wild choreb. There was no crystal.

Most of this second day was spent in crossing the rock ridges above the blood-cane valley. We were still climbing. At one point we opened a vista toward the mountain, into a much lower, crater valley, with snow beyond it, and in its eye, circled by huge screes, a dark lake like an eye.

'Udan-Adan,' said Rosanna, 'the Lake of Not-Being.'

It seemed like a vast ant trap. Anything which had ventured on those screes would have tobogganed directly into it. We looked down briefly, and turned away west, into the ridges leading to the next valley, the final northward point of our sweep before circling toward Entuthon.

From the ridge, we looked down into the next valley. It was flat-bedded, a dry lake, and had an astonishing look to it, that of a vast black pattern or honeycomb – as though paved with dark cartwheels laid rim to rim, filling the area from one cliff to the other. We stopped and looked down. They were not basalt columns, like those of the Devil's Postpile or Fingal's Cave – they seemed rather to be discrete circles: not cracks in mud, not rock structures. They appeared to be plants.

I had no great love by now of badlands vegetation. We took the Tetrarch, picking his way, down a steep trail to the valley bed. At the foot was a clear, cartwheel-free sandy area, and beyond that the nearest of the cartwheels. They were indeed plants – enormous flat rosettes of metallic red-black leaves, about six feet from tip to tip, bearing wicked amber spines three or four inches long. They might have been made as ornaments in the Forge of Los himself. Moreover the Tetrarch was making it clear that he for one had no intention of treading on them. They were plainly of the nature of thistles. One or two had stout, ribbed thorny stems rising in the rosette, which ended in an enormous scaly bud. One such had opened into an orange thistle of great beauty, a sunburst at least a yard across. The striking feature of this valley of caltrops was the character of its silence – not a bird or lizard moved, and there was no wind, and yet there was a fidgeting rustle of vegetation, like that of a palm head.

'What next?' I said.

'I don't think he can cross those,' said Rosanna, 'and there's something odd about them, not just the thorns.'

'Yes,' I said, 'there is. Hang on.' I dismounted from the Tetrarch and looked around until I found a baseball-sized rock which had fallen from the valley wall. I tossed it into the nearest rosette. The leaves closed – not with an audible snap, but with a force which held the rock suspended, well off the ground. The outer leaves followed more slowly, and the thorns interlocked.

'We go round,' I said. 'From now on, no more night travel. Some of those things may be solitary.'

We remounted and circumnavigated the valley, finding another, across the saddle, running parallel to it. Far up, at the end remote from us, were dark patches of the carnivorous caltrops, but the rest was clear. A small specimen beside the track closed at the Tetrarch's footfall – it was under a foot across, but even so its spines were an inch long. We took course over the valley bed, well away from the ominous plantation.

The only other feature of the valley was an irregular domed hillock, perforated by dark entrances of caves or burrows at its lower border. It looked artificial but not manmade, like an ant's nest. Nothing moved in or around it, but I noticed that deep grooves and scuffle marks converged on the burrow entrances. Evidently it had inhabitants, which I was not specially keen to meet. The Tetrarch, however, showed no great interest in it, sniffing and munching demonstratively, but I spurred him past. Presumably he thought there might be hyasa about.

'It looks like a city without people,' said Rosanna.

'I'm just hoping it isn't an ants' nest,' I said. 'What were the cities of salamandrine men that Sarvas talked about? That could be one – who lives in it? People?'

'I don't know,' said Rosanna. 'But let's get past it quietly, before we find out.'

I agreed, and the Tetrarch, voting contra, found himself in a minority of one, which required a little persuasion with the ankus. We covered a full twenty miles and placed several valleys between us and the hillock before we selected an observation point on a suitable crest, and a vegetation-free area to set camp. I was not about to trust anything with leaves. The only visible caltrop was a dead and dried specimen, though tiny spiked seedling rosettes closed as I dragged it off to make the basis of our campfire. The sky was just about reddening – Rosanna let me go alone to take the reading – she was tired, the camp and its approaches were in full view, with the Tetrarch on guard, and the climb down in the sudden Losian twilight might be difficult for one carrying a fragile instrument. I took a sword and the mandala in its case, and climbed to the crest, looking out for caltrops and other hazards against the descent, but saw none. The sun was about fifteen minutes from the critical point. I had a good horizon all round. Both valleys were lit from the west: about a mile off to eastward was a range of dunes, turning pinkish at this time. I was preparing my sighting when I saw, through the clear central lens of the mandala, figures moving behind the nearest dune. I looked directly. There were four bobbing heads, moving in procession. The bodies were hidden, and the heads themselves passed below the crest of the dune and out of sight as I watched. But they appeared to be the cowled heads of monks, wearing each a black, rough habit, with the cowls hanging in folds around their necks. They were going away from us, towards the lower valleys. I thought of solitary Adepts, and the elusive Agrippa. The only trouble was that these monks, from a quick reckoning of size and distance, stood about nine feet high.

I said nothing to Rosanna. The reading was negative as before, and the descent rather dangerous in the dark. Rosanna, wearing my asvin gloves against thorns, had a roaring fire going. It cast a wide circle of red light, enough to keep off most predators, and I thought it wiser not to cause needless alarm. The Tetrarch was dozing, too, and I relied implicitly on his alertness and judgment.

I had turned from the fire to open rations when, for the first time since I had known her, I heard Rosanna scream in earnest. I turned, and saw suspended in the rim of the firelight, and over seven feet from the ground, the two most horrible faces I have ever seen.

They were side-by-side, shaped like horses' skulls but larger, the teeth covered by scaly white-rimmed reptilian lips. There were no ears. The rest of the skin was composed of wrinkled black flakes like the scum on a pool of tar, and, like it, iridescent. The eyes were large, cross-pupiled and staring yellow. Around the necks were three folds of the tarry skin, like a monk's cowl drawn back, or a retracted foreskin, but there was nothing reassuringly phallic about these faces. They were the faces of devils. Below I saw ridiculously small clawed hands which seemed to be held monk-wise out of black rough sleeves. Both faces bobbed and made a deep chuckling sound.

'What *are* they?' said Rosanna.

The Tetrarch opened one sleepy eye, did not believe what he saw with it, opened the other, then gave his battle whinny, reared and charged to the end of his tether. I ran to untie him from the picket.

'Stop,' shouted a voice. 'Don't turn that asva loose! There's absolutely no danger!'

'Who's there? Where are you?' I called. 'Advance and be recognized!' I grabbed the bow and loaded.

'Here – don't shoot.' A man stepped into the firelight circle.

11

We Encounter Enormous Demons, and the Chain of Jealousy

He was young and bearded, wearing a black, four-pointed biretta and a tattered velvet coat, with a chain around his neck. In his hand was a quarterstaff, like a boy scout pole. 'I'm terribly sorry you had such a fright,' he said. 'I came to see who you were. I'd no idea they were following me; they're terribly inquisitive.'

'What in hell were they?' I said.

'Salamandrines.'

'Oh,' said Rosanna, nearly collapsing, 'salamandrines. It's nice to know.'

'Yes,' said the young man, 'they're reptiles, of course, not salamanders. Don't know how they got the name. Probably the Losians think they live in hot lava.'

'They're horrible,' said Rosanna, 'the most horrible things I ever saw.'

'Well, in firelight they would be spooky – they're as ugly as sin anyway. But in daylight they're just big hulking lizards.'

'Are there more?' said Rosanna.

'Oh, hundreds,' said the young man. 'They'll be all around us now, staying out of the light. If one comes, they all come.'

Indeed we could hear hissing, rustling, chuckling and the sound of heavy dragging tails which crossed tails. The Tetrarch snorted and began to munch anticipatorily. To him 'lizard' meant only one thing. He had the air of one laying a knife and fork.

'They're scared of the asva,' said our visitor.

'And they're harmless?' said Rosanna.

'Oh, quite – they aren't aggressive. Of course, if you attack them and they get frightened they'd be dangerous: they can

218

bite, or knock you down with their tails. But I live with them, and I've never ever had any trouble.'

'Are you by any chance Agrippa?' I said.

'I am, at your service,' said the young man. 'You knew of me?'

'Henricus Cornelius Agrippa of Nettesheim,' said Rosanna, 'Doctor of all Four Sciences, sometime Public Orator of Metz and author of a book on *The Vanity of the Arts and Sciences*, and another on *The Excellence and Preeminence of the Female Sex*. What are you doing here with those ghastly lizards?'

'You know my vita by heart,' said Agrippa. 'Well, it's nice to be remembered. I like lizards – rather as most Losians like Klars.'

'Don't tell me these too are born philosophers?' I said.

'Hell, no – they're utterly witless. Saving your presence, they'd make good professional Adepts. But they're most amusing. For example, if we three set off now walking in Indian file, after five minutes we'd be followed by a mile-long procession of lizards also in Indian file. I make myself Abbot of Salamandria and organize wonderful religious processions on all the major feasts of the Church. And then if two or three of them are gathered together, no matter who or what is in the midst of them, all the rest gather around – not doing anything, just staying stood there. Actually they aren't entirely stupid. I find I can train them to let a simurgh lead them back to me, wherever I am. They'll come plodding fifteen, twenty miles and stand there, and if I don't seem to want anything they stand bowing for a bit and then plod all the way back to where they were – no hard feelings. I find them comic beyond words. They're the paradigm of poverty, chastity, of a sort, and obedience.'

'You spent your life annoying monks,' said Rosanna.

'Right, right,' said Agrippa. 'I love it.'

'Agrippa,' I said, 'you know we're looking for the Losian crystal?'

'I didn't – that wild goose chase again?'

'It's said you know where it is.'

'Well, if you really want it,' said Agrippa, 'I know where it was. Probably still is, if you look.'

'Where?'

'About twenty miles up-valley, just on the edge of Entuthon.'

'How did you find it?' I asked.

'I didn't – the lizards found it a couple of weeks back. Apparently it looks striking or peculiar to them – a party of about six gathered round to goggle at it, and pretty soon there were two or three hundred of 'em holding a meeting. I went to see what they were looking at.'

'Didn't you look in it?' I asked him.

'Oh, yes.'

'And you didn't bring it away?'

'Why should I? There was nothing I hadn't seen before. Nothing which hadn't been shown me often and often by a woman. By two women. They're both dead. Nothing, in other words, I care to think about now.'

'How do you know,' said Rosanna, gently, 'that they're dead?'

'I've looked for them here. And I saw them dead on the Other Side. I watched them both die. I buried one with my own hands, when nobody else would. They're dead, unless they could have done as I did.'

'What did you do?' said Rosanna.

'The "Terminal Transfer", they call it here,' said Agrippa. Then his words came in a flood. 'I spent all my life fooling with Cabbala – for that I nearly got burned as a Judaizing heretic by the holy lizards of the Inquisition. My first lovely wife showed me all that's in any crystal. She died in childbed. My second wife was an Adept, a beautiful, gentle Adept, of the Female Portal. She died of plague, through my foolhardy obstinacy – I was a physician by then, the only one who didn't run for his life. My third wife was a whore and a bitch. She closed the Female Portal for me and threw the key away. Without the others it opens nowhere, except into complications. Certainly not into Beulah.

'Then, when I was dying myself, I whiled the time away, waiting to cease existence, playing mathematical games in my head. I saw a fat fly trying to get through a veil curtain, buzz, buzz, and suddenly it dawned on me how, if he'd known, he could have passed through to the other surface without tearing the fabric or destroying himself, and as I felt my existence slipping I tried the same thing on my sense of self, out of curiosity, to see what happened. This Losian world is what happened. At first I was sure I'd find one or both of my darlings here. But I didn't. Evidently they simply died. As for me, I'm marooned, for I can only have beaten my own death by ten heartbeats – if I go back now, it will be to finish dying, or less probably to start the whole idiot business again. Odd that all this life fits into ten heartbeats.'

'Tell me their names,' said Rosanna, 'if you can.'

'Giulietta – and Jehanne Lois Tissie,' said Agrippa, 'may they rest and love in peace.'

'Did you go to Adambara?' asked Rosanna.

'And searched it,' said Agrippa.

'And did you worship Enitharmon?' said Rosanna. 'You might have found them in Her temple, perhaps?'

'Oh yes. But that door goes nowhere. As for those gentle Losian swingers, not one of them can reopen the former door for me. I tried.

'Not,' said Agrippa after a while, 'that it was all honey. I was a jealous lover, so jealous of my darlings that it hurt – if they so much as spoke to a man beside me. I wake up still, dreaming that they are here, but with someone else. I think that, and not losing them to death, is what is destroying me. I don't know in any case why I'm telling you this. Except that I can't talk to lizards, any more than to monks. Lizards wouldn't understand a word, monks would tell me to lay hold on God and accept His chastening and neither would inwardly care a damn.'

Rosanna said nothing, but went and took Agrippa in her arms and kissed him on the lips. Then she took off his biretta and kissed his forehead, to his great amazement. He released Rosanna and looked at her, up and down, as if she were a ghost.

'You're beautiful,' he said, 'and far too nice for an Adept.

You're very like Jehanne, though you are not she.' Then to me, 'I beg your pardon. I meant no harm.'

'Of course not,' I said. 'It's perfectly true. Why should I mind you liking Rosanna?'

'But you are lovers.'

'Yes,' I said, getting the drift of Agrippa's remark – which, since it had never occurred to me that he might expect me to be jealous, I had completely missed.

'We don't own each other, Agrippa,' I said. 'Rosanna and I can love anyone we wish. It doesn't separate us, you understand; it makes us closer.'

'I don't quite understand,' said Agrippa.

'We think,' said Rosanna, 'that "love which drinks up another as a sponge drinks water" is phoney and isn't love. Our love is genuine – and for that we have to be two people, not a sort of two-person chain gang.'

'I see now,' said Agrippa, 'why you could use the crystal and I couldn't. Frankly, looking in it hurts too much. I'd better go now, if you don't mind. I'll be back tomorrow if I may. You needn't fear the lizards – I'll leave you the pole: if they get inquisitive, just bop them on the nose. I don't think they'll come into camp with the fire burning and the asva around. And you needn't fear me. Love well!'

He got up. Rosanna went and took his hand.

'Why don't you join us, Agrippa?' she said, and started to pull him gently towards me and the love bed. Agrippa looked at me.

'Yes, please do,' I said. 'We'd both be delighted.'

'Don't we have, in this literal-minded country, to be four for these exercises?' said Agrippa, trying to make up his mind. He was looking at Rosanna, and I had the feeling that the Feminine Portal wasn't so tightly closed that a good shove might not open it for him.

'This isn't for Enitharmon,' said Rosanna firmly. 'It's for Oothoon.' She continued to pull him towards the skins. Agrippa slowly unbuttoned his doublet.

As always, Rosanna's judgment was correct in affairs of this kind. Neither the munching of the Tetrarch nor the shuffling of the salamandrines disturbed that starlit and very moving observance. The Tetrarch snapped at a foolhardy lizard halfway through the night and woke us. Rosanna was between us, her head partly on each of our shoulders, holding a hand of each, and without comment she put our hands together.

'That makes us titular brothers,' I said to Agrippa. He seemed too astonished to comment – we had blown his mind. We went to sleep again, I certain that, if not enlightened as to the lesson of Oothoon, he was at least educated by the experience. I myself hadn't intended it to be consciousness-raising, thinking that Rosanna was acting out of spontaneous sympathy for a lonely person, but she had evidently been wiser than I as to the implications of our worship.

We were woken at dawn by uproar. The Tetrarch, having been balked of lizard, was making up for it by digging up and eating eggs which lay within the scope of his tether, surrounded by outraged salamandrines at whom he snapped and screamed menacingly. I muzzled him before he had finished his breakfast, apologized to the bereaved parents and went back to breakfast. Agrippa was deeply silent.

'We want to go after the crystal,' I said. 'Would you mind showing us exactly where to look?'

'Let me just go back to my cave,' said Agrippa, 'and pack some things. It could be quite a hunt, in this country.'

'You'll bring some salamandrines?' I asked.

'Won't need to – they'll come. I'll return in an hour. Know well.' He plodded off.

'I'm glad you got him to stay the night,' I said. 'You've got great savoir-faire, Ros.'

'If you thought that was a charity hump, you were wrong,' said Rosanna.

'I could tell it wasn't,' I said. 'The Feminine Portal seemed pretty well open to me.'

'We're making headway against Theotormon,' said Rosanna. 'Agrippa's gone in spirit to release Oothoon and Bromion who were prisoners in Bromion's cave. Can I borrow the simurgh for a few hours?'

'To tell Thapsis we found Agrippa and we're on the trail?'

'No – I want to cable the Department of Immigration,' said Rosanna. 'Giulietta, and Jehanne Lois Tissie, he said.'

Agrippa found us saddled and ready to set out. He mounted behind Rosanna, with his arms round her waist. The hideous, but by daylight unalarming, salamandrines surrounded us in a huge circle. They were upright reptiles, shaped like frilled lizards or erect dinosaurs, who stood as immobile most of the time as grayish-black tombstones. The Tetrarch was still grumpy, but Rosanna was at ease with them, looks and all.

'I have a suggestion,' said Agrippa. 'Don't ride off. We'll set out in single file walking, and lead the beast for a mile or two.'

We did so, to the Tetrarch's further disgust, for he hated dawdlers. By the end of the first mile, a slaty procession, also in single file, was goose-stepping behind us like devout pilgrims, with a steady swish of dragging tails.

'I find that hilarious, however often I see it,' said Agrippa. 'That's how great ecclesiastical movements start. Orate fratres lacertae – Dominus vobiscum.'

'Responsio nulla,' I said.

'Yes – sed erit tamen forsan; one day I'm sure they'll come back with "Et cum spiritu tuo",' said Agrippa. 'We could mount now.'

We did so, and the goose-step changed to a leaping progression, the Tetrarch making speed, but still regretfully conscious of the provision train behind him and proceeding cornerwise, munching angrily. I think he blamed me personally for the whole frustrating affair.

We threaded the defiles and rocks all day, avoiding the plantations of the vast caltrops. By late afternoon the rocky desert had given place to dunes. The salamandrines kept up an untiring pace, halting when we halted, keeping station. On low hills ahead we could see the outposts of Entuthon, the first low bushes, and the green wall behind. There were now reeds and green pools, at which we watered the Tetrarch. He drank like a locomotive.

'Slow down,' said Agrippa. 'It's hereabouts.'

We were at the lip of a sandy cup with a few reeds at its

bottom. 'We needn't hunt,' said Agrippa. 'Let *them* do the work.'

It was already getting late, and flocks of simurgh were going over: they apparently saw nothing to attract them, but a straggler detached from one passing flock, and I saw his flaps go down and the slots in his wingtips open. He glided in: undercart, airbrakes, reverse thrust and a neat stall onto Rosanna's outstretched wrist. She read the message but said nothing.

'I'll get down and round up some lizards,' said Agrippa. 'They're still scared of your asva. Let me off a minute, will you, and hand down that quarterstaff.'

While he walked back, Rosanna handed me the message foil. It read: 'ADAMBARA CABLE OFFC 1035 BZ 1200 – IMMIGRATION CONFIRM BOTH ARRIVED FOUR FIFTEEN YEARS RESPECTIVELY WHY INQUIRY GOOD LUCK DUTY OFFICER.'

'We'll get him back to Adambara,' said Rosanna, 'when this is over. He'll be ready by then. Poor Agrippa – four years of lizards!'

The salamandrines, with Agrippa herding them with cowboy yells, wandered about aimlessly. They showed no interest in anything underfoot.

'Any luck?' I called.

'No. But it was here. I remember that rock. Damn! I'd like to look in it again now.'

'Keep off the lizards a minute,' I said, and dismounted.

Agrippa was standing in a small cup of sand under a white rock. There were scuffling tracks, not ours, not those of salamandrines.

'Someone's been here,' I said. 'Not people – but they've taken it off into Entuthon, by the looks of it, whoever they were.'

The critical sun time was approaching. We stood on top of the rock, leaving the Tetrarch still sulking. Salamandrines were now beneath his notice, but he thought dangerous thoughts, I judged. Rosanna raised the mandala and scanned.

'No. Nothing,' she said, as the light finally died.

'It's evidently gone, then,' I said. 'Never mind. Camp now, and we'll ride into Entuthon tomorrow. Too many verras to go on by night.'

'May I come with you?' said Agrippa, as if the question expected the answer 'No.'

'Of course, we were counting on that,' I said, 'Blood Brother.'

'You aren't mocking me?' said Agrippa.

'Of course not.'

'Then I accept,' he said. 'I have stayed here too long.' He helped us make camp and spread the love bed.

When I awoke during the night, Agrippa was in pillow-talk with Rosanna – he talking, she consoling him.

'In Verula,' Agrippa was whispering, 'I thought the first day that I'd found Giulietta, in the slavemarket. I was sure I saw her, among a lot of women, bound hand and foot in a cart, lying there like fish in a hold. I couldn't get close, but I thought I'd know her body anywhere. I yelled and pushed and bought her on the spot, then and there, and dragged her out through all that filth and uproar – when I got the slave-gag out of her mouth, it was a stranger. It had been so long ago. I turned her loose, and the ungrateful girl reviled me, saying that a woman alone in Verula would be enslaved again inside an hour, and probably get eaten by the rich cannibals in the Palace City, and that I wasn't man enough to own a woman . . . After that, having no money, I kept seeing them, again and again among the slaves, first one, then the other, bought by other men. That place was more like Hell than Hell itself. I thought of becoming a slaver, hoping to find them that way.'

'I know,' said Rosanna. 'In Verula they really did own people like things. I was there too.'

'Not as a slave,' said Agrippa, 'not you?'

'In a way,' said Rosanna. 'Edward was an outlaw and I was his slave, for purposes of the assignment. Actually I *was* a slave in Adambara for a while, but that was a sort of misunderstanding.'

'You don't mean,' said Agrippa, 'that you were the two who harrowed Hell for the Losians? They said in Adambara that it was the spirit of Milton and his Emanation Ololon. I didn't believe it.'

'No,' said Rosanna, 'it was us.'

'And he – he doesn't mind about us?'

'He told you not,' said Rosanna. 'Why can't you believe him?' I heard more consolation as to a child, then love sounds, then gasps and a scream. Agrippa lay on his back, getting back his breath and weeping openly. Rosanna turned to me.

'I know you're awake,' she said. 'My goodness, what's this?'

'You know perfectly well,' I said, 'what it is.' Agrippa watched us. He had stopped weeping, he was evidently at last convinced. Rosanna took his hand while she and I made love.

'You don't think they could be in Verula?' he said, after we had done and lain all three silent for a while.

'No,' said Rosanna, 'I know for certain they aren't.'

That night we all slept soundly, while the Tetrarch, appeased, kept watch for us. It had to be worse, I thought, for Agrippa than for us. He was a medieval character: for him, reality was real.

I had forgotten the bark package given me by Tjurip. I now opened it. It was heavy, and when I unwrapped it, I found packed in many layers of wrapping a long, oval stone, flat and shaped like a whetstone. On it were carved concentric circles, lines and arrow-shaped markings. I thought at first it was a weapon, then I knew it for what it was. It was a tjurunga, the symbol of identity given at puberty to every man of Tjurip's people, its four circles charting concisely the fourfold structure of self, on which Losian philosophy expended its ritual and discourse – all of it set forth in a few scratches upon a stone. I saw how little is achieved by discourse – Tjurip had summarized in this archaic object all that I had learned in my travels so far. I realized how formidable was his Adepthood, and how much Adepts in general had yet to learn about economy of thought.

12
Into Entuthon

'Who do you think found it?' said Rosanna, next day, as the trees closed around us. 'Klars?'

'That's quite possible,' said Agrippa. 'It would take some-thing quite extraordinary to get Klars into open ground like that. Is anyone else after it?'

I told him about Chorim, Thapsis, the Verulans and the archer.

'That's bad,' said Agrippa. 'That swine sounds like an abbot. Anything with Verulans is bad. Did you say there were Verulan bands in Entuthon?'

I told him that, so far as I could gather, there were, and that they were Palace-City Verulans, the filthiest kind, who now seemed to have acquired enlightenment and to be converging on the city.

'Do you know the plan?' said Agrippa.

'I can guess. The trouble is that Chorim is probably sincere. My theological guess is a chastity trip, backed by recon-structed Verulan sadists with guilt complexes, which will effectively replace Losian yoga with the yoga of Urizen, the yoga of Thou Shalt Not, in other words.'

'Bad, bad,' said Agrippa. 'How many swords have you?'

'One,' I told him.

'A pity,' he said. 'I used to be a good swordsman. Men feared me, on the Other Side. When we stop, I'll cut a club. I'm handy with that.'

'I don't think somehow,' I said, 'it's going to be that kind of occasion.'

'Pity,' said Agrippa. 'I could use a good fight. Two days ago I was in a mood to die fighting. Not now, but I'm still game for a scrap.'

'We could have used you,' I said, 'on our last assignment.'

'How was it, in Verula?'

So we told him the story.

'You two,' he said, 'are people after my own heart. I could have used an asva on earth. Many times. Adepts are lily-livered. They fear death. You, of course, had lives in hand – but one forgets that in a place like Verula.'

The trees were larger now – it was the deep forest, full of metallic birds, clouds of insects, all which flourishes on the hill of Entuthon where the curtain of rains begins. There was no track, but certainly a trail. Others had passed this way, and the vegetation showed bruised leaves and bent stems which had not recovered from their passing. The closeness of the leaves to a rider became hypnotic as day passed. We found one of the fruit trees to feed ourselves and the Tetrarch. Our simurgh, released to hunt and scout, circled back to us at half-hourly intervals. The bewildering leaves and the greenhouse smell made us all fall silent.

It was mid-afternoon. I heard absolutely nothing – I saw only three grayish-white streaks come from behind us. The attack was so swift and silent that not even the Tetrarch saw it coming. A verra was at his throat on each side, and a large triangular head fixed its teeth in his neck not two feet in front of me. He yelled, not with fear, but with annoyance, and shook his head. His jaws seized one verra and broke its neck. He wheeled in place, there was thud, and the body of the second verra flew into the branches and hung there. Then he half-turned to me – I knew he was leaving the third attacker to me, for with riders he could not roll on it, as he would otherwise have done. I saw its black snout and red eyes, unreally close, and brained it with my battle-ax. The Tetrarch methodically trampled it into a doormat. It was all over so swiftly that nobody spoke. The Tetrarch seemed uninjured. I let him trample. In a few moments he resumed his previous pace, whinnying to himself. The blood on his neck was that of the verra I had killed.

'They must be mad with hunger,' said Agrippa. 'They never attack an asva. That was a pack, and in full daylight.'

Rosanna said nothing. We continued on our way. The simurgh came back again, dropping through the foliage. The forest was dripping, calm and soporific again. I think we all resolved not to let our attention wander. I kept the drawn ax in my hand, and gave Agrippa my sword. Rosanna, between us, to my surprise strung and set an arrow to the power-sighted asvin bow.

'Not much use in jungle,' she said quietly, 'but I can use it. Don't worry – I won't shoot you, or the Tetrarch.'

We found a clearing to camp that night, large enough for the risk of ambush by verras to be negligible. When we reached it, we came on a party of Klars, dividing fruit – a kind of Klar picnic – but they fled in terror before we could address them. 'Good,' said Agrippa, 'they'll tell the others. Some of them will realize we're people, if the asva didn't scare them too much. You and I had better take turns and watch.' Accordingly, I slept first beside Rosanna, until Agrippa laid his hand on my shoulder and took my place. I sat with bow and ax, hearing their whispers, and watching the dawn come up, while the Tetrarch, sniffing, walked our perimeter, and the fire of damp wood smoked and glowed in the middle of the clearing, and the simurgh, head under wing, slept on a branch overhead.

At the morning he took off. Before we were fully roused, he was back, signaling us to follow. We reentered the woods, then, in a few hundred yards, came to a long clearing, up which advanced a party of the Klars. Seeing the asva, those behind signaled 'Forward' and those in front signaled 'Back' – they halted ahead of us, chattering and jumping. They bore fruit and offerings. We were welcomed.

'Everyone off,' I said, and leading the Tetrarch I approached them. 'Greetings, friends, you loved well?'

'You – also – good – push-push?' signed the leading Klar. He was not the Archichimp I knew, but a younger male. 'You – halo – beard – fist – beard – fist – breasts?'

'Yes, my lad. Two male and one female Adept.'

'Greetings – greetings – roll on ground.' They did, rejoicing. 'You come. We – show – wonder – joy.'

'I think they have it,' said Rosanna. 'They want us to see it.'

I tethered the Tetrarch in a slipknot, so that in emergency he could respond to the silent horn, and we processed down the green clearing, surrounded by Klars. Fruits were loaded into our arms. We had gone only a few steps when the Archichimp burst from the trees.

'Greetings – greetings – you – halo – chew – snarl – wallop!' he said, jumping and pushing out his lips.

'Yes, indeed I am, old friend.' We took hands. 'You knowing loved well?'

'Well – well – happy – sun circle! Come!'

A small Klar, riding on his mother's back, was put in Rosanna's arms. Red flowers were shyly presented. Ahead was the Klar village, en fete. Klars were pressing from the huts, surrounding us, rolling on the ground. The Klar child looked anxiously over Rosanna's shoulder at an encouraging mother.

'You – three – snarl – snarl – chew – wallop!' said the Archichimp.

'News travels fast,' I said. 'I wonder how they knew?'

'Klars see most things,' said Agrippa.

'Three – snarl – snarl – chew – again – kill – Klar – shake head. Good, good.' Evidently the taboo on bloodshed didn't include verras.

'No, old friend. They certainly won't. They're as dead as doornails.'

'You – three – great – halo – people.'

'Thank you. We're not great Adepts. But we are friends to Klars.'

At the end of the village, a great pile of offerings had been set up. 'You – all – take,' said the Archichimp. 'Hallelujah, praise the Lord!' gestured the village, jumping and rolling.

I spoke to the young adult, the Archichimp's deputy, it seemed, or his son, in signs, as follows: 'Four-footed – chew – trample – friend – Klars.'

He looked doubtful.

'Klar – brave – take – pineapple – offer – four-footed – chew – jump,' I signaled.

231

Silence fell on the village. The deputy seemed to be nerving himself.

'Take – offer – pineapple,' I said. All eyes were on him. Slowly he took the largest pineapple and, in a dead hush, walked back toward the Tetrarch. The Tetrarch snorted and chewed in anticipation – the deputy almost fled. Then nerving himself he tossed the fruit under the Tetrarch's nose and ran for his life.

The silence gave place to resounding Klar applause.

'Chew – jump – friend – Klars.'

'Chew – jump – friend – Klars – Glory Hallelujah!' echoed the village. The Tetrarch munched, unheeding of his acceptance by those who thought him a monster and had summoned me from earth to exorcise him.

'Chew – jump – wallop – three – snarl – snarl – chew: three!' I signed.

A paean rang out in praise of the killer of three verras. The Tetrarch, if he appreciated it, said nothing, but finished his meal.

'I don't think,' said Rosanna, 'this is all for us. I think we walked into a festival.'

It was true. Behind the pile of offerings stood a newly erected Klar hut, on which the leaves were still green. It was much larger than the village houses. White river stones had been laid in a circle round it. Scarlet flowers had been pushed into its rough thatch. As we were ushered towards it, our simurgh, doing its bounden duty, perched screaming on the roof, to show us that he knew what was inside.

'You – halo – inside,' said the Archichimp. Again the crowd fell silent. One after another we crawled on all fours into the temple, for such it was. A short log had been covered with fresh leaves, and on this lay the holy things of the Klars – shaped stones which resembled natural objects, a bright feather, sticks marked with Klar teeth which rehearsed matters unknown to us. There was barely room inside for three humans and a Klar. On a broad leaf above the sacred objects, set on a stump, stood the red cup of a kalpa-tree fruit, a woody lacquered seedbox. In it lay a small shining thing.

'I knew they would have it,' said Rosanna. 'That's it. That's the crystal.'

'Let me look again,' said Agrippa, like a child.

'Hold it,' I said. The Archichimp motioned to the cup. I took it, removed the crystal, offered it to him, pointing to my eye. He held it up and looked long inside it, in light which fell through the gaps in the rustic temple roof. The Archichimp replaced it reverently and extended both hands to us. For a moment, taking them, we joined hands ourselves, and knelt or squatted in the Losian tessaract. Then each of us in turn looked into Beulah. Agrippa stared and stared.

'Yes,' said Rosanna, 'you will find them.'

'Perhaps,' he said. 'I found you.'

We returned to the sunlight. Offerings were being divided. Around us Klar pandemonium marked the jubilations of the village. I took Agrippa aside.

'This is tricky,' I said. 'It's now their crystal. We can't take it from them.'

'I agree,' he said. 'They've built a shrine for it.'

'Wait,' said Rosanna, 'and see what they want to do.'

So we waited. Hour upon hour the happy row, and our darśan, continued. Klars, seeking the approval of Klar maidens for their daring, followed the example of the deputy Archichimp, and first one, then another, approached the Tetrarch, hurled their pineapples like grenades and retreated. He munched steadily, conscious of a good thing, even though it was beyond his comprehension why apes should pelt him with the fruit they had not wanted him to eat in bulk. Finally, he found himself behind a wall of pineapples, behind which stood more and more hardy Klars. He whinnied and they ran. The Tetrarch set to work in earnest to demolish the wall. It was growing towards afternoon when the Archichimp stationed himself before me and called for silence. He pointed. 'Temple – hut – sun – wither,' he signed. 'One – sun – circle – kaput. Crystal – kaput – shake head. You – halo – show – crystal – all – halo. You – temple – one – sun – many – sun – circle – kaput – shake head.'

'This temple was built in a night to perish in a night,' I

said, 'but Adepts shall build for this crystal an imperishable temple.'

'Klar – see – crystal – point to head – all – suns?'

'You, the Klars, live in perpetual enlightenment?'

'Crystal – see – humans – point to head – shake head.'

'It should go to humans, who do not rejoice in that perpetual innocence.'

'You make him sound like the Pope,' said Agrippa. 'Urbi et Orbi.'

'You,' signed the Archichimp, 'take – crystal.'

He brought it forth, cupped in its red container, holding it before him in both hands.

'No, we couldn't, old friend,' I said. 'It belongs to Klars.'

'You – take – crystal – friend.'

'You – take – crystal – friends,' signed the waiting crowd, like waving branches, the noise having fallen utterly silent. Rosanna took it from him and raised it in her two hands. A rolling, jumping, celebratory uproar broke out on all sides. The Archichimp covered his face and jumped with religious emotion. Klars clasped one another in an ecstasy of zeal.

'It's by popular acclamation,' said Rosanna. 'We didn't have to ask.'

At sunset, we were escorted to level ground, and our camp piled with offerings. The site was some way from the village, and a jubilant procession led us there and got in the way while tent pegs were knocked in, and the Tetrarch watered at the pool of his first apparition among Klars, which he seemed to recognize. Wood for a fire was brought, and astonishment expressed at its flames when we lit it without an ember. They stood waiting until we were ready.

'You – halo – well – push-push – love well,' signaled the Archichimp. 'You – halo – love well,' echoed the crowd. Then weary and happy, carrying already sleeping young, they left us, under the deep foliage, melting away towards their village, and chattering to exorcise the dangers of the falling darkness. In a few moments, all were gone.

'We did right?' I asked.

'Oh yes,' said Rosanna, 'it was what they most wanted.'

'I used to mock the Losian talk of Klars,' said Agrippa.

'Now I see it is true. These creatures are so truly enlightened that they are unspoilable. Have you it there?'

We gave it to him, and he looked into it. I could see the mandala in its case light up as he held the crystal. Withdrawn it shone like a church window, and the crystal itself, small as it was, reflected fire into the leaves around as no diamond could do. We had brought a leather case for it, and in this we placed it, hiding it in the asva pack, inside the tent. So easily and after so little searching, our assignment was over.

'I thought it had to be here,' said Rosanna. 'I think Thapsis knew perfectly well where it was. He arranged that assault course to deceive Chorim, and possibly also so that we might find you, Agrippa.'

'Which I value,' said Agrippa, 'more than the crystal. She has her own enlightenment, doesn't she?'

'She does indeed,' I said. 'I think she has Klar blood.'

'That,' said Rosanna, 'I wouldn't personally mind.'

Our meal was prepared. The campfire burned, the trees dripped honeydew, the moon came up. Frogs chirped, bellowed or sang. The whole of Entuthon seemed to be full of innocent movement – we heard no verras, and the only larger beast moving was the Tetrarch, finishing the last of his goodwill offerings. All was well with us. The love bed in the tent was prepared, and the meal of fruit and dry, flat Losian loaves was set upon it.

'You know,' said Rosanna, 'that in this forest, Los and Enitharmon first enjoyed each other. Although we are not four, I think we can do them justice tonight!'

13

A Flock of Wolves

The meal, in this setting, with our mission accomplished, was idyllic and peaceful – or would have been so, but for the arrival of a terrified Klar.

We could hear him coming, hooting and yelling, long before he rushed into the camp and tripped over the Tetrarch's tether. He was, in fact, so full of lamentation that it took minutes to make sense out of him, for a Klar cannot make legible signs while beating his breast and putting dust on his head. It was Rosanna who talked him down, calming him like a child.

'Woe! Woe! Many – snarl – jump – chew – Klars – snarl – chew – cover face!'

'What's he say?' said Agrippa.

'A pack of verras are killing the Klars.'

'Oh, no!' said Rosanna.

'Action stations,' I said. 'Rosanna, give me that scare locket. We'll take the Tetrarch – he can handle them. You're safe here with the fire, but don't on any account go away from it – there may be more verras about. We'd all go, in case there are casualties, but someone should stay with the crystal. Keep that fire blazing, and don't on any account come after us.'

'Be quick,' said Rosanna. 'I'm fine – just get going.'

Agrippa and I mounted the Tetrarch, and hauled the Klar, who was nearly as scared of an asva as of verras, up behind us, and we were off, crashing through bushes, whooping and yelling Gideon-style to increase our impact, down the track and towards the Klar village. It was completely silent when he reached it. The damage had evidently been done. Not a living Klar was in sight. Nor, however, were any signs of bloodshed. Our messenger uncovered his eyes and gibbered with amazement. I gave a series of Adambaran war yells, expecting the hiss of a verra to answer them. Instead, branches were pushed back from hut doors and sleepy Klars, alarmed by the noise, peered out to see what on earth was going on.

'False alarm,' said Agrippa, 'or the wrong village.'

The Archichimp bustled out, full of concern.

'He told us you were under attack by verras,' I said, pointing at the messenger.

'No – shake head – snarl – chew – Klars. Circle – sleep – snore,' said the Archichimp.

'Is there another Klar village?'

'Nod head – one half-sun – run.'

'Not if it's that far,' said Agrippa. We were now surrounded by anxious Klars.

'What made you think there were verras?' I asked the messenger, who was covering his face in embarrassment. It took about twenty minutes to get sense out of him, with the pair of us, the Archichimp and the entire village working in relays. He was filled with shame. He rolled on the ground. Finally, too embarrassed to face us, he let the Archichimp relay his story.

'Klar – no brain – say – human – beard – fist – tell – say – snarl – chew – snarl – chew – cover face – shame, shame!'

'What man told him to say that?'

'Human – beard – fist – not – see – recognize. Not – halo – not – sword – shield – human – beard – fist.'

'A stranger, not an Adept or a soldier, just a man?'

'Nod.'

'Human – beard – fist – look:' said the messenger. And he mimed a bathrobe-style tunic and a girdle around it.

'Bugger!' said Agrippa. 'He means a Verulan – a Verulan told him to give us that message, and the ape believed him. Come on!'

The Tetrarch, who seemed to take in the situation faster than we, turned and was off like thunder. He cannot have taken fifteen minutes to the camp. The fire was still blazing brightly. Rosanna and the crystal had disappeared. The

Tetrarch gave his whinny of defiance. He had smelled asvaya. There were asvaya prints.

'Do we go after them?' said Agrippa. 'To fall for a trick like that!'

'No,' I said. 'They've got an hour's start, and if they have sense they'll have left a bowman to pick us off.'

'But Rosanna?'

'Isn't in danger, I think.' I was, in fact, sure of it. I guessed Chorim had given some pretty strict orders. Apart from a rough ride, the Verulans would be too scared to hurt her on purpose.

'You think it's Chorim? It could be stray Verulans, and she'd be far from all right. You know their cannibal tricks,' said Agrippa.

'It's Chorim,' I said. 'Stray Verulans wouldn't have known about the crystal. They've wrecked the place finding it, but they've taken nothing else. Verulan stragglers wouldn't have left a bow and an ax behind.'

'I hope you're right,' said Agrippa. 'Then what next?'

'In four hours,' I said, 'it'll be light enough to fly a simurgh. We'll tell Kari to rendezvous behind the inn outside the city, and we'll ride a circle so as to avoid the causeway. Then we can concert plans.'

Accordingly, as the sun rose, we watched the simurgh circle for bearings and streak off, and we began our circuit to outflank any ambush. We had to risk the plain of elephant grass, which could have held a regiment of Verulans, but evidently they had not been in sufficient force to leave a rearguard, or even a sniper, for nothing untoward happened. Toward midday, as we reached the paved roads leading to the city, we saw a hurrying pedestrian in a yellow robe. It was the Lama Chonpa, staff in hand, evidently shaking the dust of the Foursquare City off his feet. 'Greetings, Adept,' I shouted, 'what's wrong?'

'Mutiny,' said Chonpa, 'is what is wrong. Accursed be all the sons of rakshasas who call themselves Adepts in this mountain. Chorim has filled the city with Verulans. Thapsis is besieged in his office – they're sitting down outside holding a hartal in protest against his lascivious heresies, and in favor of a spiritual rather than a fleshly yoga!'

'The old morality number?'

'Precisely. They say he has betrayed the archimagiate to Losian and Tharmian heresies, and they want a purer religion of the Intellect.'

'Did anyone pass you going in?'

'Two asva loads of Verulans. They had a sack, and the sack was struggling.'

'Journey well, Adept,' said Agrippa. 'We are returning to put a stop to this folly.'

And Chonpa plodded off.

'Hold tight a minute,' I said.

It had suddenly occurred to me that I had forgotten the communicating capacity of my asvin ring. What worked in one culture might work in another. Agrippa watched. I blew cautiously. The ring gave a beep. 'Breaker nine for Adambara React with a ten thirty-three,' I said. There was a pause and a crackle. Then a female voice on my finger replied, 'Go ahead, ten thirty-three.'

I gave a brief account of the situation.

'Ten four, that breaker, it has already been called in. Will you please communicate by simurgh and not use this channel? Adambara React clear and standing by at fourteen twenty-eight hours.'

'What was that about?' said Agrippa.

'Well, at least they know about it in Adambara. If they've got any sense they'll have rolled some asvin already. And I was a fool to use this thing – Chorim's people were probably listening.'

'I didn't understand any of that,' said Agrippa. 'Sounds like earth stuff, and after my time. I suppose you know what you're doing.'

I could have kicked myself. Instead I prodded the Tetrarch, who was going full steam already, and who resented it.

I saw a black speck circling. It homed on us, and a simurgh dropped on my wrist. 'RENDEZVOUS DAUGHTERS BEULAH ALL HELL LOOSE ASVIN ON WAY 48HR MINIMUM ETA WILL PLAN COMBAT OPERATION KARI' ran

239

the message foil; then 'BRING REINFORCEMENTS IF POSSIBLE.'

'Give me that simurgh,' said Agrippa. 'I can't get people, but I may be able to raise some lizards. Can you program him to home on the first salamandrines he meets?'

I drew a salamandrine on the Tetrarch's broad back with Rosanna's lipstick, which was still in the asva pack. I surrounded it with a mandala. The bird looked at it with intelligent interest, ran up his motors and took off, circling. Then he set course for the badlands.

It was the next afternoon when we reached the woods behind the Daughters of Beulah. Adept traffic on the road had almost ceased, but at least we saw no Verulans.

'Drop me here,' said Agrippa. 'I hope the simurgh understood. If he did, I may have a rendezvous. With luck he'll have met a party of my friends. They may be waiting or they may get here later. They only travel at night.'

The Tetrarch and I pushed on, making slow going in the woods to avoid noise. The city above us seemed quiet enough. I hoped they would take Rosanna out of the sack at the first possible moment, and kicked myself again for having taken her locket. Even the Losian weather seemed to have gone bad on us: the sky was full of flying gray rainclouds. A quarter of a mile on behind the roofs of the inn I heard a frog calling.

'Blibbit, blibbit,' I replied.

'Blibbit, blibbit, blibbit.' I followed the noise.

General Kari was waiting in a small clearing. He was dripping and cursing the rain. 'Psst, come on,' he said. 'Not healthy here. Those Verulan buggers are everywhere. I know a better place.'

He led me and the Tetrarch to a crack between two high ferny rocks, which just about held an asva without the risk of impaction, and gave us a view through ferns of the causeway. The rain, luckily, had stopped. Half-a-dozen Verulans came up the road as we waited.

'They fooled us out of the camp,' I said. 'They've got Rosanna, and the crystal.'

'The devil they have,' said Kari. 'If they hurt a hair of her head . . .'

'They won't,' I said. 'Chorim wants her in one piece.'

'I don't trust Verulans,' said Kari. 'We have to plan tactics. The gates are shut, we're outnumbered, and if we barge in with the asva they'll get us with arrows. But if you're game, we can take a few of the misbegotten hyasas with us.'

I told him that this was the moment for coolness under fire rather than desperate deeds, and he subsided.

'Well,' he said, 'if we can wait until tomorrow, my asvin will be here. I'd dearly love to see a squadron of asvaya chewing on those Adept bastards. I told you they were scum, all of 'em. Playing patacake with Verulans and letting them besiege Thapsis in his office! Cowards, to a man.'

'I think,' I said, 'that we probably can wait. If Thapsis can out-sit Chorim, he can't be made archimage, crystal, śakti or no.'

'He'll probably kill Thapsis – send him in poisoned food, or put an arrow into him.'

'He might,' I said, 'but only if he's a fool. He's only got to bide his time. Thapsis will be starved out, and Chorim will take over.'

'And so we sit and twiddle our thumbs,' said Kari. 'Nothing else we can do, except reconnaissance.'

'Right,' I said, 'but if a Verulan comes out we can grab him. If I threaten to feed him to the asva he'll talk.'

The Tetrarch seemed to relish the notion, or else he realized he had not been fed and was thinking of pineapples, for he started to chomp loudly.

14

Tygers of Wrath and Horses of Instruction

'Watch it,' said Kari. 'Keep that asva quiet – someone's coming.' He unshipped his battle-ax.

Whoever was coming was making an extraordinary noise. It resembled gargling, or talking with the mouth full, but was still magical.

'What the devil . . .' said Kari. The musician came in sight. It was Tjurip, hopping along in a sprightly manner and playing on a didgeridoo, or nose flute. As he passed our ambush he looked around, stopped playing and dropped with great agility into the bushes.

'Greetings, Adepts,' said Tjurip. 'You hid well?'

'Not well enough, it seems,' said Kari. 'How in hell did you know we were here?'

'I smelt you,' said Tjurip, 'and I smelt the asva. No problem.'

'And how in hell did you get out past the guard?'

'I'm a senile savage,' said Tjurip, 'playing a didgeridoo. No problem.'

'What goes on, Tjurip?' I said.

'Well, brace for it,' said Tjurip. 'Thapsis died last night. It was the strain, I suppose. He had a heart attack. He's now lying in state in the Square of Adepts.'

'Oh, my God,' I said. 'So Chorim is now the archimage?'

'He will be tomorrow. Funeral oration on Thapsis, then installation, and then he presents his spirit bride.'

'Is she all right?'

'Oh, yes, fine,' said Tjurip. 'The place is full of Verulans, but nobody's been hurt so far as I know. Chorim has Olowende and Sarvas locked up in the basement of the gatehouse, but I don't think he aims to do anyone a mischief

242

– except you, Colonel Eda. Probably not you, even, now he has the woman and the crystal.'

'If I could get in there and lay my hands on that pillock,' said Kari.

'You will, General, you will,' said Tjurip. 'He's not archimage yet.'

'There are three of us, plus an asva and three or four company strength of Verulans. My asvin can't be here for a day, and the gates are shut,' said Kari. 'Talk sense, man. If you have a plan, say so.'

'Well,' said Tjurip, 'I had a talk with Chorim. I am the only Australian here. I insisted on my ethnic rights. In no way can an archimage be appointed unless my ancestral serpent Tjurungur is present to attest him.'

'What ancestral serpent?' said Kari. 'Are you out of your mind?'

'Probably,' said Tjurip, 'but Chorim agreed. He needs one respectable Adept to endorse him. And he's afraid I shall put a curse on him, I wouldn't wonder. I pointed a kangaroo bone at him and threatened that I would if he didn't respect my national customs.'

'So?' said Kari.

'So the ancestral serpent of my people will be present. It will enter the city from the forest and return to the forest. Interesting because it's the first time Tjurungur ever became visibly manifest, so far as I know. I pray he will forgive me the deception. I spent all today making him out of burlap, ochre and feathers. He hangs in the inn called the Daughters of Beulah. He will require three painted savages inside him, and one elderly savage Adept to lead him. Anyone who stops him I will horribly curse. No problem. Now the basement of the gatehouse is in the outer wall. If you can get a purchase on one of the stones, an asva could pull it out – that will give you Sarvas and Olowende. How many men have you got?'

'Three,' said Thapsis, 'when Agrippa gets back.'

'My old friend,' said Tjurip, 'is he too here?'

'So with three men inside Tjurungur, plus Olowende and Sarvas, makes five,' said Tjurip. 'We get as near the ceremony as we can. Then Kari and you de-serpent and go round to pick up Rosanna – Tjurungur goes in and takes station where he can do most damage; I'll come with you two – when my ancestral spirit speaks I may not myself be present. One of you has got to be able to blow this thing,' he indicated the didgeridoo, 'and one of you, the front man, has to operate a bull-roarer. That should be good enough for Chorim – he knows as much about our rites as a New York taxi driver. Now, we have about three hours. It'll take an hour to get Sarvas and Olowende out of the basement. We'll go as soon as it's dark.'

'Damn my eyes,' said Kari, 'why aren't you in my regiment?'

Agrippa slipped silently out of the bushes. Behind him were three of the salamandrines. He embraced Tjurip silently, and listened to the plan. 'Great,' said Agrippa, 'I can't shoot, but I've got a club. And some reinforcements.'

'Lizards, by God,' said Kari, 'or am I seeing things?'

'Lizards, Sir,' said Agrippa, 'and as formidable as they look. I suggest that when we spring the two Adepts, these gentlemen take their place. That should give someone a nasty surprise.' I looked at the thick, ringed necks and hooded heads of the salamandrines, and heartily agreed with him.

'Everyone briefed?' said Tjurip. 'Then let's get blacked up for action. Lucky for us the rain is over. I smell a nice dry evening. By the Four, it's fifty years since I had a good fight. I was a warrior too, you know.'

Two hours later a party of naked and painted aborigines, their faces and bodies striped with white ritual clay, spears and bows in their hands, appeared silently beside the wall of the gatehouse. Tjurip carried the skin of Tjurungur, disappearing under it. He was naked too, except for a waist-string, in which was stuck his boomerang. We scouted the wall – Tjurip sniffed at it and listened, then pointed silently to a square block of stone. Kari produced a pair of sling-jaws from the asvin forge. It was difficult to make them bite between the cyclopean blocks, which joined as snugly as a pavement, and we were obliged to muffle Kari's battle-ax to hammer the points into place. Then I blew the silent horn, and the

Tetrarch came out of the wood like a gray cloud. We backed him to the wall, attached the chain, and he bowed his enormous back. The stone groaned and slid out, falling to the ground with a thump which should have been heard for miles. Nobody stirred, however. Tjurip put his head in the hole and called softly. A moment later, Olowende scrambled out followed by Sarvas.

'Are we glad to see you!' said Olowende.

'No time to explain,' said Tjurip. 'Clothes off, war paint on and get in that snakeskin. Agrippa!'

Agrippa whistled, and I saw the three nodding dinosaur heads and the glazed reptilian eyes outlined against the red sky. They climbed into the hole with their small hands, the scaly thighs followed, and the long tails vanished inside.

'Forward!' said Tjurip. 'Music!'

I had never before spun a bull-roarer, and its unearthly bellowing staggered me. Tjurungur unwound as the others took him on their shoulders, a terrible and beautiful thing covered with great ochre marks and feathers which shone even in the dying light. Tjurip's ruse had still the beauty and augustness of his whole culture. It was indeed his ancestor. Spinning the bull-roarer, I took its shining, wide-jawed head upon my head, and let Tjurip lead me. We moved towards the gate.

We walked with the stamping motion which Tjurip had taught us, chanting 'Ho!' at every fifth step. I could see nothing in the darkness of Tjurungur's head except a strip of lighter darkness where his jaws opened. We zigzagged in our dance, to the sound of a bull-roarer and didgeridoo: the Verulans at the gate stood aside and let us pass, chanting and stamping, into the street, and on towards the square of Adepts. At the corner before we reached it, other Verulans were posted. Some of them laughed and then the laughter died away, awed by the ancestor as he continued his progress. We reached the last arch. 'Now,' said Tjurip quietly. The changeover was made quickly and silently. I passed the bull-roarer to Olowende, who took the head of Tjurungur on his broad shoulders, wishing me luck – Sarvas took the middle, Agrippa the tail. We blotted in the arch and Tjurungur passed on like a train, making his way through the bewildered, arguing crowd of Adepts in the square, who took no note of three blackened and painted aborigines dancing under the archway.

Before the double doors of the House of Luvah a dais had been set up, and in front of that was an open coffin in which lay the remains of Thapsis, my unfortunate fourfold friend overcome by his responsibilities. The crystal lay on a cushion before him.

'Wait a bit,' said Kari, 'until Chorim comes out.'

At that moment he did so, the crowd of Adepts fell silent, and he began to address them.

'Friends,' said Chorim quietly, 'we have come to pay our last respects to this great Adept and archimage, who has returned to the Other Side, to wish him a good rebirth there, and to appoint his successor. This is the saddest moment of my life, and I ask you to stand in silence to pay him honor.'

15

In Which We Take the Ape for Counselor

'Go,' said Kari.

Three naked aborigines slipped out of the shadows of the arch and into the alley flanking the square, behind the Sun College. We ran to the side of the House of Luvah, where the roof was lowest; Kari threw the climbing rope with its padded hook and tested its hold, then held it while Tjurip, with an agility which astounded me, ran up it and cursed me quietly for being slow. Kari joined us, dropped the rope, and we each slid down it into the empty courtyard.

'Open the side gate,' said Kari. 'Now, follow me, and quiet!'

We were behind the arched vestibule facing the square. Its further doors were those through which Chorim had just come out – its inner doors were shut, but there was a postern ajar in one of them. Luckily it was well-oiled. Kari stood behind it and swung it wider, peering through the hinge, then waved us forward, and each in turn slipped inside.

We were behind a kind of counter, normally occupied by the shoes of the devout, and at the other end of the vestibule, two Verulans were holding Rosanna. One had cords and a gag, and a long white cloth was draped over a chair. Evidently the idea was to tie and gag her, Verulan slave-style, then cover her with the veil so that she would not appear reluctant and propel her through the doors to be presented by Chorim as his spiritual bride. Like a good girl, she gave no sign, but I knew we could count on her cooperation.

Kari got out his bow.

'No,' said Tjurip, 'hold it until they get their heads together.'

Rosanna intelligently waited until they started to tie her up, and then began to give trouble. Tjurip stood up like a shadow and also waited patiently. Then there was a whizz and two sharp cracks, the Verulans went sprawling and the boomerang skidded into a corner.

'Good,' said Kari. 'Put the boot in, man: that bastard's down, not out.' Having no boots, I jumped on his stomach with both feet. We dragged the Verulans into the shoe cupboard, locked the door and put the counter in front of it.

'I rather thought,' said Rosanna, 'you'd be around presently.' She might have been at a garden party, and we bringing the sandwiches.

'Are you all right?' I asked her.

'Perfectly,' said Rosanna. 'It wasn't very alarming. More like the *Perils of Pauline*.'

'Chorim didn't try . . . ?'

'Oh yes,' said Rosanna, 'he tried. He pegged me out on a bed, put a cushion under me, and said he was going to ravish me. He called it a spiritual marriage.'

'I'm sorry,' I said.

'You needn't be,' said Rosanna. 'I asked him what he was going to ravish me with. And he couldn't get it up. I can have that effect when I want to.'

'Chorim's still talking,' said Tjurip. 'Let's get round the front and be in at the death.'

I blew a toot on my asva horn, opened the pass door into the square, and three aborigines and a Losian lady mounted a staircase to the musician's gallery and looked down. The dead face of Thapsis stared up from the coffin. The crystal shone like a minute diamond.

'I must now,' said Chorim, 'take the burden which is laid on me. I shall need your spiritual support. I am deeply privileged to have my candidacy attested by the ancestral spirit of our oldest Adept, my friend and mentor Tjurip, whom these dancers of his people represent. I honor Tjurungur the ancestor of Tjurip.'

'For two pins,' said Tjurip, 'I'd boomerang *him*.'

'Steady, the Buffs,' said Kari. 'He'll get his medicine shortly.'

'I know,' said Chorim, 'that there are divisions amongst us. There are Adepts whose vision is limited by ambition – I was forced, as you know, to detain our friends Olowende and Sarvas, but they will attest my succession, as indeed they must. I have invited them to join us. Before we commit the body of our archimage to the flames, do you accept me as his rightful Tanist?'

'We do, we do, we do,' chanted the Verulan claque. The bewildered generality of Adepts joined in.

Chorim raised his hand in benediction. 'I accept your decision, and I promise by the Four that I will try to deserve it. In that heavy responsibility, I will have the comfort and instruction of an Adept greater than I, my spiritual bride, through whose courage and wisdom I have attained the Philosopher's Stone.'

He raised the cushion. A murmur ran through the Adepts.

'Bloody idiotic lot of sheep,' muttered Kari.

Chorim set down the crystal. 'Bring in the Lady Rusana,' he said.

Nothing happened.

'Bring in the Lady Rusana,' repeated Chorim. 'Idiots, that's your cue.'

Evidently the doors were supposed to swing dramatically open. Instead there was a hollow thump, and rather than opening, they bulged, splintered and collapsed. Between the remains of them stood not the spirit bride but my old friend the Tetrarch. He was breathing heavily and eyeing the assemblage with grave disapproval. He gave a blood-chilling scream.

I have seen a few panic rushes in my time, but the exit of Chorim and his Verulans resembled that of baboons who surprise a lion. It was met, neatly and precisely, by a counterwave from the rear of the square as a bunch of Verulan guards rushed in screaming, 'Dragons! Devils! Run, everybody!'

Behind them came in great leaps the three salamandrines. I saw a Verulan archer aim at the Tetrarch. The arrow stung him. The Tetrarch charged. And Tjurip, who had watched the scene with relish, swung his boomerang not at the man but at the single alabaster lamp which lit the entire square. There was a crash followed by darkness, but before it went out I saw the body of the deceased Thapsis rise in its coffin, rush after the fleeing Chorim, yelling the slogan of the clan McPherson, 'Craig dubh!' and bring him down in a flying Rugby tackle.

Then pandemonium broke out again.

'Call off that asva,' shouted Kari, 'before he goes berserk. And get the crystal. Agrippa, get those lizards out of here.'

There was enough light from a half-moon for us to see Tjurungur disintegrate. Agrippa was in among the Verulans cracking heads right and left. Olowende and Sarvas were rushing about adding to the confusion. The salamandrines stood bowing and hissing, abreast in the entrance. Adepts were climbing the walls and piling into archways. Then outside in the street I heard the pounding of asva feet and the sound of an asvin trumpet, and Kari's troops were in the square. At their head was Lieutenant-General Faesto.

'That's enough,' shouted Kari. 'Lights, Sergeant, before someone gets killed.'

It took a full half-hour, after the torches arrived, for the asvin to restore order with their spear butts and drive the Adepts into one corner and the Verulans into another. They were reduced in numbers, many having run out of the square into the street, through the gate and into Entuthon Benython without drawing breath. Thapsis was sitting on Chorim, methodically trying to brain him with a boot he had picked up, but being unused to practical violence, he had done only superficial damage, and Olowende and I dragged him off.

'Well,' said Kari, 'shall we take this bastard out and hang him?'

'Nothing of the kind,' said Thapsis. 'Is anyone hurt?'

'Cuts and bruises, Sir,' said the Major, 'and one man dead. The asva kicked him.'

'That,' I said, 'will be the archer. Rosanna, you said there wasn't going to be any violence.'

'Well,' said Rosanna, 'there wasn't much. And he did try to shoot the Tetrarch.' Faesto came over, embraced me and kissed Rosanna. 'I'm glad you're all right,' he said.

Chorim got unsteadily to his feet. Kari unrolled a rope and started to tie a noose in it. Then he dropped it over Chorim's head and dragged him up on the dais. The Tetrarch stood over him, breathing hard and munching, as if he were thinking of pineapples.

'Quiet, please,' said Thapsis, as if nothing had occurred. 'Tjurip, will you please stop that war dance? Well, gentlemen, you can all see what has occurred. Every Adept among you should be ashamed of himself. Are we supposed to be intellectuals and sages, enlightened by the Four, or are we earth people? Verulans I will not include – they are what they are, children of the Great Selfhood. You see what occurs when Selfhood masquerades as enlightenment. I resign as your archimage. Choose whom you will. I'm through. And as my successor I nominate Rusana, finder of the crystal.'

All eyes turned to Rosanna. 'Go on,' I said. 'This is your big chance.'

'No,' said Rosanna. 'As your archimage I name the great Agrippa, and Adept Tjurip his Tanist.'

'Agrippa! Agrippa!' yelled the Adepts, the Verulans starting the demonstration as usual, glad that they weren't to be hanged on the spot.

Agrippa walked slowly to the dais and mounted it. 'Scum,' he said quietly, 'sons of bitches – I wouldn't be your archimage for the whole Palace of Urizen. You do not deserve an archimage. I would rather instruct lizards.'

There were mutterings: 'He insults us – Agrippa is arrogant.'

'You can bet I am arrogant,' said Agrippa. 'Do you not know that an archimage is one in whom the Four are truly united? Blaspheming humbugs, which of you can say that? I cannot say that, and neither will I pretend to it. Now, will you accept as archimage one of whom it is true?'

There was silence. Someone said, 'We will accept. Who is it?' And they took up the question: 'In whom are the Four united?'

'You will accept him if I show him to you?'

'We will,' said the Adepts, Verulans still to the fore.

'Come in,' said Agrippa quietly.

The door opened. It seemed nobody would enter. Then through it came the leader of the Klars, half-walking, half on all fours, after the fashion of his kind, blinking at the lights.

A gasp went up from the Enlightened.

'Greetings, fourfold friend,' said Agrippa.

The Archichimp paused, placed his hands over his eyes and extended his arms to the square. 'You – circle – friends,' he signaled. 'I – see – wallop – sadness. Wallop – shake head – halo.'

'He says it grieves him to see Adepts fighting,' I said to Rosanna.

'Shut up,' said Rosanna. 'I don't need an interpreter.'

'I – friend – all circle,' signaled the Archichimp. 'See – crystal – circle – good. You – see – crystal – circle – good. Embrace.'

They did so, joining hands in the Losian gesture of solidarity.

Thapsis went over to the Klar and gave him the archimagial greeting.

'What,' said Olowende, 'is to be done with this?'

He pointed at Chorim.

The Klar stood before Chorim with an expression of extreme sadness, and shook his head. Then he addressed him.

'You – look – crystal.'

Chorim demurred.

'You – look – crystal,' signed the Archichimp gently.

'Look in it, you pillock,' said Kari, 'or by God I'll break your neck.'

Chorim came forward in complete silence to the end of his rope, took the crystal and looked in it for a full minute.

Nothing dramatic occurred. He seemed simply tired and confused.

Chorim turned to Thapsis. 'I'm sorry, fourfold friend,' he said. 'I was on the wrong track. I shall have to begin again. May I go?' The Klar signed assent, and Chorim went.

'Well, I'll be damned,' said Kari. 'You aren't letting him get away with this?'

'No,' said Thapsis, 'I'm not. And he hasn't. Shall we

disperse the Adepts and go ourselves? It has been enough for one night. Strife too has its place in the process of learning. We'll talk tomorrow.'

Faesto and Rosanna were in a deep colloquy. Rosanna said, 'Let's all go home. Ask Agrippa to join us, Edward. We don't have to be two men and two women to make a tetrad.'

'Presently,' I said. 'Let's take the Tetrarch back to his stable first.' I considered myself lucky that he was not to be the necessary fourth man for a Losian minyan.

16
Human Forms Identified, Going and Returning Wearied

Agrippa and I left Rosanna and Faesto sleeping. We owed it to them – after all, they had not seen one another for a long time. In Thapsis's office, the Archichimp was installed behind the desk, and Thapsis sat in the chair.

'You don't know,' he said, 'how good it is to see someone else in the hot seat. My old headmaster told me what a strain it was setting an example to eight hundred boys. I thought it funny then, but not now.'

'Example nothing,' said Agrippa. 'You're casting artificial pearls before genuine swine. Come and study lizards. I spent years on earth trying to convince imbeciles that I wasn't a wizard. Lizards are a pleasant change. They don't spend their time prying after Good and Evil.'

'We – also – not,' signaled the Archichimp.

'I know, I know,' said Agrippa, 'but it's easy for you, fourfold friend – your Adepthood is inborn. Selfhood doesn't overshadow you as it does us.'

'Where are Faesto and the lady?' said Thapsis.

'Sleeping – or they were. I expect they'll want to go to the Temple of Enitharmon,' I said.

'That was beautiful,' said Thapsis.

'Yes, Rosanna said last night she could have loved the whole world,' said Agrippa. 'The Four were with us, certainly.'

'And you, Thapsis?' I said.

'I shall take a brief vacation – probably on Your Side,' said Thapsis. 'I think on the whole, ye ken, I shall return a wee while to the teaching of anthropology.'

'I thought as much,' I said. 'I saw through your Highland humbug long since, McPherson.'

'And when I come back I shall travel a while. First of all,

though, I'm going back to Adambara. Come with me and see your own statue.'

'If Rosanna wants to, I will,' I said. The crystal lay on his desk, still on its cushion. I took it up and looked into it, viewing once more the Land of Beulah and Oothoon's Palace. I passed it to Agrippa.

'Yes,' he said, 'we saw that last night, didn't we?'

'I couldn't give this to some of our particle-physicist boys, could I?' I asked.

'You couldn't,' said Thapsis. 'Try teaching them some yoga. Or make them an implicate computer – that'll take care of the ontological side – then introduce them to the lady Rosanna to finish the job.'

'Thapsis,' I said, 'was our journey really necessary? This thing is beautiful, and what is in it enlightening, but is it more so than simpler experiences?'

'No,' said Thapsis, 'and that is precisely what Chorim did not know. Every grain of sand has similar properties, if you are truly on course. If Chorim had been a proper successor to the archimagiate, he'd have known that.'

'Rosanna knew it?'

'Well, of course. Though she prefers the Feminine Portal, as you do.'

'And I certainly guessed it,' I said.

'And had to be prevented from saying so in front of Chorim, or he'd have mouthed it without believing a word of it,' said Thapsis.

'Where's he gone?' I asked.

'Out of the Losian Gate. He was looking for Udan-Adan – he wanted to jump into nonentity. But he won't,' said Thapsis. 'I sent Clia after him on an asva – he'd only got a choreb, and he's scared stiff of asvaya, so she'll catch him, and I imagine she'll show him. She's a fine Adept. If he can get over his performance anxiety she'll initiate him. She's not only a good weapons technician, but she's a very competent therapist. Out in the desert, he can experience a woman in a non-demanding situation. It'll do him a world of good – provided he's not too scared of her asva to try it.'

'This has been odd,' I said. 'The thick-ear stuff with the

Verulans was nasty, but I understood it. This I didn't. It seemed dreamlike.'

'You came, you will recall, for enlightenment this time, not for play,' said Thapsis. 'That's more puzzling in the nature of things.'

And so it was that leaving the Foursquare City we passed down the causeway, past the Daughters of Beulah in its greenery, and on into the green mass of Entuthon Benython. Rosanna, Faesto and I rode on the Tetrarch; Kari, Thapsis and the unwilling Agrippa, who had been persuaded for a while to leave his lizards, on another asva behind, and after them came the asvin in double column, the ground shaking as they went. The first night we encamped in military order and ate around the cookhouse fire, while Klars came out of their villages to stare at the asvaya in their pickets and to bring us fruit. Next day we pressed on through the forest and along narrow tracks in a wide rolling upland where choreb herds grazed and Tharmian boys tended them, setting the tents that night and unrolling our love bed among groves of orchard trees filled with the red pears of the Losian mountains, hearing the hunting cry of verras in the woods below us, while the soldiers of Or-Cu sang at the prospect of returning to the plain. Called early by reveille we dressed, washed in a clear pool, splashing each other like children, and the cavalcade formed and moved on. This was the edge of the plateau. The mountain was low on the horizon behind us, capped with cloud, and blue as ink. Rocks began to sprout from the soil among the Losian flowers, simurgh circled, and we were looking down into the plain of cities. The descent was steep and worn by choreb flocks. Springs ran in the rocks, and then everything grew drier. The cliff wall was behind us, and we were in the familiar dusty light of the great plain, where wild asvaya moved and whinnied, and hyasa holes began to appear. We rode through that night, the Tetrarch pounding steadily, and behind him his congeners, scenting home. Under the Losian stars we made good speed. At dawn we were far out, and by evening, as the dust reddened, we saw the watch-masts of Adambara, and the Sixth Fire burning on top of the great ceramic tower. We were coming home.

As we reached the asvin barracks, Kari and the squadron, at full salute, wheeled away. I halted the Tetrarch, who seemed in two minds about resigning his commission when we did not follow the regiment, and let Faesto dismount to debrief. He was to join us at dinner. Agrippa too had dismounted.

'I'd better be off too,' he said, gathering his kit. 'Good-bye, Rosanna, good-bye, Blood Brother. I've learned things I never thought I should learn. I'm going to try once more – Rosanna, my dear, you have more hope than I – where to start, do you think?'

'The Temple of Enitharmon?' said Rosanna.

'I suppose that will do.'

'Let us go with you,' said Rosanna, 'we all three owe Her a greeting, and you'll feel more comfortable if you're not alone.'

Agrippa said nothing, but mounted with us. I set the Tetrarch in motion.

It was a feast day, and Losians of all ages thronged the temple approach. We muzzled the Tetrarch and left him at the hitching-rail. We passed through the onyx bath and naked into the semi-dark of the dome.

'The inner circle?' Agrippa asked.

'No – you can't touch there, and everyone is nameless,' said Rosanna, in a whisper. 'The other circle – you're looking for people, not charisma.' So we turned back from the wicket where the Daughters of Enitharmon were binding initiates for their passage into the central Presence. Rosanna and I sat down on one of the vacant love beds.

'I'll come back,' said Agrippa, 'when I don't find anyone.'

He walked slowly on, looking into faces in the half-dusk, peering anxiously at the entwined figures.

'I hope he doesn't run into one of them with somebody else,' I said.

'It will be all right,' said Rosanna, 'even if he does. We're here to see him out of therapy.'

Rosanna and I did not make love – instead we lay listening to the sounds of love, which were all around us.

It was barely a minute before we heard another sound, a cry of mutual recognition, not of orgasm. It was followed by another.

'He made it, Ros,' I said. 'You're a marvel. You've saved a great Adept.'

'Let's look,' said Rosanna, 'but not join them. They are three, and this is for Oothoon, not Enitharmon. Enitharmon will understand – Oothoon's her daughter-in-law, and knows what it is to be plagued by Theotormon.'

We found them – they were lying unheeding, closely embraced, not speaking or moving.

'That's beautiful,' said Rosanna, 'and they're perfectly ordinary women. Theotormon made Agrippa waste four hundred earth years. Let's make love and go home. I want to see our home again.'

We took the Tetrarch back to the regiment and walked.

Rosanna and I were alone, unpacking, when Agrippa tapped at the open door of our room. He seemed sweetened, remade, younger.

'I found them both,' he said simply, 'thanks to you.'

'We know,' said Rosanna. 'We're so glad.'

'How did they come here?' I asked.

'As I did. In the last few heartbeats. On earth they are still about to die. We all three are – so we are Losians now for This-Side life. It was the House of Enitharmon, Rosanna, but it was Oothoon we worshipped.'

'We saw you,' said Rosanna. 'It was beautiful.'

Agrippa embraced us both, so that we stood as three, Rosanna between us. 'You two brought this about – Lady, Blood Brother. I can't ever thank you,' said Agrippa.

'Theotormon's left you,' said Rosanna, 'and I'm glad for that most of all. You won't go back to the lizards now?'

'Oh yes, occasionally; I like them,' said Agrippa, 'but now I know four genuine Adepts, besides Tjurip – three are women, and one a blood brother.'

'Stay and see Faesto,' I said. 'He'll be as pleased as punch to hear your news. And he's also a blood brother to both of us. In fact we're quite a large family.' Rosanna kicked me gently.

'No,' said Agrippa, 'I have work still to do and much to say and hear. I have not spoken with Giulietta and Jehanne about you, but I will, believe me.'

'Please yes, say greetings to my sisters,' said Rosanna.

'Knowing, love well!' said Agrippa. 'And thank you.'

And so he left us.

Faesto, Rosanna and I shared the room and the asva-skin love bed we had shared on the eve of our journey into Verula. Outside the stone asvin sat on his steed, and we heard the human, un-Adeptlike sounds of a living city, one to which we should always return as a place familiar, where abstract enlightenment was conjoined with ordinary life.

'I don't want,' said Rosanna, 'to visit the statue yet. When we do that, it will be time to go.'

'You have to go back?' said Faesto.

'Yes,' she said, 'we have to go back. Now neither of us needs the door, we shall be here very often, Faesto. I shall be here very often.'

'And I,' I said, 'separately and together. One doesn't pass over the privilege of an extra life. And anyhow this is our real home I imagine.'

Faesto was obviously both sad and comprehending. 'She could be mine here and yours there, Blood Brother,' he said.

'I don't belong to either of you,' said Rosanna. 'I'm me. But I love you both, and I'll come.'

'When you come,' said Faesto, 'tell me.'

'I will,' she said, 'and anyhow you will know.'

The other person who would miss us, I felt, was the Tetrarch. On each day we loitered in Adambara, visiting the House of Play together, where Rosanna was her old slavegirl self with great abandon, or worshipping together in the inner or the outer circle of Enitharmon, I always made time to put on uniform and ride him once or twice round the parade ground under the respectful eyes of Takis, my former riding master. In uniform I was recognized and mobbed by Losians wanting to shake my hand, but the popularity was worth it for the Tetrarch's sake. Thapsis came finally, as we knew he would, ostensibly to take us to see the Smithy, where we descended into vast clanging workshops and saw the furnaces of Los roaring out streams of iron, and his men working at their varied projects of art, religion and strange armament. But we knew that his real intention was to tell us that time was up. 'Tomorrow,' he said, as he left us, 'you really must go and see that statue.'

In the morning I fetched the Tetrarch, and all three of us made on his back the circumambulation of Adambara – the wall of the Bowmen, which he had once cleared at a bound, the green canal with its fruit and vegetable boats, the College of Adepts and the Halls of Council and Record, familiar places. We ate together at the Iron Choreb. Afterwards we went once more to worship in Enitharmon's house, and light lamps in the Iron Chapel to Urthona, and Los the Spirit of Imagination who reigns in this city. Then we returned to the room, and I changed into my military dress, with sword and shield, and we set out. Faesto came with us to the edge of the square. There was the statue, and there we stood in stone. The Tetrarch knelt for Faesto to dismount. He kissed Rosanna and embraced me as his blood brother, linked by her favors. Then he stood watching. Beside the statue was Thapsis. He bowed gravely to us.

'They did us well,' I said.

'Go on,' said Rosanna.

I rode across the square, bringing the Tetrarch closer and closer until the life-size stone, the asva, the hero and his emanation were beside us and looming over us, until they fused with us, the Tetrarch's motion ceased, and we merged with the carved figures. There was the brief suspension of thought, I felt the colder air of Our Side, and dawn replacing sunset, and we lay side-by-side in our bed in my apartment in Edinburgh, turning to one another for enlightenment, knowing new things and secure in the understanding that now, at any time and in any place, we had the recourse of a second and a different world.

v idd h_a t s_a tk_a m_a ya s t e

BOOK THREE

Beyond the Night of Beulah

1

Shadows of Tharmas and Enion, in Vala's World

'Edward, are you asleep?' said Rosanna.

'No.'

'When shall we go back?'

It was about three real-time months that we'd been back. Oddly enough we had hardly mentioned what had happened, except when Rosanna wondered how Agrippa was getting on. Rosanna was having her long vacation and spending it with me *en menage*, but she'd have to go back to school shortly. The trouble was that although these trips didn't need leisure, because they did not score against real time, they tended to upset one's sense of continuity, and it was damned hard to get restarted. That was the only reason we didn't rush to go back daily.

Thapsis had given us an open invitation. We couldn't tackle him in the person of McPherson, because McPherson probably deliberately, had gone off indefinitely to do field work with some bunch of hairy shamans – thus avoiding awkward questions now his cover was blown. I wanted to ask him how to handle matters so that trips to the Losian world didn't compromise our efficiency in this one. I think we both resented a little the way our spontaneous visits had been turned into instruction for us and gamesmanship for him. The first time round had been scary in the extreme. The second had been a kind of instructional pantomime – Magic Flute stuff. I didn't see much point in repeating either of these just yet, and I said so to Rosanna, who was sitting up in the dark.

'But we shan't,' she said. 'We've moved on from those. I feel that next time will be more serious – less fictional, if you understand.'

I understood right enough, and wondered what kind of seriousness we would find.

'Couldn't we go simply for pleasure?' I said.

'Yes, yes. If we could get to Beulah.'

'I thought that was an inaccessible part of the Losian scene.'

'It may be. We know one gate to it. We could try that.'

'The crystal? We don't have it.'

'No,' said Rosanna, 'but we've got me. The gate between the thighs.'

'It sounds,' I said, 'a little like entering into one's mother's womb to be born again. I think it's metaphorical.'

'It's not metaphorical.'

'Then how . . .'

'We go together one time when we come exactly together.'

'If we can hang on enough to perform the necessary Game of Adepts without spoiling the climax,' I said.

'It would be difficult,' said Rosanna, 'but let's practice a little. Then one day when we come exactly together we can try it. I don't see any risk. How can it be bad to go there at a holy moment, anyhow?'

'We usually don't come exactly together,' I said.

'But sometimes – actually more often than you realize. Even if I've come several times already I usually have another peak when I feel you come. Let's be ready. We shall know when to try.'

'We'll have a signal. Which of us will call?'

'Either one – just say "Now!" and we'll try it,' said Rosanna.

'I'll call,' I said. 'You can't say "now" and scream at the same time.'

'I didn't even realize,' said Rosanna, 'that I scream. Always?'

'Usually. I'll tape record us some time.'

'Yes, I'd like that.'

I did in fact do so the same night. We found the tape a certain lead-in to a reprise. Rosanna listened to it wide-eyed. 'I do make a noise,' she said. 'It's beautiful. Come.'

It was a full week before the time came to make the

attempt. I knew the opportunity was upcoming, in that there was something about Rosanna's response which cued me. It was shortly before dawn and she had woken me with her touch; I was ready before fully waking. She had put a pillow under her. 'Open the gate,' I said.

'It's open. Ever so wide open!'

This was not her usual posture. I felt her knees in my armpits. In the event neither of us called the attempt – or rather, both called it together – 'Now!' and 'Now!' Evidently one can both scream and perform the Game of Adepts. Certainly one can ejaculate and do so. The suspension of thought which marks the Adeptic transition was not distinguishable from the suspension of thought normal to orgasm, but both of us knew it had taken place, kissed, and lay gasping to see what had been achieved by our exercise.

2

The Pleasant Shadow, Beulah

At first nothing appeared to have changed. We were lying naked side-by-side. The heat and the perfume of love did not go – they were in the air, a humid stovelike warmth and a strong greenhouse odor of wet fern. Moreover the bed was moving, or rather gliding. We were in a boat. I put out my hand on the side away from Rosanna and touched bundled reeds. We were in a reed boat, between high passing walls of reeds, moving forward with a steady unsplashing motion. The sky was yellowing over the reed tips. The prow beyond our feet was high, pointed where it crossed the lines of reeds, and ended in a knot like a corn dolly. Two lines ran out taut over the thwarts on each side of it, dipping and drawing. We were being towed.

Rosanna did not ask where we were. She put her head on my shoulder, and the two of us waited without further exploration for the light to rise. As our two breathings returned to rest, I felt something missing. The lack was an apprehension – my skin twitched. I realized that I was waiting to itch from the bites of the insects one had come to expect in such situations; but there were no insects. The path of water between the stems was about six feet wide. We could touch them on either side. A fluffy canopy of mist was passing over and roofing us as the light rose. The bow wave ran with a steady, unsplashing crackle characteristic of reed boats.

Rosanna moved her head and turned away into sleep again. I crawled forward, stood up gingerly and looked over the prow into the mist. The two tow lines ran straight ahead, dripping, and at the end of each was a submerged, brownish, swimming form, ending at its forward point in a v-shaped, round-eared head, paws paddling steadily. We were being towed by otters, large as dogs, long tails lying like rudders behind. The port otter sensed me, checked in his paddle, turned and looked back with a bright, tame eye, then resumed his work. They were in fact water verras. But there was none of the angry meanness of the great forest verras of Entuthon. These knew their work, approved it and were our friends.

Birds were beginning to move and whistle. The reeds were full of fluttering and piping. At first I could not see them, then first one and then another appeared in the reed wall or flew across ahead of our bow wave – scarlet crested birds like cardinals, making no attempt to avoid us. Indeed, they behaved like an escort. I looked back to the stern. Rosanna was sitting up, her eyes full of wonder, one hand holding back her hair, while on the other sat one of the red birds, bowing and whistling. The browner hen was perched on the gunwhale beside Rosanna's shoulder. A hummingbird whizzed past like a purple-waistcoated bullet. He tried to buzz the cardinal from his seat on Rosanna's hand, but the red bird stood its ground. The hummingbird hung motionless in front of Rosanna, looking her up and down, then tilted his wings and spun off to the summit knot of the prow and sat there beside me looking down.

'It's beautiful,' said Rosanna. 'This is different, different from where we were before.'

It was indeed different. We both of us realized the nature of the difference – this was a place wholly without dangers. We had no basis for the conviction; the reed beds might be full of alligators, large snakes or ill-intentioned persons, but we had the absolute confidence that they were not, and that what was there, if anything were there beside birds, our two verra friends and the immense regiment of stems, was amicable as well as fearless. I looked around in the boat. We had neither garments of any kind nor equipment, and it was evident that neither was needed. Our love bed was a great white verra pelt, with two pillows. There was a paddle, in case we needed that – though the engine room ahead knew exactly where it was going. There was also a round wicker basket. One of the water verras turned aside without slacking pace, threw up a bright silver fish, caught it and began to munch. It was breakfast time. I opened the basket. In it, folded in white napkins, were the yellow Losian loaves, the spiced pulse of a Losian breakfast, and an earthenware bottle of some tisane or other to replace the herb tea of a Losian inn. A second pack of provisions lay below. Our journey was clearly plotted out as to meals and provision made. As we poured the tisane into two earth cups, the hummingbird on the prow started to fuss. I held out the cup and he hovered, sticking his beak into the cup and balancing like a small helicopter with flicks of his tail, then spiraled back to his perch and began a long discourse about something or other.

'His name,' said Rosanna, 'is obviously Woodstock.' She put one arm round me, and trailed the other hand in the water. The stream, for all its reed beds, was so clear that every pebble showed as a bright scale on its bed. Rosanna and I, too, were changed. Usually we were Beatrice and Benedict. Now we were both children. We were warm together rather than striking sparks.

'Where is this, Ros, if you know?' I asked her.

'Beulah,' she said. 'It must be.'

'What we saw in the crystal?'

'Yes, but real. That was ideal. They must know we're ready now.'

'No assault course this time?'

'This is a loving place.'

'You reckoned we'd get here,' I said, 'coming like that.'

'I hoped we might. And I opened the door wide for you, didn't I?'

I put my hand over the door she had opened, and Rosanna for her part took hold of the key.

'Whom do we worship here,' I said, 'when we make love?'

'Los and Enitharmon, to begin with. But here, Tharmas and Enion – the Senses and Generation. Beulah's theirs. Look at the moon on the paddle blade.' It bore a burned-in crescent. The knot of the prow was a circle containing a crescent. We were in moon country. Now, by day, the sunlight was diffused by the skeins and layers of mist like ground glass. At night it would be clear Tharmian moonlight.

'Look,' said Rosanna, 'we've got our rings.'

Each had the plain Adept ring we had received in Adambara, and I had the iron ring pierced in two places, the asvin's silent horn.

'Don't blow it,' said Rosanna. 'Not now. The Tetrarch will come when we need him. I want to stay in this boat. I don't want an asva crashing around – I don't want the water muddied or the reeds broken.'

The reed palisades were already dividing into platoons and the channel opening. We passed through patches of floating, bladder-stalked green plants which groaned and crackled against the reed flanks of the boat. The third such patch was studded with tall budded stems, the fourth was in flower with waxy white spikes of bells, overpoweringly fragrant. Rosanna picked one and began to put the flowers first in her hair, then in mine, then to make a necklace.

I asked her if this was to be her Lady Chatterley number, and at once felt the flippancy unseasonable. Instead of saying so, however, she smiled and went on plaiting, then began to make a flower arrangement which by that time had a sizeable erection poking out of it.

'Time for worship,' she said, and we sacrificed gently on the verra skin to each of the four Immortals of our present sadhana.

By the time we drew breath the escort of reeds had wheeled right and left and we were moving through what seemed to be a meadow of the floating water flowers. Then we left them behind and entered a mist-veiled lake. A fleet loomed up ahead and passed on each side of us – they were not ships but floating islands of vegetation, bobbing in our slight wake, and alive with the red birds. Woodstock was still seated on the Tharmian crescent at the prow, flying sorties now and then, but always returning to deliver another agitated discourse; like one who assures a nonexistent crowd that there ain't no justice, he seemed to be unburdening himself of personal wrongs. Urizen's sun was overhead for midday, asserting itself in the mist as a yellow disc, but powerless to scorch in Beulah, and all the time there was the heavy greenhouse odor of wet ferns and soil, the scent of generation. Two wild water verras came up at the head of twin v-shaped ripples and played with our team, but those serious beasts, after a few somersaults and an exchange of courtesies, returned to their work and the visitors disappeared with their ripples into the mist. We ate again, slept again, made love again – Rosanna conducted a long colloquy with the still complaining Woodstock, who came down from the prow, sat like a large amethyst on her finger and lectured her from there. There seemed nothing else to do, or which needed to be done. Such a gentle entry into the Losian world seemed to speak for Rosanna's feeling that we were now ready. I wondered how long the gentle warmth would last, and whether new instruction lay ahead. The asva whistle I knew had not been provided for nothing. But for now we were on holiday.

3

Mild Moony Luster in Soft Sexual Delusions

Towards evening the mist reddened steadily. Then, as soon as the sun set, it cleared like drawn curtains, and we saw the enormous Tharmian moon, a dark circle whereon the crescent of light was outlined in earthshine, the black almost waveless expanse of the lake, and ahead its further shore, low hills and vast black trees. Woodstock flew his final circuits and settled philosophically in the wicker circle of the moon emblem on the prow, like a toy bird in a hoop, merging with it, a small black excrescence. As the moon rose we padded on, spits of land came to meet us, then ranks of large leaves like shields, and we were in a broad inlet running inland. For a few minutes we ran up its middle; then the engines stopped. This was our destination – for the night, I thought, but one of the two verras turned in his harness, reared a wedge-shaped, sagacious face over the gunwale and hissed at us.

'I think,' said Rosanna, 'that this is where we get out.'

We were several feet from the bank. The stream in which we rode seemed more like air than water. Even the crescent moon showed the pebbles three or four feet down. Rosanna slipped over the side. I followed. The water was as warm as air. The two verras spun and played a little round us, then as if at a signal they turned the boat, now empty and riding high, and set off at steady speed back to the lake, taking the sleeping Woodstock back with them. We held hands and watched it out of sight. Then, half-walking, half-swimming, we moved off together up this clear, dreamlike river into the wood beyond. Anywhere else it would have been lunacy – we were naked and without recourse to clothing, our previous journeys had prepared us for forest verra, for the lumbering, unpleasant, alligatorlike hyasas of the Entuthon rivers, stinging plants, broken glass, even.

'It's like the River of Life,' said Rosanna.

I knew the picture to which she referred, and surmised that its artist had been here.

'Oh yes,' she said, 'he lived here. Come with me.'

'I'm coming.'

Swimming was effortless, we seemed buoyant, as if in the Dead Sea.

'I believe,' said Rosanna, 'that we could fly.'

'We are flying,' I told her. 'How shall we know when to land?'

'There,' said Rosanna. It was indeed the place to land. There were old stone columns and a mouldering wooden staging from which a path ran into the wood, puddled with huge patches of the moonlight. Beyond it was a round basin of pebbled water, too shallow to swim further. We landed and went hand in hand into the warm aromatic wood.

We had not gone a hundred yards, and we were beginning to embrace, when we were aware of another naked couple walking with us. We could not see their faces, but they brought a jar of recognition.

'Who are they?' said Rosanna. 'Who?'

'I know them, I'm sure,' I said. The familiarity was disturbing. I saw that she had long black hair like the hair of Rosanna, and he a small beard.

'Greetings,' she said, 'did you love well?'

'Greetings,' we answered.

'May we walk with you? I imagine you're going to the festival.'

'Yes,' I said. The girl slipped her arm through mine, the man slipped his through Rosanna's. As we walked on we came into full moonlight and I saw who it was that walked with us. They were our selves, but transposed, so that Rosanna seemed to have a male and I a female twin, as if we two had silently divided into four, the Losian tetrad. I opened my mouth to speak. 'Ssh,' said Rosanna. 'I know.'

I would not stay silent, however. The girl was holding to my arm with a warmth which suggested that if the festival ran to Losian form, I was about to make it with myself. I had Rosanna on the other side, but electricity was being transmitted through her body from her new partner, and I could feel her ticking.

'Are you our emanations?' I asked the girl. My voice sounded absurdly loud in the moonlit wood.

'Silly,' she said, 'we're Edi and Ruso – we live here. Are you Losians?'

'Yes, I suppose so.'

'I thought you were. Tharmians say shaktihaya, you say saktihaya. We say ashva, you say asva. We will show you how Tharmians worship.'

'Is the festival in the Temple?'

'We don't have a Temple. Who wants to worship indoors? They'll have drawn a circle. That's all our goddess needs. Pick some of the flowers to throw in the circle.'

Rosanna and her fetch were already in whispered colloquy. I kissed Edi without letting go of Rosanna's hand.

'This is out of this world,' Rosanna muttered.

'Did you come in the verra boat?' said Ruso.

'Yes.'

'We saw it sail away. Are you from Adambara?'

'No,' said Rosanna, 'from the Other Side.'

They withdrew their arms, and each in turn embraced and fondled each of us for a full minute. I knew that Rosanna would find nothing strange in being so embraced by a woman, but was surprised to find that I felt no qualms in being embraced by a man, for Ruso seemed an extension of Rosanna, a part of her I knew made visible. We stood a moment in the fourfold circle, then went on.

Already we were surrounded by other couples, of all ages, often, like us, walking in fours. The air was full of the smell of the flowers they carried – some girls had flowers in baskets on their heads, flat saucerlike baskets heaped with flowers, others of both sexes were wreathed in leis of the same flowers. The path became paved. The little Tharmian town, when we came to it, was surrounded by an ancient wall and entered by a huge carved gate, bearing the moon shield on its cornerstone: the streets were paved with shiny yellowish alabaster which reflected moonlight and shone like a dance floor. The only such street I had seen on Our Side was the main street of Dubrovnik, similarly polished by centuries of passage. The town had a Mediterranean air, with high houses and colonnades, as if built against a sun which no longer parched it – sunk by the moon and its cult to the bed of a blue lake. On all the shadowy house walls there were paintings: dancing maidens like those of Bali. There were stalls dispensing the yellow bread, but since all were naked, none carried money, and the basis of trading was unclear. We all four took the hot bread and ate it and no one asked for payment. In a small piazza surrounded by arched walks and the tall houses, four cressets were alight, and here the circle of flowers was being strewn. We added our flowers to the circle and ourselves to the worshippers within it, where skins and cushions had been spread. From balconies other couples looked down. In a small space at the eye of the circle a man and a girl danced fiercely and tirelessly, falling at last among the other couples and their place being taken by other dancers. There was no music, but each dancing girl had brass finger cymbals; feet scuffled, voices whispering or gasping, Edi and Rosanna crying out together, the moon passing behind a wide tower so that for a space one knew neither the face nor even the sex of the co-celebrant, then moonlight again, people talking in low voices or sleeping, covering sleeping partners with the skins, Rosanna's head on my shoulder. Edi and Ruso had gone.

'Where are they?' I asked Rosanna.

'They moved away, with another couple. That was incredible,' she said.

'Where do we sleep?'

'Here. It's warm. The others are sleeping. Pull that skin over us.' I did so, covering our eyes from the Tharmian moon, now fully overhead. The town was asleep save for a few breathings and murmurings.

'But who were they?'

'Does it matter? They worshipped with us. Our brother and sister, say.'

I was about to comment on the implications of this analogy,

but Rosanna was asleep. For once I outslept her. She woke me in full misty daylight with more of the yellow bread and herb tea from a crock of it which stood on a stone table. Others, rubbing their eyes, were dipping pannikins in the crock and carrying the tea to still-sleeping partners. Yet others sat half-embraced in small groups conversing in perfect contentment. Edi and Ruso were nowhere to be seen. It was only when a choreb herd, driven by whistling boys, passed through the piazza, scattering the circle and pausing to graze on the flower petals, that the Tharmian festival broke up.

We were gathering ourselves together, at a loss what to do next, other than walk further into the town, when the last choreb herd came up. The herdboy left them to chew at the surviving flowers, and walked round the square, jumping over still-sleeping couples under the skins, looking into faces and finally stopping before us, as people whose faces were strange.

'You are Eda and Rusana?'

'Yes.'

'You loved well? I have this for you.' And he handed us a folded piece of reed paper.

On it was an address in Losian: 'At the Crescent Moon. Breakfast is ready.'

'It seems,' I said, 'that even in Beulah there will be instruction and perhaps duties. Shall we just not show up?'

'No,' said Rosanna, 'better go. We'll have to find it.' In daylight in the Tharmian town, we had ceased to be children and were Edward and Rosanna again.

'Something's gone,' I said.

'No. We can get it back at any time,' said Rosanna, 'but one can't live forever in Beulah. It would be like staying a child.'

'I wonder where those two went.'

'They live here. In Beulah. *They're* always here,' said Rosanna.

'Come on. The note said breakfast is ready.'

And indeed we could see the sign of the crescent hanging

from a bracket in the street we had traversed with Edi and Ruso the night before. It was a small inn, like a Losian inn except that its whole front wall was covered with naked dancers in red and white clay. Inside the people were naked in the Tharmian manner, the girls making up for clothing with necklaces, waist chains, bracelets and huge earrings, the men with intricate leather belts. At the main tables sat half-a-dozen Tharmians, and in a booth in the window two figures familiar despite their undress.

'Greetings,' said Thapsis, 'so you got here on time. I've brought Agrippa.'

Agrippa rose and embraced Rosanna. He then shook my hand, a gesture which attracted attention among the Tharmian men further off in the room.

'They can see we're Losians,' said Thapsis. 'Tharmian men kiss men as well as women. In fact Tharmians kiss everything, even choreb. Did you enjoy your first night in Beulah?'

I told him about Ruso and Edi.

'Yes,' he said, 'I think most of us have relatives here.'

'I thought Beulah was a mystical state and one only saw it in your infernal crystal,' I said.

'It is, it is. Or rather, it's a place to visit. You and your lady were familiar with it already – you told me so.'

'Yes, but that was different. Here it's real.'

'Yes. The Tharmian world is real. But if you now went back and had the whole experience again, the boat, the birds, childhood, the fiesta, it would have lost its magic – now wouldn't it? I'm glad you decided to come this way, however. We don't pay enough regard to the World of Tharmas. Most Adepts simply avoid it, and they're much the poorer for it. I come here at least once a year.'

'I think,' said Rosanna, 'that you look great like that. That Adept's nightshirt you wear in Adambara doesn't suit you.'

Agrippa roared with laughter – personally I thought that Thapsis in the buff resembled Rodin's studies for his *Balzac*. 'I make a good Tharmian too,' said Agrippa.

'Yes,' said Rosanna, 'but I've seen you naked before.'

'Sit down,' said Thapsis, 'and let us eat.'

'Speaking of dressing the part,' said Agrippa, and he handed Rosanna a package.

In it were Tharmian moon earrings, a moon pendant, bracelets and ankle bangles, and for me a woven belt with a shepherd's knife in a sheath.

Rosanna kissed him.

'How are they?' she said.

'The women? Well. They're in Adambara. We have a house, the three of us. I miss them. After so long, and with perhaps too little time ahead, I didn't want to leave. But this must be done.'

'Thapsis,' I said, 'what precisely "must be done"?'

'Agrippa and I have some surveying to do,' said Thapsis. 'You may like to join us later. For the moment you're both on holiday. Enjoy Beulah while you can.'

'Where exactly is Beulah? Where does it fit in?'

'Normally it fits in between, say age two and age five – we go through it horribly fast, and before we're sexually mature: it's wasted on toddlers.'

'It's an extraordinary place – the lightness, the lack of danger,' I said.

'It's a perpetual high,' said Rosanna, 'peak experience land.'

'Good name for it,' said Thapsis. 'Actually it's where the śakti opens her eyes and knows herself separate. We're all glad to revisit here. It's the basis of all other highs, and I suspect it's where all genuine worship takes place. Losian swingers, the Temple of Enitharmon, even being alone in virgin country – they all recreate Beulah. That's its use. One couldn't take it undiluted – one would come down.'

'Yes,' said Rosanna. 'I want to talk with Ruso and Edi more.'

'You can do that,' said Agrippa. 'They were round asking after you. They want to go in the verra boat with you – they called you the beautiful strangers. I told them to come back around Second Fire and you can all go and explore together.'

'Incidentally,' said Thapsis, 'you won't get any instruction from them. Tharmians aren't like that. Take them for what they are.'

'Touch-people,' said Rosanna.

'Precisely.'

'You mean they're innocents, like the Klars?'

'Not like Klars. Klars have discursive depth. In Beulah there isn't discourse.'

'But everything is sacred?' said Rosanna.

'Everything is sacred everywhere,' said Thapsis, 'as you well know.'

'But we know it's sacred when the reminiscence of this place touches it,' said Rosanna, 'especially sex. When it isn't worship it's dull, or nasty; when it's good, it takes us here.'

'I wish I'd known you long since, Rosanna,' said Agrippa. 'You could have saved me time.'

'You two aren't Tharmians,' said Thapsis. 'You bring yourself to Beulah and still talk like professional Adepts. You'll spoil it for yourselves. Be Tharmians for a week, or a day, or as long as you can keep it up.'

'One more question, Thapsis,' I said. 'Why do I have my asva horn?'

'Because you're an asvin,' said Thapsis shortly. 'Meet here for breakfast again in four days, and we'll tell you what Agrippa and I are doing. If you care to join us you can; if not, stay on in Beulah as long as it works for you. You won't need accommodation; people sleep anywhere, in the streets – it's too hot most of the year for beds. Incidentally, the bread and fruit are free. All those reed beds are tandul-grass – they produce enough wild rice not to make it worth selling, and when people bake it's the rule to over-bake and put out what you don't use. You hardly ever see money here – they pay off in choreb. If you want milk, ask a herd boy, and don't be shocked if he says "let me kiss your breasts" or "let's share a love bed" – it's the normal transaction here.'

'Either sex?' said Rosanna.

'Oh yes, either sex. They've got no hangups over male and female. If you find that bothersome, say "we're strangers" – Tharmians mostly know that strangers have reservations. But it's natural to them – so many are other-halves, exiled by Your-Side folk and left in Beulah, so that their twin can play male and female in real time.'

'Do you think Edi and Ruso recognize us?' I said.

'I doubt it. If they do they'll say. Tharmians don't keep their own counsel. They should be here soon. Or maybe,' he added, 'they know you and take you for granted. You two are pretty much in touch with all yourselves.'

'Last night,' said Rosanna, 'when Ruso was loving me, he kept saying "We're one person" – I thought he just meant in intercourse.'

'I think,' said Agrippa, 'they know you and don't know it; they just interpret knowledge as attraction. I think I hear them at the other door.'

'Any rules or warnings?' I said.

'No, my boy – you're in Beulah. Not the city of Nobodaddy. Just don't shock them by covering your body. And embrace, don't shake hands – they find that campy and a bit off-color.'

'If it's cold?' I said.

'It's never cold in Beulah.'

Edi and Ruso embraced us both at length, touching us all over.

'We lost you last night,' said Ruso. 'The love circle moved on but you were both asleep. Come in the verra boat – we've brought food and a love bed.'

We took hands. Agrippa and Thapsis watched. 'Love well,' they said.

Edi and Ruso had a gaily painted choreb cart with bells. The choreb was combed and its fleece had been washed.

'Pick us up like sheaves and put us in,' said Edi. I picked her up; Ruso picked up Rosanna, and we seated them in the front of the cart. Edi took the reins.

'Now you are real Tharmians,' she said. 'Do you like our town?'

'What is its name?' I asked her, climbing in behind with Ruso, who promptly put his arm around me.

'Tarnindhupura,' she said, 'New Moon Town. All our towns have "moon" in their name. My middle name is Indhu too.'

The town was tiny, half as big as Mdina or Valletta and very like them, within its high wall. Whoever built it had fortified it, but there were now no gates, and trees grew between the stones of the wall, their tops in the lemon-colored Tharmian mist.

I asked Ruso why the town was walled.

'It was built long ago,' he said, as if that settled it. At the gate we took a different paved road, passing Tharmians walking or lounging – only the choreb herdsmen seemed to have work to do, though in the houses people of both sexes were baking, and children brought out the piles of yellow chapatis to fill the reed-covered stalls on street corners. Over everything hung the scent of flowers, fern and lake.

'We are so glad we found you,' said Ruso. 'We love you because you are so like us. She is like me, you are like Edi – that turns us on more than we can say.'

'Us too,' said Rosanna. There really seemed no more to be said. There was a basin here with many boats, some larger, loaded down to the clear water with piles of the wild rice, some small, and among them our verra boat, its two verras stretched out in the paws-forward attitude of resting otters. They jumped up, bowed and dived like arrows. We climbed in, lifting the girls again 'like sheaves', because this, Ruso said, was lucky – the choreb ambled off to graze and wait for us. An amethyst spot buzzed down on Rosanna's hand, expostulating loudly. Woodstock had stayed with the boat.

'We'll go to the floating islands,' said Edi. 'We'll show you how to play with the hummingbirds.'

The verra boat swung round and moved off into the veils on the lake. We all four seemed to embrace continuously – not with any arousal, simply with complete ease and pleasure in each other, male and female, of This Side and of That.

'We need red flowers,' said Edi, 'to play the jewel game. Try the first island.' It loomed up, rocking on the water like a mattress afloat. A creeper bore large red blossoms. Edi picked as many as she could in passing. We headed out towards other islands.

'Stand up, Rusana,' said Edi. Rosanna got to her feet, balanced in the float soft reed bottom of our boat, and Edi proceeded to decorate her like a Christmas tree, putting the flowers in her hair, behind her ears, between her fingers, in her armpits, in her pubic hair. 'Now stand still,' said Edi, 'and you'll have jewels.' We passed between two islands. The birds came down to her, ruby and amethyst, covering her, settling on her fingers, while Woodstock, with a mistaken sense of proprietorship, buzzed them and gibbered, but he was outnumbered. The shiny green mates, less enterprising, formed file on the gunwale.

'There,' said Edi, 'you have your jewels, Rusana. Put the flowers on me too.'

We did so, and Edi too was jeweled with birds. Then we passed the last island and the birds withdrew, whirring back to their place. Edi and Rosanna, shedding flowers, were laughing in each other's arms.

4

In Which Embraces are Comminglings, From the Head Even to The Feet

All day we cruised about – that night we slept in the boat, landing at dawn to pick up breakfast from a village, where it was conveniently exposed on the pier of greenish piles. We swam in the lake and splashed each other, rode in the choreb cart through long causeways built by a more obsessed or industrious people, which the inhabitants of Beulah took as patrimony: 'We don't build them now – we have these, so why should we?' said Ruso. All the time there was the continual intimacy of body, hands, fingers, sometimes sexual, sometimes social, but so unceasing that both Rosanna and I, who neither of us undervalued physical intimacy, began to feel not so much invaded as depersonalized. Our identity was slipping and merging with that of our two companions – whose was this hand, anyway, mine, hers or his? There was mental intimacy too, but never exchange. For Edi and Ruso things were as they were. There was no 'why' in their vocabulary. Birds are unafraid here because they are unafraid. Hummingbirds are quarrelsome because they are quarrelsome – 'Everyone,' said Edi, 'knows that.' It was a trip, it was ecstatic in its lack of concern or anxiety, but the three days were enough. We loved Edi and Ruso and were willing to let them go back into Beulah and seek other playmates. On the fourth morning we all bathed and made love together, lifted the girls into the cart, and made our way back. There were no parting scenes – the usual prolonged mutual embraces when we got down at the Crescent Moon, then 'See you soon – love well!' they said, and drove off.

'Well,' said Thapsis, 'how were the Tharmians?'
    'It was a trip,' said Rosanna. 'They were beautiful – but I understand what you mean.'

'Your holiday was long enough?'

'I'd like to see more of Beulah,' said Rosanna, 'but on our own. Possibly even alone, without Edward.'

'You would never be alone long. Being alone isn't Tharmian. They'd want to ensure you weren't lonely. A Tharmian who has nobody touch her in six hours begins to feel isolated.'

'I know,' said Rosanna.

'Ready to talk about work?' said Agrippa.

'Exactly what sort of work?' I said.

'Travel,' said Thapsis. 'We have a journey to perform. It is one which I've never taken – few Adepts have, but I postponed it until you came. I want you to take it with us. Will you?'

'Journey to where?' I said.

'Into the interior.'

'Not another assault course? Can't we ever come here in peace?' I said.

'Nothing of the kind you experienced before. We've all moved beyond that – you, Rosanna, I, Agrippa. There's one journey left however.'

'Is it dangerous?'

'No – not like your Buck Rogers reconnaissance in Verula; not even like that extraordinary, farcical hunt you had for the crystal, when I was trying to cope with Chorim.'

'What became of Chorim?' said Rosanna.

'He's well, and living quietly in Adambara. He no longer calls himself an archimage.'

'Good,' I said, 'I hope his ears drop off. Now, where are you suggesting we go? Down a volcano?'

'Don't fool, Edward,' said Rosanna.

'I'm sorry, Ros, but every time . . .'

'The lady understands,' said Thapsis.

'There only is one more journey,' said Rosanna, 'which belongs:

> '"In the midcourse of this our mortal life
> I found myself lost in a darkling wood
> Having wandered from the path. No words can tell
> how thick and terrible that forest grew . . ."'

'Yes,' said Thapsis, 'but what he saw was tinted by theology. I want to see for myself.'

'I could believe Dante saw Verula,' said Rosanna. 'Isn't that what he meant by Hell?'

'No. Verula strikes me as uncommonly like Your-Side earth,' said Thapsis. 'And you can put Hell out of your mind. Places of reward and punishment after death have nothing to do with reality – you know that. Some shamans have mistaken This Side for a post-mortem experience. The interesting things, including judgment, salvation, damnation and all the other matter of eschatology happen while one is still alive to experience them.'

'That's obvious,' said Rosanna. 'Then whom did Virgil and Dante visit?'

'Live people – including some, like Agrippa here, who were out of time-synch. We want to know whom they met.'

'So where are we going?' I asked.

'Inland from here. We want to see for ourselves. That's what our vocation is about.'

'I think, Thapsis,' I said, 'that you've involved us in enough of your experiments. This one isn't play – it's heavy.'

'Well, yes, those were play and training, and this is serious,' said Thapsis. 'After all, it's a trip we must all make. Why be a trivialist like Ivan Ilyitch and leave it for your last few hours of physical life?'

'You nearly got us both killed in Verula,' I said. 'How do we know there won't be more paramilitary heroics?'

'There won't,' said Thapsis. 'Agrippa, go and ask them for some more of that breakfast dish and six more chapatis, there's a good chap. And two more pots of tea. And blach – right-hand, of course.'

After he had gone, Thapsis said, 'I didn't want to say this in front of him. He's on borrowed time, you know. But you have no need to be life-careful here, Adepts. In fact, the best thing you can do is run some risks. If you are unlucky, and die here, you simply go home and if you choose to come back to us after that, you have the experience on your next visit of birth, a Losian childhood, your clock here is set back to zero, all without cost in real time. He who loses his life will save it, and if he loses it often, he's nearly immortal. Agrippa can't – he hasn't the real-time capital to go back and then return. He's living in the Anomaly. We don't discuss it, but he knows it, and you don't imagine I'd run him into any unnecessary danger.'

'Don't,' said Rosanna, 'will you?'

'Not if I can help it. But he does need to make this journey. Why do you think we train and labor to be archimages? Why do you think we trained you? You thought this whole experience was a caper, and the Game of the Adepts was a simple magic trick. One starts to learn counting in kindergarten, so that one can achieve mathematics later. Here comes the food.'

As we ate, Thapsis said: 'We are simply going to visit people. Who they are we don't know – they avoid all the places where Losian life is lived – and Tharmian, and Luvian. That's why we don't know. Some have wandered here as you did, but by accident. Most I feel sure are living simultaneously on Your Side. Every person here must have a real-time nervous system somewhere to support him. We will try to make contact. If they are tormented, as Dante thought, nobody is tormenting them but themselves.'

'Why,' I asked, 'does it matter?'

'Because,' Thapsis said, 'knowing, you can go back where you came from and see life differently. I wanted you both to see Beulah – not only as a holiday, but to realize that Beulah is outgrown.'

'Beulah is Paradise?' said Rosanna.

'Oh, no,' said Thapsis, 'by the time we get to Paradise we have grown beyond Beulah, and committed the sin which makes people go running to Urizen and torment themselves and other people.'

'Meaning Original Sin?' I asked.

'Yes and no – meaning, messing about prying into good and evil, instead of living in the unity of the Four. If the people back there,' he indicated the hinterland, 'are in trouble, it's not through "doing evil", but through asking questions about ethics. All the filthiest things on Your Side have been done by soi-disant ethical experts. The one thing which damns people is blithering about ethics.'

'So we are going to harrow Hell,' I said.

'You could call it that, provided you know what is really going on: Dante didn't,' said Thapsis. 'Milton had a better insight, and if he'd listened to Ololon he'd have come closer still. You should have no trouble. You come from an empirical tradition. It's the great gift Urizen gave to Your Side, empirical science. We will go and see.'

'We'll come,' said Rosanna. 'But I want to stay a little longer in Beulah. Neither Edward nor I had much childhood.'

'As long as you wish,' said Thapsis. 'Edward?'

'I will go where she goes,' I said.

'We've got a room for you here,' said Thapsis. 'You can't go on sleeping in a boat.'

When we were alone, I asked Rosanna what she made of it.

'In spite of what he said, not frightening,' said Rosanna. 'I'd be more scared if he said it was like Verula, like Our Side. That's really horrible.'

'But viewing Inferno seems a big change from Beulah.'

'Inferno isn't wicked people – that's Our-Side life and politics. It's unhappy people.'

'Maybe cruel people?'

'Only to themselves, I think. People only punish themselves in that world – after all, nobody else is punishing them. Let's go and see. Thapsis is right – it's the next thing we have to do. We should be honored that he chose us.'

'Thapsis chooses volunteers out of his own devious motives,' I said.

'But they've been good motives, haven't they? Good for us, I mean.'

'Yes, I suppose so.'

'I wonder who they are?'

'Thapsis seemed to think that they're mostly half-selves of Our-Side people. Like Edi and Ruso, but unhappy instead of childlike.'

'You're probably right,' said Rosanna, 'and also I think in some way he wants to help Agrippa. Agrippa is getting old in Losian time. It doesn't show much, but he is. And he has no real time left. Not even enough to go back for a few seconds, perform the Game and be reborn as a Losian baby. If he had even fifteen minutes in hand, that would be plenty.'

'But he's into extra time already.'

'Yes.'

'We all have to die some time.'

'But it's crueler for him. He thought he'd beaten it, and found his two lost Alcestises, and now they're going to be lost again soon. Or eventually.'

'We all lose people eventually,' I said. 'That's what being human is.'

'Yes,' said Rosanna, 'but don't you see it's harder for Agrippa now?'

'I see it. The two women are into extra time too. I don't see how we can help. Or Thapsis. Or this journey.'

'We'll think,' said Rosanna, 'if there's a way.

'And about living dangerously here,' she added, 'I'd like to be reborn, to be a Losian baby, and a Losian child.'

'Let's try,' I said, 'and time anything like that together. I don't want to lose synchrony with you here, Ros, even if I've got you on Our Side.'

'You haven't,' said Rosanna, ' "got" me. I thought we went into that. I belong to me.'

'Sorry. But you know what I mean. It was loving.'

'I know,' she said. 'Let's lie down a bit. This is like our home in Adambara.'

We did so.

But she was still fretting over Agrippa. Finally she dragged me round to tackle Thapsis. We found him – unusually for Beulah – alone, drinking herb tea at a table by the window. I had an unnerving impression that he was expecting us.

'Agrippa,' said Rosanna, 'isn't there *anything* we can do to help him?'

'Naturally,' said Thapsis, 'we're working on it. I'm no less sympathetic than you are, my dear. Consolation will have to come from within, I'm afraid.'

'He's terrified of dying,' said Rosanna.

'Hardly,' said Thapsis, 'after all, he's done it often enough before: we all have.'

'Doesn't he know that?'

'Well, he ought to. He's an adept. He also knows it's like being hauled out of bed at midnight by the police and told to evacuate: leave everything – clothes, achievements, people. Doesn't want to lose the Agrippa clothes. I remember, when I was a kid, crying because a story I liked was over. Doesn't want to lose the women, either: though they'll probably figure in the next production – different parts, of course, but the cast's usually unchanged.'

'I'd feel the same,' said Rosanna.

'Well, naturally – it's called "attachment". *I* quite like being archimage. You probably don't want to lose Edward.'

'That,' said Rosanna, 'but I also don't want to lose me. I like the Rosanna clothes. It's wasteful. It would be better if one could remember, not start from scratch.'

'Natural,' said Thapsis, 'in the young – at eighty you may feel different. After two thousand performances of *The Mousetrap* the part palls. Agrippa's relatively young too. As to remembering, it might not be a good idea.'

'Some people do,' said Rosanna.

'Jatismaras,' said Thapsis, 'it takes stamina. There's usually enough forgettable in any one life; we can just about cope with so much *dukha*. To deal with total recall you'd need to be very far along the road.'

'It's idiotically wasteful. What do we gain if we don't recall anything?'

Thapsis poured himself another cup. 'Ever play one of those chess machines?' he said. 'They've got a read-only memory with the rules of chess, which is hard wired, and a random access memory for the moves in this game. When you switch off, it clears the RAM and the game's gone. What isn't gone is the added experience you've gained of chess. If you force it you can get back – there's an arhat here who can do it. He usually won't – he finds it harmful.'

'I want,' said Rosanna, 'to meet him.'

'With a view to helping Agrippa?'

'With a view to helping me,' said Rosanna.

'If you did,' said Thapsis, 'you probably wouldn't recognize him, and he probably wouldn't play. He stays out of our Fourfold World – lives in the other hemisphere mostly. Only stays here because he's sworn to stay in middle-Order reality to give other people a leg up transcending it. My considered advice would be not to push it. By the time you get his powers, you'll be able to handle the results. Damn it, you're both physicists: you know time is a human position artefact, you know these "lives" are actually a coherent superposition. Just stick with that. And let Agrippa deal with his own feelings – *he* doesn't have access to quantum ideas: might help if he had.'

He was looking at Rosanna to see if the advice had been swallowed and decided it hadn't.

'Incidentally,' he said, 'the arhat already knows about you two. I talked to him before we got you here. The last time you died, Rosanna, you were seven, and it happened in Auschwitz. Edward here died after three months on the Somme. There is a carryover – you're terrified of general anaesthetics, and Edward can't stand loud noises even now. Want to go on? No, I didn't think you would. Just take my word for it that I'll do anything for Agrippa which seems wise, and try to control your inferior benevolence. The arhat would give you a lecture: I won't. And I've got to be off now. Love well.'

'Thapsis,' I said, 'I've got a long memory for theory. You once told me that reincarnation was hogwash. Any explanation of that – or was it simply adeptic deception?'

'The only adeptic part of it is that we don't volunteer detailed information on theory,' said Thapsis. 'What is hogwash is the beads-on-a-string, return-as-a-pig-if-you're-greedy model. Moreover, what you call *you* is temporary. It refers to the costume. Edward is temporary: you aren't. Satisfied?'

'Seems clear enough to me.'

And he stumped off.

In the next days we made no preparations and undertook no training. There were no libraries in Tarnindhupura. In the moist warmth of the Tharmian weather Rosanna and I wandered about, sailed in the verra boat, made love and slept. We found that in spite of what Edi had said, there was indeed a small temple of Enitharmon – a clay-brick circular chapel with no inner circle and no perpetual sacrifices: Tharmians see all sexuality as magical. The Tharmian couple who came into the darkened chapel and joined us there told us that they were Enitharmon's devotees. We asked after Edi and Ruso.

'Oh yes – we know them, everyone knows them; we swing with them often. You are like them, you two strangers.'

'How can you tell?' said Rosanna. 'It's too dim here to see our faces.'

'Your bodies are like theirs. Are they your brother and sister?'

They left us at the door of the shrine and ran off arm in arm. At night, with the seemingly perpetual Tharmian moon, which still rose with earth-shine even when its disc was dark, we mixed with Tharmians in the streets. It is strange to walk in a naked crowd where everyone touches each other as much as possible, and where strangers embrace closely as a matter of course. We had not known how fiercely the people of Our Side fortify and defend their frontiers. 'It's strange, with these boys,' said Rosanna, 'one doesn't feel invaded. It's nice: like making love to another woman.'

'You feel invaded by me?' I asked, 'or Faesto, or Agrippa?'

'Well, yes. There's always some invasion in lovemaking; there's a letting-in at least,' said Rosanna. 'But not with them.'

'Let's ask Agrippa over to spend the night with us,' she said later.

'How about Thapsis?'

'I don't know,' said Rosanna. 'He never asked me. I don't know what precisely his trip is.'

Agrippa spent next day with us, in the verra boat. He was as amusing as ever, but we could perceive his sadness. It was consolation he wanted from Rosanna, as much as when his two spirit women had been lost to him and he had lived with the salamandrines in the desert. Next morning he excused himself, embraced us both like a true Tharmian and left.

'I don't just know what we can do for him this time,' said Rosanna. 'He loved me three more times after you fell asleep and cried all the time.'

'I don't see what we can do,' I said. 'In a way he's lucky to have had this much of the Losian world. And I still don't understand the mechanics of this time business. Or how he keeps running without a nervous system back home to keep things going. If, as I suppose, we are inside our own heads here, we have to have functional heads to be inside.'

'I know,' said Rosanna. 'I wish Thapsis would set it all out clearly, in good factual Urizenian terms.'

'Why,' I said, 'doesn't Thapsis just show him the implicate – I mean, without any frills? Why don't we get a better look at it, come to that?'

'Ask him,' said Rosanna. 'We can't help Agrippa with a lecture on quantum logic. It's the explicate he doesn't want to lose. We don't want to lose it either.'

'Maybe we all get to be real Adepts and stop worrying about it.'

'Yes,' said Rosanna.

'I think Thapsis is cooking something to help him,' I said. 'Thapsis would say, stop understanding and use your imagination. He'd also say that a skull-knowledge approach wouldn't yield a solution.'

'I wish,' said Rosanna, 'Faesto was here. Then we'd all be together.'

'We'll go to Adambara,' I said, 'and see him when this exercise ends. I like him as much as you do. And we agreed that you had a special relationship on This Side.'

'That,' said Rosanna, 'was big of you.'

But her sadness for Agrippa spoiled the abandon of Beulah. We both felt it was time to be on our way. Later that morning we came on Thapsis, sitting on the boat pier, with a Tharmian girl climbing over him.

'Greetings,' he said. 'You loved well?'

'Well, and you?'

'Well!' said the Tharmian lady.

'That answers your question,' I whispered to Rosanna.

'Does Beulah pall?' said Thapsis. 'There's another festival tonight. We could make a foursome.'

'No,' said Rosanna, 'it doesn't pall, but we should get going soon. About tonight, yes, as a sort of sayonara party for Beulah. But what about Agrippa? I don't want him left out, particularly not now.'

'He isn't,' said Thapsis. 'He said goodbye to Beulah with you two, last night. He asked for a simurgh and went for a long walk – he's writing to Giulietta and Jehanne. Let him handle it his way, Rosanna. I'm not unmindful.'

'Then we'll meet you at moonrise, in the square?' said Rosanna.

'Yes, yes. This is Argyra – Argyra, Eda, Rusana.' And she embraced us both.

We were the last of the festival celebrants to sleep. Rosanna came back to me and we covered ourselves with a verra pelt. She was warm and satisfied.

'How was Thapsis?' I asked.

'He's nice,' said Rosanna 'and loving, which I never realized. I was still thinking of his dour Highland professorship, but he's not like that. And he cares about Agrippa.'

Thapsis woke us at moonset. Agrippa was with him. 'Don't wake the others,' said Thapsis, 'but we should be moving.'

We picked our way over the embraced sleepers. Argyra did not even stir, but lay scattered and outspread like a child. Thapsis bent down and kissed her without waking her.

'Clothes, equipment?' I said.

'Taken care of,' said Agrippa.

'Transport?'

'Walk on a little way.'

We passed out of the gate.

Among the trees outside was a stone bench and a stone drinking trough. A cresset had been lit at moonset to guide home any of the worshippers who might return early to the homes and boats. Thapsis sat down.

'We have about half an hour,' he said. 'We may as well be comfortable.'

'Until the bus arrives?' I said.

'You could say that. I want to make a dawn start. We'll go round the walled town, not through it – we'll disturb everyone. That will be easier with a little light. And we can strike the main causeway at the gate opposite to this one.'

'You should have been with us, Agrippa,' said Rosanna.

'Thank you, lady. But after being with Tharmians I needed to reset my own boundaries. So I took a day alone.'

'Well, Agrippa,' said Thapsis, 'we've seen them all – Tharmians, Losians: the Verulans I won't count, because not all who profess Urizen are like that. You have made the circuit of the Fourfold world, and so have our friends here. We should all be just about ready for this journey.'

'It's the consummation?' said Agrippa.

'I haven't any idea,' said Thapsis. 'It was something that ought to be done – I'm quite sure that it won't be anything like what past Adepts have led us to expect; it may turn out to be trivial. We can only go and see.'

'Nobody,' said Rosanna, 'says anything about the Luvians, Thapsis. Why? Aren't they part of the Four?'

Thapsis looked at her shrewdly. 'Oh yes, they are part of the Four. It may be that they are the best part. They are a part whose time was, and I strongly suspect it is they who own the future. You see, not many of Your Side whom you would know find themselves there. That will change. In your world, Los and Urizen have been fighting for the crown. Adambara and Verula you seem to understand, and it's not surprising. People who live by creativity and enthusiasm, rich pigs who starve and murder other people to get wealth they squander on trivia – both quite familiar. Most of humanity has been on the sidelines, except when your culture enslaved them. Luvah has the answer, and his time will come on Your Side.'

'And the Luvians?'

'Well,' said Thapsis, 'you know the Amish. None of the soulless technology of Urizen, because it is senseless and leads to death. None of the wealth of Verula, because it makes pigs and isn't worth having. None of the creativity of Los, because it disturbs the Fabric – Luvah is the Weaver, you know; not because Luvians make cloth – in fact they're mostly gardeners – but because he makes men into a fabric. In the past, none of the innocence of Tharmas. But that will change.'

'You say their time will come on Our Side,' said Rosanna.

'Is coming – is almost here, in fact. When your cities fall down, when wealth stops buying anything, when if a man wants to eat he must grow what he eats, not buy it, deny others, and waste half. Luvah is Compassion, but on earth he is Orc, overturner of wrongs and triviality.'

'I suspect we call Luvians Maoists. They're also Urizenian prudes,' I said.

'Well, no offense, but on Your Side what did you expect?' said Thapsis. 'All the Four must unite, or we're back where we were, replacing one evil with another. Los is the Uniter – that is why he is the Smith – he melts and welds the Four together. There will be time to visit the Luvians, Rosanna. Many from Your Side who come here find themselves among them, but hardly ever your skull-knowledge friends. Peasants understand them at once. Incidentally, they own the future on Your Side if only because subsistence living works, and it's also invincible. You will watch, and see this, and be on their side if you're decent, as you are, and see them beat your cadillacs into windmills and your washing machines into henhouses and your pig rich into the ground, and see Los and Tharmas sleep for a while. It will be the task of decent Adepts not to side with the trivial and the inhuman, and yet to see that no new iron books are written. What you learned from our Tharmian friends may help. Luvah and Tharmas together are a formidable brotherhood.'

'I know what you mean,' said Rosanna. 'I think they perhaps are the true radicalizers. People talk as if imagination and sensuality were trivial, like wealth. Luvians probably think that middle-class trivialists keep them for pets.'

'Show them that they don't,' said Thapsis. 'You realize, don't you, that your next assignment will have to be on Your Side, not ours?'

'That's why we come here,' said Rosanna.

I for one marveled at her. I knew what she meant, and

sensed what she sensed, yet always Rosanna said it before I had shaped it.

'You will meet them anyhow on this journey, the Luvians,' said Thapsis. 'If we pass through the Empty Quarter and don't have to retrace, we'll come to their cities. At least you'll see their gardens from the high ground there, if it's clear – like a big chessboard, each family its own provider.'

Agrippa looked up. 'Time's up, isn't it?' he said.

'Yes,' said Thapsis. 'Blow your asva horn.'

I did so, and in a few moments I heard the claws of the Tetrarch on the stones, and his heavy tread, and saw the huge face and long neck coming out of the shadows of the marsh road. There was no touching reunion. He gave a long sigh, and I noticed he was munching. He was in full saddle order, his saddlebags were full, and on his back sat a minute Tharmian boy.

'He's been properly fed and watered?' said Thapsis.

'Yes, Adept, yes. And thank you for the ride!'

'Down,' I said. The Tetrarch knelt, and Agrippa lifted down the boy.

'There,' he said, 'asvin! You've ridden a war asva of Adambara. Tell all your friends. Off home!'

'No,' said the boy, 'I'm going to the square – Chitra's going to stay awake for me. Bye, Adepts!'

And he dived into the shadow of the gate. We heard his feet pattering off on the alabaster dancing floor of the street.

'They start early,' I said.

5

States That Are Not, But Seem to Be

The causeway from Tarnindhupura ran across the flat lands reclaimed by former and more industrious inhabitants from the delta, haphazard Tharmian gardens interspersed with lots covered in reeds; fruit trees, tame choreb, reed houses, narrow channels with reed boats, the little stalls of bread, and everything capped with the moving mists which shaded daytime Beulah. It was early, and the Tharmians, late risers, lay sleeping under their porches. Here and there someone waved and called, 'Did you love well?' and we answered their greeting. As time passed, the herds began to move. Unafraid of our asva their curly backs and soft eyes streamed on either side of him. In one porch I saw a choreb lamb resting, legs folded under him, chewing the cud, and beside him stretched out like a vast dog a great forest verra, tame with the universal tameness of Beulah, the verra lying down with the lamb, household pets both. The daughters of Beulah appeared, flat baskets and pitchers on heads, long-haired, round-buttocked, covered in silver finery, and all of them greeting us, asking for rides, admiring Rosanna's Tharmian ornaments and Agrippa's beard with the innocent, friendly impertinence of the country where there is no reserve or privacy and everyone is, in Thapsis's expression, a co-child. Gradually we left them behind. The causeway mounted steadily. It was now punctuated between the stones with reeds – few Tharmians evidently used it. We overtook a cart drawn not by choreb but by two rangy, fast-stepping horned beasts like eland. It was full of choreb wool in bales, and in it were a man and a woman. They were clothed in blue simple blouses and trousers, dressed alike, and on the man's head was a wide, Quaker-like hat. As we passed them, they too greeted us. 'Good morning, brothers. Good morning, sister.' One instinctively did not ask them if they loved well – though very possibly they did. They had a gravity which would have made it a little like asking a nun if she loved well – if she said 'yes,' it would not be in the Losian sense.

'Greetings, comrades,' said Thapsis. They smiled gravely.

'Luvians,' said Thapsis. 'Choreb wool for the looms. They've got a fair step to go.'

We came to a crossroads. There were old carved pillars on three of its intersecting arms. That along which we had come was marked with a naked maiden, like a vrksasa, leaning languidly against a tree which sprang into flower at her touch and had a crescent moon in its branches. That to the left had a pair of weaving figures, bent over their loom, and above them a star. That to the right bore reeds and a fish. The road ahead, which looked disused, had no pillar to indicate its destination, but a branch had been laid across it.

'Straight on,' said Thapsis.

'That looks like a Tharmian "No Through Road" sign,' I said.

'Probably is,' said Thapsis briefly.

From that point on, the causeway was broken with bushes, but it was continuous and climbed steadily. It mounted a low range of hills covered with dripping woodland, the bluffs fringing the delta, then into flatter wet thickets just below the lid of mist, then into the lid of mist itself, until finally we were traversing the side of a hill, looking down in bright sunlight on a wide, an endless field of choreb wool, the mist filling the valley of Beulah, hiding the Tharmian world completely from what was outside it. Then the causeway turned inland, climbing yet more steeply in yet thicker woods. The sun went behind another deck of clouds, and when we had risen another thousand feet or so it began to be cold.

'Clothes,' said Thapsis. 'That is the end of Beulah for a while. From now on we shall need them, whatever our principles.' And he put on a kaftan and an enormous cloak. We all followed his example. The Tetrarch munched audibly.

At about three thousand feet the Tharmian road simply

ceased. In front was a tangle of branches, bushes, high timber growing over and among them and stumps covered with bright yellow fungi. The Tetrarch crashed and slithered his way through it like a tank, stumbling on muskeg, snorting when dead wood pricked him or whipped at him. Moreover he could clearly smell verra.

'Yes,' said Thapsis, 'Dante met one – took it for a panther – must have been the spotted kind. Keep a sharp lookout. We're not in Beulah now.'

It was becoming an infernal place – cold, wet and dark, full of the obstructions of a temperate rain forest with clouds just about clear of the highest treetops. Periodically it rained.

'I think,' said Thapsis, 'that there is a track under all this.'

It did, indeed, become rather easier to progress – the dense forest debris thinned, there was more high timber and finally we were crossing the floor of virgin forest. Then rocks began to sprout. The Tetrarch threaded between them. At last we struck a bare crest, and the track became unmistakable. So much for the horrendous wood, I thought. The ground was heathery, and the rocks lay about like large gray choreb. In a few minutes we could see the next valley. It lay under driving gray clouds. A wide river flowed along it, as black as ink with peat-water. On the far side were bare crags and a track running up. On the hither side stood an enormous, gray building. It might have been a Greek railway station, a nineteenth-century prison or a library in industrial Manchester before the Clean Air regulations – it had that moldering and forbidding appearance, enhanced by its size, isolation and squareness. On top of its façade stood an enormous gilded sun, the sole bright object in sight.

'Temple of Urizen,' said Thapsis. 'This must be the arrival point. They have to come through his sanctuary – it stands to reason.'

'There's nothing in the previous voyages about a temple,' said Rosanna.

'Probably recent – a labor of love by the newcomers, I shouldn't wonder,' said Thapsis. 'It used to be a cave, apparently. Caves are among the earliest human sanctuaries. They've put up something worthier of Nobodaddy.'

'I take it there won't be stray Verulans around?' I said.

'They wouldn't, if you'll forgive the expression, be seen dead here,' said Thapsis.

'The Infernal airport,' said Rosanna.

'Precisely. And that, ladies and gentlemen, is the river Acheron. Who would have thought that it flows into Beulah, and if one went down it, not across it into the badlands . . .'

And, indeed, movement was taking place. The whole of the temple face towards the river was a vast mouthlike arch, and out of it there flocked what appeared to be refugees, or pioneers – a gray, bundle-carrying collection, converging on a long pier which ran into the river. The pier was furred with them. Others had settled in piles.

'The dead leaves,' said Rosanna.

The boat, when it poled out, was ridiculously small and overloaded. It made its way across, returned poling, and there was a rush as it repassed behind the pier to get into it.

I set the Tetrarch in motion. 'No,' said Thapsis, 'sit tight and watch. We'll be mobbed, and we don't want to interview them. The flow seems to have stopped for a while. Outspan here and let's eat. It may take all day to clear these, even if no more arrive.'

It was indeed sunset when we went down. Only a few immigrants remained, camped by the landward end of the pier, and they took no notice of us. The boat came slowly back. The boatman was a wizened Losian with the iron pendant of his country of origin around his neck. His boat was called the *Good Hope*.

'Greetings,' he said, 'you loved well? What are you doing here, fourfold friends?'

'He's an archimage,' said Rosanna. 'We might have guessed it.'

'You know well, fourfold friend?' said Thapsis. 'If that's the last crossing, join us.'

So we sat beside our asva, on Charon's pier, and ate supper with him.

'Why you?' said Thapsis. 'What is an archimage doing ferrying immigrants to the badlands?'

'It's my sadhana,' said the old man. 'I don't take them if I can stop them. Every time I come back I stand off the pier and yell – "this way only to the badlands, Beulah's two days' walk in the other direction, or you can make reed boats and get there downstream in three days." They're hellbent on crossing. I reckon I manage to stop about one in fifteen. They're frightened, and angry, and all they want to do is to get across to what somebody told them was their destiny. It's pathetic.'

'You only ferry one way?'

'Of course not; I'd bring them back if they ask. But they don't.'

'And once across, they're cut off from civilization?'

'Oh no, there's a very pleasant town a few miles on, with the best university on This Side. I go there whenever the ferry closes. Quite a lot of them stop there – it's full of good Adepts and good conversation and some excellent inns. If they'd stop there they might get their bearings. Pagans usually do, because the Christians tell them they aren't allowed to go further, and they believe them. But most are just hellbent and press on into the badlands. You'll see squads of them going through, when you get to Limbo, like the old-time Mormons headed for Deseret.'

'The Mormons did a pretty good job when they got there,' said Rosanna.

'These don't. You call out "Did you love well?" and they say "Lord have mercy on me a sinner, avaunt!" or something like that.'

'I always thought,' said Rosanna, 'that this was how it really worked. Tell me, in the badlands, as you call them, is anyone preying on them? Do they kill each other, and things like that?'

'Usually not, I gather,' said Charon. 'They're all bent on punishing themselves, and they cooperate to do it. Do it very efficiently, too. There's nobody *to* injure them in the mountains – verras, perhaps, but as they go in droves, even verras only pick off stragglers.'

'Who exactly are they?' said Rosanna.

'Other-Siders who get here by accident, a few. Twins, chiefly, if you know what I mean by that. There was a girl here yesterday who arrived in chains, like a convict. I asked her where she got them, and she said "He put them on me."'

'Someone who keeps his anima in Hell,' said Rosanna.

'I can remember someone else who turned up in Adambara as a slavegirl, Ros,' I said.

'But that,' said Rosanna, 'was different.'

'I'm going to talk to them,' said Agrippa. He walked back.

'Please yourself,' said Thapsis.

'Cheers, Adepts,' said Charon. 'If you're wise, you'll move on a bit and camp – then go on before the next batch arrives. Not too far, or you'll catch up with today's consignment and they'll want to hitch rides. Limbo's about twenty miles on. You'll enjoy it – full of the illustrious dead.'

'If they were dead, would they be here?' said Rosanna.

'The Anomaly, he must mean,' said Thapsis.

'But only Adepts know that device,' I said, 'and Agrippa only learned it at the last moment. How then . . . ?'

'You seem to be under a misapprehension,' said Charon. 'Most of the Other-Siders who come this way do it in the last few minutes or seconds of life – they're living in the Anomaly, in extra time. That's why we can't just show them how to get back. It seems to happen naturally – probably premortal anoxia turns off *maya*, or something of the sort. Adepts they aren't. Others get called back again, will they nill they, because somebody resuscitates them.'

'Yes,' said Thapsis, 'we've seen that happen in Adambara – some get turned back in immigration before the Time of Choice is over. Others stay longer, but feel they have to go back. You need to be an Adept, or into the Anomaly, to have full control.'

'Mind what you say, Charon,' I said. 'Agrippa's in the Anomaly, and running out of Losian time, and he's dead many years on earth.'

'Glad you mentioned it,' said Charon. 'Poor chap! How tragic for an Adept!'

'Is Hell really terrible?' said Rosanna. 'It seems chiefly – stupid.'

'That can be terrible,' said Charon. 'It's less spectacular than it was. People used to light fires and jump in them.

They used to wallow in sewage and lie around on ice up there because they thought that was expected of them. Now they're just lost, as a rule, and remorseful. You don't see many bad folk here. They're too arrogant to be self-punishers. Those drift to places like Verula, where they can get fat on injuring others. Or they did, until the Great Adept and his Emanation dealt with the Verulans.'

'These,' said Thapsis, 'are the Adept and Emanation you're talking about.'

Charon's jaw dropped.

'And I have to add,' said Thapsis, 'that courageous as that whole caper was, it was just a caper. It was earth-side playfulness – one thing Verula could not handle.'

Rosanna and I stayed quiet. It had been nicer when the Losian girl in Entuthon believed I was the Spirit of Milton. Evidently Thapsis still thought he had been very clever.

'The archimage Thapsis can be playful too,' said Rosanna. 'On the Other Side he masquerades as a Scottish professor of anthropology.'

'Whist, woman!' said Thapsis.

'You say the bad don't get here?' Rosanna asked.

'Pretty rarely, the real swine. You get to Hell by bothering about Good and Evil instead of Love and Intelligence,' said Charon.

'Dante talked about Purgatory,' said Rosanna.

'Purgatory is simply when you have the sense to learn from self-punishment to stop doing it,' said Charon.

'And Heaven?' said Rosanna.

'Is anywhere else except this patch of badlands and what people have come expecting to do to themselves. It can be Adambara – it can be Beulah – it can be Luvia if you've got a social conscience. It can even be Urizen's world, if you know the other Three.'

'That,' said Rosanna, 'is what I thought. Dante was bending it.'

'Yes,' said Charon, 'he had to. Even he realized the people here weren't dead – you remember Fra Alberigo?'

Agrippa was back in a few minutes.

'No use,' he said. 'Either the Adept ring doesn't work with

them, or they think I am a devil tempting them. I told them to go to Beulah and they put their hands over their ears.'

'I gather it used to be different,' said Charon. 'When Virgil came here, for example: that was several archimages back, of course – Charon's a title – my real name's Christopher: we take it in turns. And before that, Bronze age Greeks weren't hellbent, they just couldn't get used to the quieter tempo, and the lack of macho prestige; spent their time in Limbo drinking blood to keep up their strength and pining for heroics. Most were the twin-selves of very put-down women, who just couldn't afford an animus. Now women outnumber men in the emigrant deliveries. There's another flight due in at dawn. Are you going across?'

'We are,' said Thapsis.

'Fine,' said Charon. 'Spend some time in Limbo if you can, and try to dine at the High Table. But I'm not having that asva in the boat, I'm sorry. If you want to get across before you're mobbed by crazy immigrants, I'll take you tonight before I tie up and go home. But *he's* going to have to swim.'

And so we crossed Acheron – Agrippa, Thapsis and Rosanna in the boat of Charon, the *Good Hope*, I following on the reluctant Tetrarch, with a long ripple following, until he shook himself on dry land.

6

Among the Cliffs of the Dead

We did not overtake the tail of the immigrant column. After our morning start, in rain and wind, we encountered a few of them sitting about listlessly under rocks. They offered us no greeting.

'I'm in two minds,' said Thapsis. 'I'd like to spend time in Limbo; it's probably the most underrated city in the world; I've never seen it, and it's the source of nearly all our best graduate Adepts. On the other hand, we have a long journey ahead. I suggest a quick visit. If the Fellows see you, Agrippa, we'll be here a full week.'

'Dante stayed around,' I said.

'And I don't blame him. Dante had his tongue in his cheek. After all, it's the place one stays, he says, if one can't qualify for his rather vulgar and exclusive Paradise. Actually,' said Thapsis, 'one can see very well how one observes what one wants to observe. I think myself that Dante never went *through* the badlands – he went halfway and came back. On the way in he saw Limbo and his own forecast of Hell – on the way back he saw Purgatory and his own forecast of Heaven – the same two places, seen with a different preconception, and probably with the sun out. Usually the weather in Limbo is foul. But that shouldn't bother you, Edward, after Cambridge.'

'And the unbaptized babies?' said Rosanna.

'Moonshine,' said Thapsis. 'They used to have a first-rate choir school in Limbo. That may have started the story – the town was full of soprano putti in Dante's time. Agree, Adepts, that we press on?'

'We could get one good meal here,' I said. 'I don't mind

forgoing dining in Hall if everyone else agrees. But I do wonder whom we should meet.'

The College City was indeed as Dante described it. He had arrived at night, when they had the tower beacon burning – we got there a little after dawn. It was in the manner of other university cities – Gothic castles, Victorian follies, Classical façades, packed into narrow streets where the Tetrarch's claws clumped inappropriately. Arches with porters' lodges opened into green courtyards – I could not tell the names of the colleges, but over one gate I noticed the motto 'Fais ce que Voudras.' That one at least was familiar. I had not thought of Francois Rabelais as a shaman.

'Oh yes,' said Thapsis, 'you see how differently things appear to different people. We'll be lucky to get our meal – nothing's open.'

We found, in the end, a small Losian place with the usual fare. By the time we had done, there were a few inhabitants moving. It was as we were leaving the town, beyond the colleges, and towards a level, gray river with weirs, that we overtook two figures of earthly appearance. One, tall and bearded, wore gray plus-four trousers and puttees – he walked fast, and beside him, deep in colloquy, was a gnome-like companion who wobbled on a terrestrial bicycle. As the Tetrarch came up I heard the rider respond to some remark of the walker with a dry, Punch-like chuckle which had no twin in any world. Then we had passed them, and it was all my sense of duty could do to preserve my conformity to Thapsis's instructions.

'You hesitated – ' said Thapsis, 'you knew them?'

'I think so,' I said.

'Who were they?'

'George Bernard Shaw and Bertrand Russell.'

'Dear me,' said Thapsis, 'we should have stayed. And then again we shouldn't. Why don't they come to Adambara?'

'I don't think,' said Rosanna, 'it would be their trip. Maybe they will, if they have time . . .'

She remembered Agrippa's predicament and held her peace.

'We do well to press on,' said Agrippa. 'I care less now for universities than I did. Almost as little as for Adepts.' The dreaming spires disappeared in a violent squall of rain. Water coursed down the Tetrarch's sides. Only a short way beyond the town, the road ran to a rock wall. In it was a long tunnel, lit by patches of the luminous Adambaran stone, and packed with the sheltering immigrants. We passed through them with difficulty. I thought of the beggar-infested gate of Verula.

'Who feeds them?' said Rosanna.

'There is food,' said Thapsis, 'if they learn to look for it. These woods contain quite a lot of fruit, but it's of poor quality. Oh well, the light at the end of the tunnel. Looks as if the rain is on the other side of the hill.'

We came out into drier country. The road was between rocks again. Though there was no sun, the Tetrarch steamed.

It was a chaotic landscape, a cracked tableland with rock pinnacles, ravines, clumps of trees. As we rose, it became colder still and a dusty wind got up. The immigrants were no longer in column. We saw figures fanning out like dots on the surface of the inhospitable ground. The road continued to ascend. There were great corries with black round lakes in them. We were on a ridge track, headed for a line of pointed crags. The road threaded between them. Then without warning the landscape fell away from under our feet into a spectacular chasm.

The Tetrarch stopped. We looked down.

It was a complete circle of cliffs, as if a plug of rocks some miles across had been removed. Its walls were two or three thousand feet high, its bottom level like the bottom of a can, occupied on one side by scattered tufts which were actually full-size trees, and these became denser until at the foot of the north-facing wall they coalesced into forest. At any time but midday one-half of the bowl was dark. The track that we were upon hung precariously in the cliff face, running round the arena and falling. The shadow facing us made it impossible to see whether it reached the bottom. The Tetrarch viewed the scene with disapproval. Agrippa inspected the rock wall beside us as if looking for fossils.

'Seen something?' I asked him.

'I was looking to see if it said "Dante was here,"' said Agrippa. 'The scenery looks infernal enough.'

'I think it's frightening but beautiful,' said Rosanna, 'and no more hellish than the Grand Canyon. What's that?'

'That' was a group of what appeared to be larger boulders, near the edge of the facing shadow: the track ran as a fine line just above them, and from them depended like a beard a patch of scree which, unlike anything else in the place, was green. The boulder outlines were unnaturally square. They were buildings. A dirty streak on the cliff above them appeared to mark a spring.

'Looks like a fort,' said Agrippa. 'Who built it, I wonder? Thapsis, did you know there were buildings here?'

'I didn't,' said Thapsis. 'I have a guess, what it is, and if I'm right it's long empty.'

'There are caves down there along the edge of that wood,' said Rosanna.

So vast was the bowl that it took three hours of careful descent to round the cliff pinnacle which lay next on the hither side of the buildings. A vast red rock needle stood away from the cliff, and the track passed in the fork between them.

The fortlike structure was a rough quadrangle – it lay below the track and we looked down on its roofs. A few ill-favored goats were moving about on the thorn scree, but the green area behind had the air of overgrown garden.

'Old Verulan slave-fort,' said Thapsis. 'I thought as much. They used to raid on foot for slaves – Tharmians, I suppose – and they put these forts in inaccessible places. Used to collect them here and break them in, before marching them off to Verula. That stopped long since. Before we cleaned up Verula, they used trucks. This is a historical monument. Come on.'

We left our mount by the spring, which ran into a man-made basin to water the fort. The way down to the fort entrance was rugged with disuse. Broken wood lay about. The door hung on one hinge, giving on a guardroom full only of rubbish. Beyond was a solider door, unlocked, and immediately behind that another; a kind of airlock designed, no doubt, to prevent escape from escort. It gave on a ruinous passage lined with Verulan cells.

I heard a sound behind me. Agrippa was supporting a collapsed Rosanna.

'Take her back,' said Thapsis. 'I'm sorry, shouldn't have brought you here – it's a bit too like the place . . .'

'No,' said Rosanna, 'no – there are people here.'

'People?'

'Prisoners. I know it.'

'Go on, Ros,' I said, 'go back to the Tetrarch while we look around. If there are people you can see for yourself they aren't prisoners – there's no front door, let alone a guard . . .'

7

We Encounter Many a Woeful Company

Rosanna pushed past me into the passage. We followed. The cells had wooden bolted doors with a broad, barred port in each. Rosanna looked in the first, then in the second and stepped back, pointing. I looked in. The cell contained a man, yellow faced, eyes surrounded by hair and beard, eyes which looked at us without hope, curiosity or even interest. I shouted; he did not move. He would have served as a waxwork of the Prisoner of Chillon. In the next cell was another.

'Hell's bells,' said Agrippa.

There was a slight scuffling. Another man was behind us. He too was made up as a medieval dungeon inmate, in an ill-fitting canvas shirt and trousers out of a Devil's Island movie. He was ostentatiously not raising his eyes.

'Who are you?' said Thapsis.

'Permission to reply, Sir?'

'Granted,' said Thapsis.

'Chief trusty in charge, Sir. Everything is in order.' And he stood there awaiting orders. We heard feet, and outside the barred corridor window six heads went past with six spades over shoulders, all in the same Devil's Island makeup, and by the sound of it, in leg irons. We heard them enter the building, then sounds of irons being removed, then doors closing and bolts being shot.

'Permission to respond to all questions,' said Thapsis. 'Who are they?'

'Gardening party, Sir. The other trusty is in charge.'

'Where's the guard?'

'I wouldn't know that, Sir. Trusties are on duty here, Sir.'

'There's nobody in that guardroom,' said Thapsis.

'Trusties are not allowed past the door,' said the scarecrow.

'Your name?' said Thapsis.

It was the wrong thing to ask.

'Don't order me to break regulations, Sir,' said the scarecrow, 'please.'

'Let me try,' said Rosanna, and she attempted to take his hand. He jumped back. 'No physical contact with any guard!' he shouted.

'My God,' said Agrippa, 'they're playing jails. They run the place themselves. They dig the garden and starve on the result. It's a self-perpetuating system. The guards have gone and they don't know it. Must have been operational, this place, until Verula was taken.'

'No,' said Thapsis, 'I don't think there ever were any guards. Trusty!'

'Sir,' said the scarecrow.

'I am the Chief Inspector of Prisons. Everyone here is under my orders – under pain of severe discipline. You will follow me.'

'Yes, Sir.'

'And you will answer all questions promptly and truthfully. All regulations are suspended.'

'Yes, Sir.'

Thapsis led him into the ruined guardroom. 'You all wait outside,' he said to us. We waited. The shadow, moving round the cliff wall, was slowly swallowing the beard of garden and the quadrangle of the fort. After half an hour, Thapsis put his head out and called 'Rosanna!'

She went in to assist him.

'I think he's right,' said Agrippa. 'Four people would be too many for them. He'll find out first how they got here.'

'And if there ever were any guards,' I said. 'You can see how it could happen. Each new one who arrives is told the system, the rules, the punishments – it's self-perpetuating. And since of course jail doors are locked, nobody even tries the door.'

It was darkening steadily, though the sky was still light. Thapsis came out.

'We've got them out of the cells,' he said. 'There are

twenty-three of them. You were right. Every one found himself in this place, nobody recalls when or how it was first occupied, nobody has seen or spoken with a guard. When a trusty dies he is replaced by the next senior prisoner. Names are forbidden, so nobody remembers them. Each newcomer is taught the routines by the others – he's put in the black hole by the trusties if he breaks them. The discipline couldn't be stricter if the entire SS was running the place. Rosanna's trying to talk them down. They don't seem accessible to explanation. You try.'

The twenty-three scarecrows sat without great interest in lines on the floor. The two trusties still stood.

'I've tried to explain,' said Rosanna.

'You men understand?' said Thapsis. 'There are no guards, this is not a jail, you are all free to leave when you wish.'

'Yes, Sir,' chanted the seated files, casting an eye on the trusties for cues.

'We're most grateful to you, Sir, for the information,' said Trusty Number One.

There was a full minute of silence.

Trusty Number One was looking anxiously out at the rocks. Then he seemed to snap shut an invisible watch.

'Er – Sir – may we dismiss, Sir?'

'If you want,' said Thapsis, 'but isn't there anything we can do to help you – er – plan your next actions?'

'You see, Sir, it's chain-up time when the shadow hits that tall rock. We get bread and water if we miss it.'

'Nobody will put anyone on bread and water. You are free to go. You are free to eat as much as you like. You two, break us all out a decent meal if you have one – we'll eat with you,' said Agrippa.

'That's good of you, Sir. But the guards wouldn't like that.'

'THERE ARE NO GUARDS,' said Agrippa.

'No, Sir. But when they come back . . .'

The two files rose to their feet. 'March,' said Trusty Number One. His colleague brought up the rear. The door closed. We heard shuffling, chains clicking shut, cell doors closing.

'It's absolutely no use,' said Thapsis. 'Get the simurgh,

Agrippa. We can't stop and give them therapy. We'll bring a party of asvin up here and pull this place down. It'll take them a couple of months to get here. Tell them they may run into opposition – from the inmates. And ask the College of Physicians to put their skates on and get some head-changing mandalas up here along with the asvin. By the Four, I wouldn't have credited it.'

'I would,' said Rosanna. 'How else did you think Hell would work?'

'I think we may see a great deal more of the same,' said Thapsis. 'We'd better go down to the floor of this place before it gets dark. I'm not staying the night here – agreed?'

It was indeed dark when we reached the foot of the track. It ran on into the tree-dotted bowl. The tops of the crags were still sunny. We could see our simurgh circling up to take his bearings for Adambara. The fort windows showed one pale light. Other illumination was no doubt against the regulations of Hell.

It was icy before long on the valley floor. With sunset, cold air poured down from the higher peaks. Thapsis, Agrippa and I collected wood and lit a roaring fire. Even the Tetrarch edged towards it with none of his usual stoicism. He had stopped thinking about the possibilities of lizards, for there were none, and ate Tharmian fruit out of a sack. The flames threw up jumping shadows.

'Please,' said a voice, 'we're so cold. Can we come to the fire?'

From among the shadows came a boy and a girl. They might have been Losians, Tharmians even, but for their dress, and they had the stunned, disciplined air of the men in the prison above us. Rosanna ran to them and led them to the fire.

'Did you love well?' said Agrippa, taking them for Losians.

'You know about that too. Don't laugh at us,' said the boy.

It was hard to know what to say next. Rosanna warmed them, fed them, and they began to look human.

'Who are you?' she asked.

'I'm Rick and she's Nancy.'

'How long have you been here?'

'Seems ages, but then it would be.'

'Do you know,' said Thapsis 'where you are?'

'In Hell,' said the boy, simply. The girl had said nothing.

'Leave them to me,' said Rosanna. We did so, for a full hour, while they talked in whispers.

She came back. The two youngsters had fallen asleep under one of our saddle blankets.

'They were in a car,' said Rosanna. 'She was running away with him, leaving two young children. They hit a bridge on the freeway. They saw what was going to happen and just grabbed one another – they think they must be dead. Also they're good Catholics. Ever since they walked here from the river, they've been wandering about freezing – it's blowing a full gale with snow where they've been. They found their way down here to get out of the wind. Can we check that they're really dead?'

'I suppose so,' said Thapsis, 'when the simurgh gets back. What shall we do with them?'

'They're young – and they've stood up to it pretty well,' said Rosanna. 'I told them that of course they're in Purgatory, not Hell. In the morning we'll tell them to start back to Limbo with a note to the Academy, and somebody can take them both back to Charon. Then they can make a boat and drop down to Beulah. That's where they belong, not here.'

'It's a pity, Ros, that Paolo and Francesca didn't run into you,' said Agrippa.

'Then if they're not dead, they can choose,' said Rosanna, 'and if they stay in Beulah only a few days . . .'

'I agree,' said Thapsis. 'But we can't help everyone here. There must be thousands upon thousands. It calls for a more concerted operation, and that may be beyond the resources of our whole Losian world.'

'Yes,' said Rosanna, 'but we are going to do what we can, aren't we?'

When light reached the valley floor the simurgh was back within minutes – he had been making circuits in the higher daylight and waiting. It was still bitterly cold. Agrippa baited him, I fed the Tetrarch, Rosanna woke the two sleepers, fed them, briefed them, and they set out, resigned and unbelieving perhaps, on the climb to the lip of the valley. We could see the two small figures mounting until they passed out of sight behind the pinnacle.

Crossing the valley floor we were at first screened by bushes from the remainder of its expanse – it was huge, and when we came into clearer ground we could see other figures moving parallel with the track. Some were processing in column, others were scattered. Agrippa viewed the procession with distaste and amusement.

'Like monks,' he said.

'Or like your religious lizards,' said Thapsis.

'I prefer lizards.'

'I wonder,' said Rosanna, 'if those two will make it. You promised to find out what happened to them on Our Side, Thapsis.'

'Yes, yes, I will, but give the simurgh a few hours' rest. What are those blighters up to, over there? Can you see, Agrippa?'

'Running after someone – driving him away, by the look of it. Should we interfere?'

'No,' said Thapsis, 'I think not. There are a lot of them, and you heard what I said about missionary work. Let's get the facts and then see what we can do in the broader context – if we can indeed do anything.'

There was something fanatic and disturbing about the wandering and the countermarching around us. It vanished in the thickening scrub, but we knew it was there when we could no longer see it. The sun was reaching most parts of the valley now. We could see the prison and its smear of garden, the climbing line of the track.

'They should have reached the top by now,' said Rosanna, 'if those others leave them alone.'

'I don't see anyone else on the road there,' said Agrippa. 'Perhaps they're in luck.'

Thapsis had been writing in the saddle behind me. He launched the simurgh, and we watched it spiral up.

'Thapsis,' I said, 'are you assuming there's a second way up out of this kettle?'

'Well, the track goes somewhere,' said Thapsis.

We ate in the saddle. The scruffy leafless wood prevented our seeing far ahead.

'At least there's provender,' said Thapsis. 'This wood is full of nuts. But nobody seems to be picking them.'

A figure lying beside the track jumped up at the approach of the asva and fled.

'I have a nose for trouble,' said Agrippa. 'Have we got weapons?'

'We are fully equipped,' said Thapsis. 'Good. We're getting to the cliffs again. We've crossed the valley at its widest part. Now we shall see.'

Finally we saw. There was a huge railway-arch of cave, and the track ran into it. There were no signs of the lighted stone panels of the previous tunnel. Wild simurgh flew in and out of its cornice.

Thapsis passed forward a torch, flint and steel. The Tetrarch, detecting what he was going to be expected to do, demurred and required spurring. He disliked caves.

We passed under the bulging side of the cliff. The torch, when we lit it, showed little.

'Go steady, there are probably people camped here,' said Thapsis. There were indeed people, but not camped. They advanced in a hostile line. They were rugged like stumps, in the drab costume of immigrants, and their intentions were unfriendly. They were headed by a scruffy figure in what had once been a soutane or clerical robe of some kind. In his hand was a megaphone of bark, constructed no doubt from local resources to greet us.

'Turn back,' bawled the megaphone, 'you who give shelter to the adulterous. Turn back or perish! How dare you interfere with the Divine Justice?'

'Theatrical,' said Thapsis. 'Here we have a preacher. Friend, are you addressing us?'

'Turn back,' bellowed His Reverence.

'I told you I smelt trouble,' said Agrippa.

'It's incredible,' said Thapsis. 'Here he is, damned, for all he knows, and he's as fanatical as ever. Let us pass, friend, for we come to do good. We come to show you the way out of here.'

'As you did to those two sinners?' yelled the little man. We were closing fast. His congregation was edging forward. He rounded, turned his back on us and addressed the faithful. 'Behold the Beast of the Apocalypse,' he hollered, 'and on his back the Scarlet Woman, holding in her hand the cup of her fornication! You see the scripture fulfilled.'

'He means you, Ros,' said Agrippa. 'Thapsis, give me that bow please. Now, you beggar, stop canting and get out of our way – don't you people listen to his nonsense: you have this kind of thing to thank for the pickle you are in.'

A stone whizzed past my head. A second hit the Tetrarch. They were followed by a shower. The devotees surged forward. 'Head down,' I called to Rosanna. Thapsis prodded me. 'Use this if you need it,' he said, and passed me an aegis.

I did not raise it and arm it at this pitiful mob. They were too like the beggars of Verula. Instead I held it up as a simple shield.

'Go,' I said to the Tetrarch.

That animal knew exactly what to do. Verras he would have torn, one snap left, one snap right, spin, kick, trample – I had seen him in serious action. This was the moment for his threat display. I believe that he enjoyed it as much as real combat. He charged. His scream, terrifying at any time, was amplified by the cave mouth to diabolic proportions. Simurgh scattered overhead. The Tetrarch struck right and left with his head, jaws closed; he trampled, taking care to tread on nobody, he reared and the rabble ran like rabbits. Only once did he pause, to put one heavy foot on the tail of the fleeing preacher's garment, while the man continued to run like a clockwork mouse on a polished floor, making no headway. He dropped his megaphone. The Tetrarch trod heavily on it with his other front foot, then raised that which held back the terrified orator, and watched him gain speed until he hit the cave wall. We were through the reception party, who were running up the walls of the cavern, and we were going like smoke into pitch darkness.

'Steady, it goes somewhere,' said the quiet voice of Thapsis. 'There's enough wind coming up to show that.'

The Tetrarch slowed, squinting up to make sure there were no low spots in the roof. In twenty minutes we were through, into a rocky defile. Thapsis doused the torch. 'Word travels fast in Hell,' he said. 'All that was because we sent those two youngsters back. You see, Adepts, what we have to deal with.'

Those Who Have Had Punishment Enough to Make Them Commit Crime

'Stop here,' said Thapsis. 'I want to talk to the troops.'

I halted the Tetrarch and felt in the saddlebag for a pineapple. He smelt it coming out, opened his mouth, and turned to munch. I could feel that he was pleased with himself but still thinking of lizard meat.

'Adepts,' said Thapsis, 'I apologize. I thought this was going to be a routine survey. I knew we should meet unfortunate and deluded people. I just hadn't thought the thing through. Now, I made certain promises to you, Eda and Rusana. Obviously, as an archimage I intend to keep them. Do we go back, or do we go on?'

'If we go on?' said Rosanna.

'There are up to seven more valleys after this – or on another view there may be only three or four: it depends if you agree with past travelers or with Charon – that they traveled in and out, not through, that is. Now on any basis of probability, the further we go, the more organized the immigrants: it stands to reason, the further from the start, the longer they'll have been here. It seems virtually certain that that means trouble.'

'You don't think,' said Rosanna, 'that they learn to cooperate?'

'Oh yes, I do think,' said Thapsis. 'It's what they cooperate in that worries me.'

'Charon said that really wicked people don't seem to come here,' said Rosanna.

'I know he did, and I wasn't about to start an argument about the nature of antisocial behavior. Dante thought people came here as a result of the passions. Your greatest Adept pointed out that they don't – "they are those who, having no passions of their own, because no intellect, have spent their lives in curbing and governing other peoples' by the various arts of poverty and cruelty." If he's right, and he may be, I don't fancy the prospect.'

'Verulans?' said Agrippa.

'Possibly worse – holy Verulans, who aren't hypocrites and believe in what they are doing.'

There was a long pause. Munch, munch, munch went the Tetrarch's jaws. I could see the sides of his face swell and subside at each jaw-closing.

'I'm game,' said Agrippa.

'I think we ought to go on,' said Rosanna. 'I'm terrified, after what you said, but I think we have to go on.'

'Edward?'

'Look, Thapsis, Agrippa's the one with most to lose. This is a dream for us,' I said, 'and one nightmare more or less makes no odds. It's Agrippa's vote.'

'I vote to go on,' said Agrippa. 'Dammit, when I was a soldier I didn't count on nine lives like a bloody cat – why now? You have to live with yourself.'

'Right, then,' said Thapsis. 'Proceed with caution – full four-man battle order, Colonel Eda. If it's any consolation, Faesto and Kari will have asvin on the ground here in one month, not three, and they're sending more simurgh, so we'll be in constant contact. Any other questions?'

I should explain that though asvaya are normally fought with one rider per beast, there are two, three and four-man battle orders arising from the asva's carrying capacity, four being the maximum: since Rosanna was light, we were still within the Tetrarch's three-man jumping capacity, but with four effectives. In this order the front rider sits well ahead and clear, with normal asvin sword, ankus and shield. The flaps of the saddlebags are turned up, like reversed chaps, to provide some protection for the three rear riders, who, having no reins to hold, can fight on either side, enclosed in a pod which is reasonably safe against sword strokes or asva bites. Of these, number two is usually unarmed and serves as commander – he is too close to the rider to be effective as a swordsman, and is protected by the mount from attacking mounts. Number three carries the asvin bow and aims to the left as a rule. Number four, in the rear gunner position, has the battle-ax, and aims at the oncoming rider after his stroke has missed. He can also strike at an attacking asva, which is virtually swordproof. Some rear men prefer the ankus in this situation.

My number two was, as it happened, Thapsis; my number three, Rosanna, who knew already how to use the asvin bow; my number four Agrippa. We did not need to change places. My only worry was that the asvin battle order is designed for use against similar armament. I doubted if there were asvin in Hell, but there might be bowmen; against any sort of infantry without firearms, I felt able to leave defense to the Tetrarch, and our operation was surely to be defensive. As a last resort, of course, we had the aegis. I took this in lieu of a normal asvin shield – its range is short, but at least in rocky country one wouldn't need to watch for reflecting surfaces and dangerous ricochets which make it such a tricky weapon in street fighting. I remember how, in Verula, that brief flash of its dying pattern as the strobes went out had nearly incapacitated me. I checked this one. The pin was in, the trigger free, and on the inside I noticed a label Mark III. I had lost track of the mark numbers since that first foray. 'This aegis,' I said to Thapsis, 'what is it? Killer, or crazy-making?'

'Oh, neither – it's nonlethal,' said Thapsis, 'unless the armorer made a boob, it's a straight Gorgon – produces catalepsy, about half-an-hour's duration. We don't let the first two marks out of Adambara. So you needn't be scared to use it.'

I checked that everyone was behind me, pulled the pin and then the trigger. I heard the iris snap open, and saw a faint play of light on the distant rocks. It was armed, and the strobes were working. That at least was in order. I returned it to safe.

'Wouldn't like to hurt these poor devils,' said Thapsis, 'and any crazy-making down here might start something serious. Are you ready to move?'

'Yes,' I said, 'but two more things. Agrippa, check the deep rear saddlebag. What's in it?'

He leaned over and fumbled.

'Helmets,' he said, after a while.

'How many?'

'Four.'

'Then issue them.' I blessed the training and foresight of the Adambara NCO who prepared the Tetrarch – four saddles, four-man order. We put them on.

'Secondly, who's in command?'

'Strategically, I am,' said Thapsis. 'Tactically, in action, you are. Agreed?'

'Agreed.'

And so, in military order, we moved off. Rosanna at number three had on her back the polished metal plate which serves the tail rider as a backward mirror. We were as armed as asvin could be, and better armed, I reflected, than our illustrious predecessors in the same dangerous country.

Simurgh flocks were moving overhead, and presently one of the birds dropped down, skimmed the ravine and came to hand. Thapsis read the message. 'Equivocal,' he said. 'They're still checking. Probably both of them were badly hurt. We'll have to leave it, Rosanna – in any case there wasn't more we could do.'

Soon after, another four simurghs arrived, in a lozenge formation, military birds no doubt, and settled on the four pommel perches where asvin carry their message eagles.

'We shall run out of dried fish,' said Thapsis. 'We'll have to put them up to hunt before long.'

The ravine fell steadily. We saw little sign of life. There were occasional immigrants to left and right among the boulders; most, it seemed, attempting to hide: none were moving purposively. We looked apprehensively for signs of organization. The first we saw was a Druidic-looking stone circle, built by rolling boulders into a ring. Nobody was about, nor was there any evidence of its purpose, but it must have involved a great deal of cooperative hard work. The stone of the walls which flanked the defile was pumicelike and soft. It began to bear graffiti – letters, names, hearts, the words 'A. F.: DEAD' cut in large letters like a fraternity slogan, the word MISERICORDIA, cuttings in scripts I could not read. There were no dates. Somebody had written 'HELL IS FOREVER' and next to it 'THIS WAY' and a pointing finger. These evidences were oppressive, the more so as there were no lost souls around to explain them. We were clearly headed into something. The simurghs fidgeted and settled down to sleep. The only interruption came when the Tetrarch suddenly paused in his measured tread, made an uncontrollable dive with his jaws and picked up step again. The head and tail of a hyasa protruded on the two sides of his mouth.

'Trust him,' said Agrippa, 'to find one here.' I had no stomach for the Tetrarch's saurophagy and had to endure the crunching of lizard bones for some minutes. Moreover when we stopped, the Tetrarch refused a pineapple. I hoped he would not go on strike.

Early afternoon we struck black sand and immense numbers of footprints, also rags of cloth, pieces of paper and refuse of other kinds. The defile widened ahead, and round the next bend we confronted an earthly-looking image. It might have been a bad copy of Mayan. A large boulder which occupied the middle of the defile had been carved. The carvers had used a fair amount of skill, incorporating the bubbles and cavities of the black pumice into their design, and in fact, rather emphasizing a shape which had been there fortuitously than cutting one from scratch. It was a crouching, bearded figure, crowned, and holding a sword in one hand, a little like a pre-Columbian King of Spades, except that his left hand held a pair of scales. Ill-defined human figures were falling from one pan of these into a pair of what appeared to be jaws. The whole thing was roughly executed but alarming enough to us, and probably more so to immigrants. In front of the figure were four black stone posts, whittled down like boulders, and inscribed.

'Minos,' said Thapsis, 'and the four pillars of tyranny. Somebody took a lot of trouble. It looks like a manifesto.'

The defile wound. It was never possible to see far ahead. About a hundred yards beyond King Minos, the Tetrarch slowed and on his own initiative moved to the left side of the canyon, almost pressing against the rock wall. Then with infinite craft he inserted himself between two rocks which just contained him, like a locomotive in a station platform, stopped smoothly and looked back for orders.

The canyon ahead was full of the immigrants, a couple of hundred of them. A small group, like a court or a committee, were sitting on a longish boulder, before which were three more posts – of wood, this time. Attached to the posts, faces to the wood and hands over heads, were three prisoners – two men and a woman.

'Here it is,' said Thapsis. 'Human sacrifice?'

'No, kangaroo court,' muttered Agrippa. 'How do we handle this one?'

'We sit tight,' said Thapsis, 'in a state of vigilant readiness. There are two objectives – to get through, and to stop any excesses if we can. By the Four, listen to them!'

The uproar was diabolical – booing, chanting, shouting and, on the rare occasions when that died down, a high-pitched and apparently ritual harangue by one of the guardians of morality on top of the rock – it could have been a sermon, a long-winded judicial sentence or a mixture of both.

'Think fast,' said Thapsis. 'There's a bastard there with a whip. What's the scenario?'

'Man and woman caught reviving the intimacies of normal life, other man guilty of aiding and abetting?' I said.

'Or something like it. Plan of action?'

'They expect the Devil incarnate. The Tetrarch will do for that. On the word of command, all yell like fiends and charge, cut those three loose, spread confusion, try to cut them out of the herd, then about turn and up aegis, to give them a chance to get away?'

'Good thinking,' said Thapsis. The harangue finished and a howl went up. The character with the whip came forward to an enthusiastic reception and rolled up what remained of filthy sleeves. He took station behind the prisoners and looked round for room. Failing to get it, he simply laid about him until the crowd fell back. The lash was a diabolical thing like a stock whip, long enough to strike all three victims simultaneously. He prepared with evident relish for the first swipe.

'In five,' I said. 'I'm going to have to take the whip, Thapsis.'

'If you have to.'

'Four, three, two, one – go.'

The Tetrarch was into the crowd and going at full speed before they so much as saw us. The whip landed once, and the crowd began to count aloud. Our conjoined yells were lost in the row, but not the whinny of the Tetrarch as he went down among them. This time he was less careful – I saw figures fly in all directions. Yells of self-righteous satisfaction turned to screams of terror. He circled the three whipping posts, spun and kicked once, and I heard the volunteer executioner hit the rock wall twenty feet away. The Tetrarch eased in to each post in turn, and I leaned out of the saddle and cut the ropes. Luckily none of the prisoners fell. Instead they stumbled off in roughly the same direction. The bulk of the crowd had headed for the sides of the canyon. Only the nasal orator on top of the rock stood his ground. I put the Tetrarch straight at him. We cleared his rostrum, and he fell off on the far side and rolled into a crevice. The Tetrarch spun neatly, repeated his leap and returned to circle the three prisoners; without prompting he took out the three posts with three consecutive rear right hooks, snap, snap, snap. Then he picked up the last in his jaws and threw it after the mob. The three prisoners were running now. I crossed to and fro behind them, to avoid heading them off. As soon as they were clear and a space opened between them and the nearest of the righteous, I turned the Tetrarch, raised the aegis and fired. The mob froze like sprayed ants. I gave them a second burst, snapped the iris to safe, let the Tetrarch do some rearing and yelling, which I felt he had earned, and put him at speed down the far side of the canyon from the three victims, who, I was pleased to see, had not stopped to contemplate the effects of the aegis, but were running for their lives.

'One dead, two or three wounded,' I said over my shoulder. 'We couldn't have done less.'

'Two dead,' said Agrippa. 'I got one of the judiciary with the battle-ax.'

'That,' said Thapsis, 'was unnecessary.' We were well away down the defile. There was no pursuit and no sign of further political organization ahead.

'You were right,' said Rosanna to Thapsis.

'Yes, but we can't keep playing St George,' I said. 'I suggest we ride at night and go as fast as possible. The next lot may be waiting for us – so long as they think we're devils, we can have the jump on them, but someone may try to see if we're arrow-proof.'

'I hate to mention it,' said Agrippa, 'but they may do that sooner than you think. There's a man with a bow standing on that rock.'

He was a tall figure, shading his eyes with his hand. He wore a buffalo-skin cloak, the horns forming a headdress. He carried a spear decorated along its shaft with eagle feathers. As we watched he jumped down and sauntered towards us. On his back was his bow.

'Hold your fire,' said Thapsis. 'That's not one of them.'

The walking man raised his hand. 'Greetings. You come in peace?'

'Yes, Adept. And you?'

'In peace,' said the man. 'Of what people are you?'

'Losians,' said Thapsis.

'I do not know that people. I am of the Sioux.'

He stood there, looking us over. 'You bring a woman with you?' he said. 'That is strange. This is bad country. Twice I have died here.'

'How did you reach this place?' said Thapsis.

'I danced,' said the shaman.

'You have a reason for coming, warrior?' said Thapsis.

'I come to fetch back my wife. Have you seen her?'

'There are many people here – this is a large territory,' said Thapsis.

'You passed many people?'

'Many. They fought with us,' said Thapsis.

'And you come with the spirit beast?'

'Yes. Two days' journey behind us, we crossed the river – we in a great canoe. The beast swam,' said Thapsis.

'That was the way she came,' said the shaman. 'So I will follow your trail, and I will meet her coming.'

'Tell him the others won't let him take anyone out of here,' said Agrippa. 'He can't tackle that bunch single-handed.'

'I hear what you say, bearded man,' said the shaman. 'If I find her, as I shall, they will find that I am strong. We will see whose singing and dancing is the stronger, theirs or mine. I have the feelings that this is the first time you have come here. Who taught you the dances?'

'We had a different way of making the journey,' said Rosanna.

'There are other ways,' said the Sioux, 'but it is dangerous if you do not know the dances. I first dreamed them when I was a child. No man of my people has been here more often than I. And I am now about to bring back my own wife, who is dying bearing my child. Five others I have brought back, so I think my dance is a good one. Twice only have I died here. That is a good record.'

'Will you eat with us, warrior?' said Thapsis.

'If I do not fast, how can I dance?'

He hitched his bow on his shoulder. 'That beast – it is neither a horse nor a buffalo. What is its name?'

'It's an asva,' said Thapsis.

'That is good,' said the Indian. 'I have dreamed of it but I did not know what it was called. Whom do you come to bring back?'

'Only ourselves,' said Thapsis.

'That is a strange journey,' said the shaman, 'to come here when you are not looking for anyone. It is good to meet with other Adepts. I will go now. If I can reach the plain before she does, it will be all the easier.'

'Do you know what lies this way, since you've been here before?' said Thapsis.

'No. It is my practice when I come here to meet the person I seek at the way down into the valley.'

'Do many of your people come here as you do?'

'Some. But none so often as I. They do not dance as I dance. Good hunting.'

And he set off, not seeming to hurry, but with a steady watchful gait which covered the ground with the economy of the Tetrarch's own speed. As he went he chanted loudly to himself.

'So much,' said Thapsis, 'for Dante. We went to the wrong place for information. I never thought of coming here by dancing. That Adept comes when he wishes. He has died here twice, he says. You two should forget all about the Game of the Adepts, go home and get some practical instruction from someone who has a really advanced technology. That man was never in the Fourfold City. Not even Tjurip has been here, unless he's keeping quiet about it. We need four Adepts and an asva – a real shaman dances and he's here.'

'We have to come,' said Agrippa, 'in the way which is open to us. Exactly as we see what we expect to see. I wonder how he accounts for the antics of the European damned. Let's press on in our own manner. That warrior can look after himself better than we can.'

9

To Be the Sport of Accident

At evening the cloud deck lifted. There was an elaborate red sunset. As we had ridden in military order, so now we bivouacked in the same way, going part-way up the left slope of the now much wider valley and settling on a level patch where we might possibly be besieged but could neither be surprised nor descended upon from above. The scenery was wild, and would have been fine if we had not been conscious of what was behind and what was probably in front. The Tetrarch was our main guard, but we agreed to set watch. We cooked on a smokeless military fire hidden in a rock gully. Thapsis fidgeted, sent off a simurgh while light lasted and kept reckoning how long it would take for the asvin to arrive.

'They'll have to cross to Beulah in boats,' he was saying. 'I've doubled the detail – probably will need more still. I wish I knew what support services to requisition. We shall have to clean this place up once and for all.'

'Why didn't you do it before?' said Rosanna.

'Before?'

'Hell's as old as human ignorance. You knew about it. You obviously had a good idea what went on here. Apparently it was far worse in the past, when people took self-torture for granted. And the Losian world did absolutely nothing.'

Thapsis sat with his chin on his fist. 'Yes,' he said, 'but there are things that I don't think are clear to you. The nature of Losian time is one – you still think about history; what goes on here is outside history. On the other hand there is ongoing change, and we will be acting in the fullness of time. Urizen's world is setting, on Your Side – so we have degrees of freedom which Dante, or Milton, or the shamans, didn't

330

have. The source of damnation is on Your Side, not Ours, and you can see for yourselves that the supply of immigrants who arrive here is drying up. We don't control the Time of Choice – we do control the thought forms which people, and parts of people, enact on Our Side.'

'But now you're about to move in with troops, like gangbusters, and clean up this venerable religious institution,' said Agrippa.

'When the Four were still at odds, we couldn't. Before the Four became separated, there was no need. This marks a stage of the putting-together,' said Thapsis.

I asked Rosanna afterwards if that satisfied her.

'I see what it means,' she said. 'People used to think Hell would be a casualty of science, but all that happened was that we started acting it out on Our Side as well as here. I think he means that now the other Three are getting the upper hand again on Our Side, or are about to do so, so we get balanced people, who move equally well in all the Four Worlds down here.'

'All of which leaves us still with a pretty hairy undertaking,' I said.

'But worth it, if it helps that along – or gets us ready to be part of it. Why do you think we play this Adept game?' said Rosanna.

'There's one thing,' I said. 'I know how you feel about anyone in trouble, Ros, but today has to be the last time we intervene. In Verula we held off until we got back to base, and then did what we could to stop any more atrocities. We just have to do that here. Inferior benevolence could blow the whole thing.'

'I know,' said Rosanna.

'This bunch will use it to trap us.'

'Are we playing it,' said Rosanna, 'by imagination and love, like Thapsis said, or by the book?'

'By the book first,' I said, 'so that the real change has a chance.'

'It has more than a chance,' she said. 'Hell's suddenly got trivial. It's the only trivial part we've seen on This Side. Beulah was limited but it wasn't trivial – one moves through it, grows and comes back to it. The point about Hell was that it was nastiness seen as a deserved dead end. Turn it into Purgatory and it's a sadhana, it goes somewhere, and it stops being trivial again.'

'I wonder if the Losians will handle it like that,' I said. 'Thapsis still thinks one can talk these people down by telling them they're mistaken.'

'If that doesn't work,' said Rosanna, 'other people will have to try. You'd better sleep now – it's your next watch. And it's a time for knowing rather than loving, so far as I'm concerned.'

I felt the same. Agrippa shook me three hours later and took my place, while I took his, on a boulder above the flat where we were camped. It was less cold here, there was the same moon which shone on Beulah, but it was small and seemed to take no interest in us, unlike the huge, warm Tharmian moon. The refugees would have no fellow-feeling with it.

After breaking camp we followed a track in the middle of the widening valley. The sky was dead gray again with drizzle. We were coming down onto the next step of the plateau. Once more the cracks and the glimpses into corries and canyons appeared in the flat strata. We saw no people, but we began to see posts bearing signs, illegible with age, and finally posts bearing skulls, the typical markers of prohibited land in Verula. Here there were no minefields, however – the prohibition seemed to be a general one against settlement, and it had been observed. I thought I saw a hurrying party moving parallel to our left, but it went out of sight behind rocks and we did not see it again.

Mountains were beginning to close in on our right. We could see nothing of them but their feet, for the tops were in cloud. The valley sides closed in again. Fine cold mist started to blow back at us, the sides soared higher and higher, and we began to feel first, and then to hear, a machinerylike roaring in the ground.

'Waterfall,' said Agrippa. 'Now, are we at the top or at the bottom? There's no river.'

We were in fact in the middle. We came out upon a

roundish pad of wet vegetation stuck like a bracket to the side of the valley. In front was a humming black curtain streaked with froth. Its top was hidden in mist and in its own spray, but its height must have been vast. It landed in a boiling pool of foam, filled with logs and trash which surfaced and sank like vegetables in a stew, then spilled over into a second fall which descended into a dark, twisting crack. Everything was soaking, the grassy pad vibrated as if it were about to become detached and follow the riverborne trash down into the gorge, and from it, to our right, a slippery track wound up into the cloud. At its foot sat a defeated-looking group of walkers. We called to them, but they scattered, climbing over the edges of the pad onto the slopes above the gorge, where the asva could not follow.

'Up,' said Thapsis. 'There's obviously nowhere else we can go.'

At noon we were still climbing into impenetrable fog. It grew colder and colder. We seemed to be off the cliff face. Snow patches appeared, then dirty snowfields, then a continuous fog-covered grounding of snow on which the Tetrarch's feet crunched. He appeared puzzled by it. He had never seen snow before. As it grew deeper, he stamped to free his feet. All the time, although we were wholly alone in the mist circle, we glimpsed movement parallel to our own, saw rocks which moved, heard coughing. We could have been in the middle of flocks of sheep. As it grew dark the mist dropped below us, and we were crossing snowfields in a rounded valley. Some of the moving rocks had come to rest, others were still moving. There was no sign of firewood. The snow was slowing the Tetrarch's pace – I had to dismount every hour to clear the snowballs from his leg feathers. And yet, though miserably uncomfortable, we were not dangerously cold. I spoke to Thapsis about this – it struck me that we might be experiencing one of the hallucinations which precede death from heat loss.

'Take a look inside your asvin cloak,' he said. An asvin cloak is woven of a kind of grayish-black duffle and lined with something which looks like suede, but is manmade. I peered inside the flap of mine. The suedelike material had gone, and was replaced by what looked like bear fur. My asvin gloves felt bulkier than usual.

'Clever idea,' said Thapsis. 'I'm glad the armorer insisted we bring them.' It seemed that the fibers made by Adambaran spinners lengthen with cold. At least we were not going to freeze.

For a while, under moonlight, it was still. We passed ground glass areas clear of snow, from which boulders protruded like frozen-in heads.

'Do we stop?' said Thapsis.

'No,' I said, 'keep going and count ourselves lucky. It must blow here at gale force, or those lakes would be snowed.' The Tetrarch had struck harder snow, and his pace quickened. We reached an almost snow-free crack between two irregular gendarmes which seemed to mark the head of the pass and began to go down. As we rounded the bend I saw a small avalanche of people converging on us, first silently, then shouting and finally screaming. The Tetrarch left them behind.

'Why do they still go on?' said Rosanna. 'Why didn't they stay in the valleys?'

I told her that I thought we had seen some of the reasons before we reached the waterfall.

'The ones who press on may be the decent ones,' she said. I had a different picture, however: the constant forward pressure of immigrants less and less human as their sojourn became longer. We reentered mist and saw no more of them, and as we did so, we heard the wind break loose overhead. Where we were, sheltered between cliffs, it only caused the fog to roll over and over in vast eddies, but we could hear the thundering of wind overhead and catch glimpses of flying scud.

'They won't any of them make it over,' said Rosanna. The Tetrarch checked and screamed, and a snow verra flashed from behind one rock and away behind another to emphasize her point.

'This must be just about the end of the journey,' said Agrippa. 'The Empty Quarter absorbs the inflow by killing them off in the mountains. That's why it's empty.'

'I think not,' said Thapsis. 'Some, certainly, but not all. Or they may find a way round which we missed.'

And indeed, when day broke and we were down into rainy forests of enormous, canelike plants where conifers would have stood in a terrestrial landscape, there were tracks, rags, even abandoned huts, several of which appeared to have been burned to the ground. Later we saw three skeletons, tidily impaled on pointed shoots of the canes, then more admonitory skulls on posts. Someone was preventing settlement even in this dismal and inhospitable area. As we came lower, the canes thinned. There were two tracks here, one on each side of the valley, and we had taken that which by chance turned out to be the lesser. It was also the better wooded with the shining black canes, so that we saw the other only intermittently, and could not be seen from it.

'Look,' said Agrippa.

The other track was about a mile off, and we could see a stretch of perhaps one hundred yards, separated from us by the valley, and somewhat above us. Along this, someone was running for his life. I reined the Tetrarch. He disappeared from view. For a full half-minute nothing happened, and then two verras bounded into view, crossed the open space, and vanished after him. Close behind them came three other running figures.

'We can't intervene,' said Thapsis. 'They're out of range. Proceed with caution – there may be more of them.'

We did so. About three miles on, the other road came in view again. On it a party of figures stood waiting. They carried spears made of the black cane wood, and our cover gave out exactly opposite to them. It was necessary, if we wanted to avoid attention, to wait for them to go.

For an hour we stood, with the Tetrarch steaming, Agrippa watching our rear and I our front, with all arms at the ready. Then we saw movement in the party, and the two verras broke cover. They were trotting side-by-side on the leash. Behind came a walking man, and behind him two others, carrying between them another, the fugitive probably, lashed to a pole like a dead stag. The entire detachment set off parallel with us. We could hear shouts and laughter. We gave them another half-hour, and then resumed our march. The second road, when next the opposite valley slope appeared, had left us. We saw nobody else on our descent. Soon we were back on stony, level ground. Behind us were the feet of the mountains we had crossed. Every few hundred yards there would be a boulder on which was scratched an arrow pointing forward, and on top of each boulder was a skull, emphasizing the point of the injunction. It seemed that the area was well policed.

At noon it became clear that a change of landscape lay ahead – there was nothing in front of us but the gray sandy light, and with a certain inevitability the Tetrarch stopped at the lip of yet another huge rock-walled bowl. It was twice as wide as the last, the far cliffs being hazed and barely distinguishable in detail. We could see another falling spiral track which touched down to our left on the sunken plain, ran a mile or so and then vanished into a huge expanse of lines, perimeters, blocks of what appeared to be buildings and moving dots of inhabitants. The settlement had none of the compactness of a city. I had seen others like it.

'Glasses,' said Agrippa, and he proceeded to study its detail.

On the outer perimeter, which was some kind of fence, I could see watch towers on legs.

'What is that stuff, Agrippa? It can't be wire.'

'No,' he said, 'thorns. About twenty feet high and twenty feet thick, then a ditch with more thorns in it, then another fence.'

'Do we go down, Thapsis?'

'No. We follow the lip,' said Thapsis.

'I'm glad you agree. That's a concentration camp. Run, no doubt, on the same principle as the prison. That was a test run. This is the real thing. It must be five or six miles across if it's a yard.'

'Can you see who are in the guard towers, Agrippa?' said Thapsis.

'No, but somebody is.'

'Any uniforms?'

'They all look alike to me, inside and out.'

We set off in silence to outflank the menacing plain. Under us the lines of thorn fence rotated slowly. There was only one larger building – hutments were packed into the corners of some of the compounds, a few with smoking chimneys, but at one point only an unsightly square bunker was rising; it was uncompleted, for we could see working parties lugging boulders towards it, and a makeshift ramp ran up its side. As it came abreast, we could see that it was the base and first two stages of a ziggurat, or stepped pyramid.

The edge of the cliff was fortunately double, with a lower ring of bluffs behind it. We could traverse without being silhouetted. Opposite us a far steeper footpath ran up to the clifftop from the valley floor, plaited like a cornice, and then ascended into mountains to our right which were high enough to have timber on them and then snow. Agrippa scanned them with the glasses. 'More huts up there,' he said. 'Another labor camp. The punishment detail presumably cuts timber above snowline.'

'I think,' said Thapsis, 'that we have seen all the circles of Hell. There may be similar things going on in some of those corries we passed; I don't think we need document everything.'

We spoke little after that – sound carried in that great basin: we could hear occasional outcries, whether of people or of animals was unclear. Most of the time there was silence. Agrippa scanned with the glasses.

'They've got a couple of gallows down there,' he remarked at one point. When night fell, bonfires were lit at intervals round the perimeter fences. Rosanna thought she could hear dogs, or verra, below us. After moonrise we turned slightly away from the lip of the lowest circle, as the screening bluffs gave out. The plateau was rough and bushy, with flat stones like roof tiles. Once or twice the Tetrarch jumped wide fissures in it, running into the circle below. He had settled to his steady pace of travel.

Dawn found us moving steadily upwards in driving rain, climbing step after step of the plateau, away from the amphitheater of rock. The summit was a low ridge, and as we went along it we saw, through a gap in the lower ranges, a much deeper plain far below us, with rainsqualls and sun patches moving on it, and spread on its surface the square garden plots of the industrious Luvians. We were coming to the end of the Empty Quarter, returning to the World of the Four. We saw no further refugees. Evidently Charon had been right. There were no deeper circles, and the traditional journey on had been in fact a journey back.

'I think,' said Thapsis, 'that we are on the right road.' We were in fact on no road at all, but the country was passable. All next day we dropped down through rocks and forest in unceasing rain. This was the watershed which feeds the warm rivers going down into the reeds of Beulah. Tall canes began to appear. At our evening stop I cut a number of these, and with the two spare asvin blankets I equipped the Tetrarch, to his disgust, with large batlike false wings, which were attached to the two pommels of Thapsis's saddle, and could be opened like oars. I wanted to increase his diabolical appearance should we encounter more of the inhabitants. As we remounted in the dark, Agrippa drew my attention to a light winking on a peak behind us. Somebody was signaling to somebody. I hoped that the message had no reference to us.

Dawn came up sunny for a wonder, the country was gentler, the air warmer and the ground under us formed itself into a semblance of a road. There was one more defile ahead, which steamed as we entered it. This looked like the exit. We passed between its sides, the track winding along its bottom beside a stream which ran to the Luvian side.

We were about a mile down when the Tetrarch registered. His ears went up. We stopped. As we did so, somebody hidden by the rocks ahead gave a distinct cough.

The Tetrarch underwent a change. From a tall, camellike profile of huge legs and soaring neck, he flattened, as I had never seen an asva flatten. His sloping back became a straight line, from head to rump, parallel with the ground. In this attitude he moved stealthily forward, looking for a vantage point between rocks, and slid into it.

We were looking slightly down on the next fold of the valley. On a flat rock beside the track a tableau was waiting, quite motionless. A woman was kneeling on the rock edge, head to knees and hands to heels. Behind her stood a headsman with a sword, and behind him a small group of the inhabitants of Hell. They were all clearly waiting, their eyes fixed on the track where we were due to appear. If we had followed it, we should have seen only the tableau. From where we were we could also see that most of the rocks flanking the valley had bowmen behind them. Moreover there was no way around the reception committee.

'We have been indiscreet,' said Agrippa. 'There's the bait.'

'What now, Thapsis?'

'Yell and raise the aegis?' said Thapsis.

The range was too long. The aegis did not have the range of the bows.

'We'd be safer on the track,' I said. 'If we charge, we're a hard target forward, unless they get the Tetrarch in the eye. This aegis is a solid shield, and in battle order they may not damage us much. Then we can open the iris and go through.'

'The way they are placed,' said Agrippa, 'we can aegis the ambush, or the execution party, but not both.'

'I'm looking,' said Agrippa, 'at those bows. They're pretty clumsy. The rate of fire and re-aim won't be anything like a longbow. If half of them were shooting at something else, they'd be in aegis range before they could get off another round. There are only five of them, and the woman, on that rock. We'll use their bait on them. Sit that asva and let me off. I'm going down.'

'Are you out of your mind?' said Thapsis.

'Completely,' said Agrippa, 'and I now claim command as senior Adept here after you. Give me a count of a hundred, then get the asva as far down as you can without drawing fire. As soon as you see them open fire, up aegis and go like the devil. Those wings will help confuse the target, and the aegis should get most of them. Understood?'

'And what about you?' said Rosanna.

'You halt as soon as it's safe and I'll rendezvous.'

'If anyone tries to draw fire,' I said, 'it had better be me, Agrippa, not you. If I'm hit, no serious harm is done.'

'Leaving nobody,' said Agrippa, 'who can manage an asva. Be your age. Also, I'm going to get that girl. She reminds me of somebody. Now, give me the asva bow and let's get on with it before they send out scouts.'

'Are you sure you know what you are doing?' said Thapsis.

'Dead sure, Adept. Rosanna, my dear – Blood Brother – see you at rendezvous.' Rosanna handed him the asva bow, and they touched hands. He slipped off the Tetrarch's back. 'Watch me down to that rock, then start the count,' he said, and he was gone. A few moments later we saw him peer over the rock. Thapsis began to count. On the hundred I backed the still-flattened Tetrarch onto the track and took him down as quietly as possible to the turn of the road where the fire of the ambush would converge. Stopped in the lee of the rock which screened it, he raised his back slowly, like a forklift, bringing me level with a notch in the stone. I alone could see what happened. None of us spoke.

The tableau on the rock remained motionless. Then, suddenly, one of the group of infernal officials keeled over and fell from his perch. I heard a suppressed gasp in the valley. The others turned. Then one after another they stumbled or rolled in different directions as Agrippa picked them off. The headsman raised his sword, and a yellow streak passed bodily through him, spilling him into the stream, where he lay face down. There was a full half-minute pause. Then Agrippa sprang on the rock, cut the woman's bonds and pushed her bodily over the edge into cover. Arrows transfixed him from every side like a squall of horizontal rain, and he went over the edge after her. The Tetrarch shot forward. Behind me the ragged wings went up like sails. I pulled the pin and trigger and held the aegis high, sweeping it back and forth towards the unmasked firing positions. Arrows flew past, hitting the aegis and the leather sides of the combat pod. I could not see where we were going, for the aegis and the Tetrarch's head were in front of me. I saw arrow feathers protruding from the wings as we went. Then Thapsis prudently jettisoned them, as they were slowing the Tetrarch, and we were out of range.

'Anyone hit?' I said.

'No,' said Thapsis.

'He meant to finish it,' said Rosanna, 'and he got the woman before they fired.'

'What he said made sense, Rosanna,' I said. 'There was no way any of us could have done it.'

'I might have,' said Rosanna.

'We weren't going to be able to find a solution to his situation,' I said, 'and he preferred to go with style.'

'But *he* found it,' said Thapsis. 'He transcended selfhood. Is that the object of sadhana or isn't it?'

'And we don't know he was hit,' I said. 'With arrows one can't ever tell – they always seem to go through the target, even when they miss. We halt for rendezvous.'

So we wheeled and halted, in a secure spot, covering our rear with the aegis. Nothing moved on the track. Rosanna was staring dry-eyed in the direction from which we had come.

Time passed, the sun declined. I reckoned we had waited four hours. We passed rations and ate in silence. Suddenly the Tetrarch raised his ears. Below us, coming the other way, there was a steady vibration, then the rattle of claws and the jingle of equipment. I backed him into the rocks, aegis at the ready.

'Asvin,' said Thapsis. 'They can't be ours, they can't be hostiles – there are no asvaya . . .'

They came in sight, asvin in squadron, riding three abreast. But they were not the helmeted asvin of Adambara. They wore blue fatigues, they carried crossbows, their guidon was red with a yellow star. Behind the first squadron came three covered carts drawn by the fast-stepping Luvian bulls, and filled with more blue infantry, then more asvin. I lowered the aegis, rode out and raised my hand. The column halted.

'Advance and be recognized,' someone called.

'I am Colonel Eda, of the Losian asvin.'

'Greetings, Comrade,' said the guidon cornet. 'Cornet Li, First Luvian Mounted Militia. What in the name of the Four are you doing here?'

'We rode through from Beulah,' I said.

10

Arrows Shot by Troops of Destiny

He obviously neither believed me nor knew what to do. Then Staff came up at the gallop, an adjutant and a major general. We repeated our story.

'Regrets, Colonel,' said the major general. 'I have to disarm you. This is hostile country, you know.'

'Certainly, comrade officer. I compliment you on your vigilance. And if you don't want to be shot full of arrows you'll deploy now. We hit an ambush about an hour ahead. We got through with this aegis, but they'll have got their head together by now and they may be after us.'

He shouted orders in Luvian, and infantry with crossbows piled out to occupy the rocks on the slopes overlooking the road. I handed over our weapons.

'We lost one man. He bravely drew fire to get us through,' I said. 'Keep an eye open, will you, and don't shoot him if he shows – he's probably wounded. Bearded man, wearing asvin uniform.'

The officer looked us over. 'You look all in,' he said. 'I am Major Wen. The woman too rode through with you?'

'Of course,' said Rosanna.

'You and the man who fell are heroes worthy of the masses. Stay here, and our commissary will look after you. We're going on to clear the pass. Cavalry, forward.'

And off they went. We dismounted from the Tetrarch. Luvian women in blue fatigues ran up a tent and placed us in it. Rice and vegetables were brought. They surrounded Rosanna, asking questions, but her mind was on Agrippa.

It was dark before the adjutant got back. He stood in the tent flap and saluted with the formality of the Luvians. 'Comrades,' he said, 'we found five dead bandits but no dead Losians. He must have fallen in the river. We set up the Hammer and the Star of Luvah and buried him in spirit. We also found a frightened woman. There were many stunned bowmen, and these we took prisoner.' And he about-faced.

'That doesn't surprise me,' said Thapsis. 'I had a feeling they'd not find a body.'

At breakfast the time came for diplomacy. Wen and his squadron had gone on up the pass, but staff kept arriving, a command headquarters had gone up overnight, and after reveille we were all ushered into a rather spartan mess to exchange courtesies with the General, Wei Po-yang. The Luvians were mostly, but not all, Asians by origin – I saw black, European and Losian-looking faces, but the officer corps was solid. Wei was a balding, genial, middle-aged man who congratulated us on our achievement, condoled and saluted our presumed casualty, treated Rosanna as a fellow officer, and then, as soon as the food was cleared, got down to business. I noticed that the Luvians used ducks, not simurgh, for message carrying. They are actually faster. I only hoped they wouldn't tangle with our simurgh when those arrived. We were thankful for our Adept rings – Luvian (no relation to the Hittite language of that name on Our Side) is intelligibly like Losian, at least as it is taught in Adambara, but since the Adambaran books were written, it had acquired a heavy injection of Chinese, and Thapsis gave up trying to dispense with his ring after a few minutes.

'Our orders,' said Wei, 'are to go in and clean up this whole area. It is a disgrace to the Fourfold World that these miserable people have not been taken in hand. We think that the historical moment has come.'

'We entirely agree,' said Thapsis. 'That's what we were doing here. Losian asvin are on their way.'

'We shall welcome them as comrades,' said Wei, 'but if I may say so, have you not lost your opportunity? We, as you know, have had much to do in our own region – you, on the other hand, have had the benefit of great prosperity, which you used in a praiseworthy pursuit of learning. But you could have acted at any time in the last millennium. You had the resources.'

'But General, you said yourself that the time has only now become ripe. What we do depends on thinking patterns on the Other Side.'

Wei grinned. 'And those, I'm delighted to say, are changing. They are acquiring a more Luvian cast. Anyhow we need not dispute. We are allies to supersede the unopposed rule of Urizen, and to put new words into the human vocabulary – we, Brotherhood; you, Imagination.' We joined hands fourfold, I was relieved to see. The Luvians looked doctrinaire to me in a familiar and unwelcome fashion. I was glad that they retained respect for the Tessaract.

'The question remains,' said Wei, 'how far your asvin intend to advance. Some kind of permanent arrangement will be necessary. Are you empowered to negotiate?'

'Oh, yes,' said Thapsis, 'Fully – and you?'

'Well, subject to our Central Committee.'

'Then suppose we form a joint administration? To give these immigrants the benefit of both approaches?'

'I think,' said Wei, 'we would prefer parallel experiments. You can have the upper two circles – that's where the intake is. We will in that case retain the lower circle, the hard core. It is our belief that these people are not ready for the approach via Imagination. One doesn't know what they'll imagine. Now Brotherhood is an easier idea. They believe in austerity – we turn it from self-punishment to concern for the wrongs of others. We have not been able to afford some of the intellectual luxuries of your approach. I mean no offense.'

'Of course not,' said Thapsis.

'Then I will offer that suggestion. Message bird, please.'

'We know, Brother Wei,' said Thapsis, 'that you have a great deal of work to do at home. Wouldn't you like us to take this whole problem off your hands?'

'It is indeed generous to suggest it,' said Wei, 'but we cannot so easily lay aside our responsibilities. And also we don't think you can do it. We can.'

'We dealt with Verula,' said Thapsis.

'Indeed you did – after it had been festering for millennia

on your doorstep,' said Wei. 'If you forgive the comparison, you and the Verulans could deal with one another, for both were elitists – good and evil elitists – you recognize I use good and evil in a colloquial sense? These folk are not Adepts. Peasants can talk best to them. Hell was long the condition of peasants.' And he dispatched the duck.

'So it boils down to this,' said Rosanna, when we bowed out, 'who can reform whom?'

'Both of us probably can,' said Thapsis.

'I meant,' said Rosanna, 'whether the Luvians teach these folk Brotherhood, or whether Hell evangelizes Luvia in reverse. It won't take much passion for equality to legitimize leaving Hell exactly as it is, unless the rest of the Four are there too; Los in particular.'

'It would seem,' said Thapsis, 'that that depends greatly on what occurs on Your Side. Which is why visits such as yours are of great importance.'

'Agrippa knew,' said Rosanna.

'Precisely. There will be two statues – one in Adambara to the Great Adept who annihilated selfhood, and one in the Luvian capital to the people's hero who also annihilated selfhood. I hear Agrippa chuckle. You see, the same thing means different things to different people.'

'It certainly does,' I said. 'Look who's here.'

We were returning to our quarters through a great deal of Luvian pandemonium – carts arriving, officers riding about on asvaya, field kitchens. In the middle of it all was the shaman. He was walking briskly down the middle of the track, and behind him was a young Sioux woman carrying her baby. The Luvians took absolutely no notice of him.

'See,' he said, 'I have both – my wife and my son also.'

'We're delighted for you,' said Thapsis. 'Did you have to fight?'

'Spirits and devils attacked me,' said the Indian, 'but my singing and my paint broke all their arrows, and I shot many with my medicine bow. You are a brave man but foolish, coming here with no songs and not properly painted. I hope you return to your home in peace.'

'How did you get over the mountains?' I asked.

'We saw no mountains,' said the Indian. 'We came by the water which roars. There is a path.'

'What do you do now?' said Rosanna.

'She must leave spirit ground and bathe in the river – then I will dance, and we will go home.'

'You said that she was dying in labor?' said Rosanna.

'I said so. Her spirit had departed from her, the child's also. So I came to fetch them both back. Now all will be well.'

'But . . .' began Rosanna.

'How can they live, if their spirits have run away?' He looked incuriously at the Luvian camp. 'I have not seen these warrior spirits here before,' he said. 'Travel well.' The family moved off.

'We seem to have been getting it wrong,' said Rosanna.

'Possibly,' said Thapsis, 'it's a different view of medicine, lady. We say, cure her and her "spirit", as our Sioux friend calls it, can return: he says, bring her spirit back and she will recover. I don't think that would have helped Agrippa, if that is what you are thinking. In fact, what happened was the best thing that could have happened. Any Adept who sorts out the self-illusion has no more need of this dream-world of ours – or of yours.'

'You brought him on purpose, Thapsis,' said Rosanna.

'But I'd no idea how far he would get. Now don't waste your regrets, Rosanna. You made this possible, remember.'

'By coming on this journey, so that he would come?' she said.

'No, of course not. By helping him turn out Theotormon and teaching him to get rid of jealousy. Why do you think he hung on like that? Now don't cry – you give other people more insight than you've got yourself – that's a penalty of being a great initiatrix. Listen – you loved Agrippa, all loves are for a time only, they are what they are and they are good in themselves – the "ever after" bit belongs with the illusion of time, and that's built into the illusion of self. He got rid of the illusion of self, and when you feel better about it you can start on the illusion of time. You know the answers, really, and you give them out to other people, but you haven't entirely mastered them yourself.'

Rosanna wiped her eyes.

'The sad thing was, his two women knew all this but couldn't get through to him. It took you to do that, Rosanna my dear.'

I wished Thapsis would desist from delivering graveside addresses – I should have Rosanna to console. But for her, who seemed to understand what he was talking about better than I did, it had clearly been the right thing to say, and no consolation was needed. It was long before she spoke of Agrippa again, and then it was with pleasure.

11

In Which Love and Pity are the Same

'I won't accompany you,' said Thapsis. 'I need to stay here, to be quite sure there isn't any friction. You can go down through the borders of Luvia to the port of Glossa and get a ship to the Shore of the Plains. If nothing holds you up, you'll strike the asvin road from Adambara about the time our second column goes through. Join it if you like – it will cross inland to Beulah and set up headquarters in Limbo. Or you can go back to Adambara if you'd rather. Faesto's going to be commanding that column,' he added looking in Rosanna's direction.

'I won't cross Acheron again,' she said, 'not even with a relief mission. They don't need me, and I don't think I should know what to do. Let's decide later.'

'You owe it to your own efforts that it will be a straightforward journey,' said Thapsis. 'When Verula was unconquered you couldn't have crossed the plain.'

'Do we have to pass Verula?' said Rosanna.

'No, no, you won't even see it. Go through Or-Cu, where the asva herds are – that's where the Tetrarch was born.'

'I doubt he'll remember it,' I said.

'He will,' said Thapsis. 'He's an old asva, and was many years wild before you got him, but I'll wager he knows his birthplace.'

'Are asvaya immortal?' said Rosanna, suddenly.

'Practically indestructible, yes. Immortal, no. Apparently when their number's up, they let you know, and take off for the desert. What happens to them nobody knows – must be a graveyard somewhere like there is for elephants,' said Thapsis. 'Sergeant Takis knows when an asva is fey, and turns him loose – he's tried to follow them to see where they go, but he never found one. They say you never see a dead asva, and you never see an asva's bones. The hides come from the odd asva that breaks its neck, and that's rare.'

'And Luvia?' said Rosanna. 'Will we be welcome?'

'I know what you mean,' said Thapsis. 'I do not understand Luvah's worshippers either. But consider whom they worship. He is Passion – love, hate, compassion, and in his earthly form Revolution, the perpetually young Prometheus chained to his rock until his time comes. His bride is Vala – mother nature, lovely, treacherous, blameless, mother and harlot, Mary the Mother of Compassion and Mary Magdalene. That is a very profound iconography, and it produces very complex worshippers. You never know with Luvians – one dynasty it's orgiasts, the next, revolutionary puritans, and then Vala reasserts herself, and goddesses, as you know, run to extremes. One day she is Hecate presiding over sacrifices, another she mothers a Messiah on Your Side, the next she builds a garden for Sensuality and Generation and has them wander there like two children. Luvians say that it is her veil that separates Our Side from Yours.'

'Yes,' I said, 'but any practical tips?'

'Don't ask puritan Luvians if they loved well – their reserve is seriousness, not prudery. Don't come the heavy Adept – these folk are Adepts too, but they don't like elitists, as Wei said. And don't, as it were, take sides between the Archons. Remember, all the Four must be present for consummation. Los melts them in his furnace and then pours a human form. I'm interested that you two find Passion a difficult thing to handle – Sensuality, yes, Imagination, yes, Legalism and Scientism – you've seen plenty of them: but Passion has become singularly lacking on Your Side, in its sense as a value. On Your Side it's either sensuality, which is fine, or jealousy, which is a work of Hell, or sick enthusiasm of the Hitler variety. I don't think anyone in our era will understand Passion.'

I waited for him to finish, but he had a point.

'Passion is the fourth arrow of intellect,' said Thapsis.

'Thapsis,' I said, 'you wouldn't also have anything so useful as a map?'

'Why? It's simply a matter of following a perfectly straight paved road,' said Thapsis. 'If you wander off on farm tracks you'll get lost, but you can ask your way. Incidentally, don't drink Luvian wine. None of these people here use it, and it's far stronger than blach.'

I knew by now that when Thapsis harangued about philosophy or the religion of the Losians he was treading water, getting us into position for something – one never knew for what until we were over our ears in it. Rosanna encouraged him, however, and then tried to explain to me (chiefly in bed, when I wanted intercourse or sleep) what he had meant. This time she did not wait, however.

'Passion isn't what you think, Edward,' she said. 'You'd call it Concern.'

And I knew well that to Rosanna, who was loving but not jealous, sensual but not careless, concern came naturally.

This time there was no dawn departure, no sense of expedition. Wei had our arms returned to us, and we stowed them. The Tetrarch had been groomed until he shone, and resented it. Luvian militia men and militia girls saw us off and waved and cheered. Thapsis saluted gravely and turned back into the headquarters tent. Then the bend of the road concealed the entry into the badlands, the camp and the way leading to Agrippa's resting place, and we were alone together again, dropping steadily down into the Luvian plain, and passing the fast-stepping bull carts bringing up supplies.

'Well, Ros,' I said, 'we have harrowed Hell. I love and admire you more than ever before.'

'I know,' said Rosanna, and leaned forward to touch me. 'Thapsis plans it well.'

'Plans what? If you know?'

'After each test he leaves us together for a while.'

'You reckon there will be more?' I said.

'Oh yes, if we come back for them, and we will,' said Rosanna. 'You don't want to stop now, do you?'

'No,' I said. 'Where is it going, though?'

'Ultimately we have to rejoin into one person,' said Rosanna.

'I thought you didn't want that.'

'I don't know yet that I do,' she said.

'I seem to recall that "in Eternity there is no such thing as a Feminine Will."'

'I am hoping,' said Rosanna, 'that we could be one person here, and ourselves on Our Side. We'll have to see. We shall know when to stop. The landscape changes, and other people initiate us, so we can't know until it begins to happen.'

'Who's going to do the initiating?' I asked her. 'The deepest character we've met so far was old Tjurip, and he didn't seem about to give.'

'He gave you your identity card,' said Rosanna. 'Have you ever looked at it again?'

'I don't think it came through customs,' I said.

'It's in your asvin pack. I saw it yesterday,' said Rosanna. So as we rode I felt in the pack and took out the tjurunga. It was still in its bark-cloth package. It was like a flat gray whetstone, and the lines drawn on it had been emphasized by rubbing in lime. On one surface were four marks side-by-side, concentric groups of circles like transverse slices of an onion. On the other, the same four circles overlapped, and two lines of footprints ran to their common point, crossed there and emerged again. The left-hand line had a spear drawn above it, the right-hand line a pear-shaped structure: male and female meeting in the fourfold labyrinth, then going their ways. It seemed to square with Rosanna's interpretation. The Tetrarch, meanwhile, unconcerned with Adeptic matters, was enjoying the warmer air. He began to do something I had never heard him do before – to sing tunelessly under his breath in a series of whinnies, creaks and rumblings. At first I thought that something was the matter with him. Then I appreciated that this was simply a song of contentment.

'What does he want?' said Rosanna.

'He's singing,' I said, and we listened to him. 'You know, Ros, if anyone is to administer a final initiation, I think it should be the Tetrarch. He is a great shaman – he's taken all the trips, he is steadfast, selfless, but with a tremendous identity in spite of it. Wouldn't surprise me if that beast turns out to be our two-person self made concrete.'

'I think he's a part of you,' said Rosanna. 'But you might be right about initiation. We've both taken more instruction from him than we realize.'

We were among the first cultivated fields – the badlands were an irregular blue range behind us. By the roadside we passed a pile of large yellow squashes, waiting, no doubt, for the cart to come by and garner them. The Tetrarch, who had the better forward view, saw them before I did. Nonchalantly he edged over, took the topmost squash without changing step and was on his way. The singing stopped abruptly – the Tetrarch had his mouth full.

We began to see the work of the Looms. The landscape itself was a fabric – its patchwork squares of green crop, brown bushes or reddish earth ran into the feet of the hills and filled the whole plain; where a rock protruded, cultivation ran right into its shadow. Sail-driven windmills rotated in unison. Nearly every field had its blue-clad figures. We passed a marching column of blue-clad children on the way to school, led by a young girl, the teacher, and a boy carrying a banner, and behind him the band, singing lustily and banging tambourines. The villages were of stone, and the walls of the houses which fronted the road were neatly inscribed, on surfaces of whitewash. A party of Luvians of both sexes were busy sweeping the street, as if it was their own kitchen. I hoped the Tetrarch had wiped his feet – it seemed uncultured to ride where they had swept.

'What does that say?' said Rosanna, as we passed a wall covered with writing.

'Try your ring – I'm driving,' I said. 'It's probably Adeptic instruction of some sort.'

'Four enemies,' she read, spelling out the writing, 'idleness, dirt, lack of concern, old thinking. Four achievements – two grains for one grain, right thought, right action, work together.'

We passed another. 'And that says: all old thinking knowledge is not only useless but positively harmful.'

That, I remembered, was practically a verbatim quote from

Agrippa. 'These people represent the Archon of Passion?' I said.

'Yes, if they mean it.'

'And what if they don't, or some of them don't? It's a fine line between wall slogans and iron books.'

'On Our Side,' said Rosanna, 'one would turn into the other. Perhaps not in this world – I don't know. I'd be happier if "right thought, right action" read "love and imagination." Perhaps that's what they mean.'

'Love should be kosher in the land of Passion.'

'Why? It isn't a passion. Pity, hate, concern, zeal are what Luvah stands for. And generation – there wasn't one love bed in that whole camp, but there are more children here than any other place we've been. I was coming to think this was entirely an adult world, apart from the few replacements when an Adept meets with an accident, until we came here. "Love" belongs in Beulah, the way you mean it.'

When we stopped in a small town to eat and to water the Tetrarch, we were surrounded. We sat at a long table in the local inn while Luvians plied us with questions – where we came from, where we were going, what we thought of the work they had done. We told them we were here for the first time, that though we were going to Adambara, we were from the Other Side.

'Where they live by the iron books, like savages?' said one of the Luvian girls.

'I'm afraid so,' I answered, 'though less than they used to.'

'No, now they live by the books of brass,' said another.

'"Compel the poor to live upon a Crust of bread, by soft mild arts, smile when they frown, frown when they smile, & when a man looks pale with labor & abstinence, Say he looks healthy & happy.
And when his children sicken, let them die; there are enough Born, even too many & our Earth will be overrun . . .
Reduce all to our Will as Spaniels are taught with art."'

'One of our great revolutionary poets wrote that,' said the first girl, decisively. 'But all that will be changed soon. What are the Losians doing about it?'

'They are too busy playing at Adepts,' said one of the men. 'It was only when they were in danger that they destroyed Sutun's clique. You should live with us, strangers, and see how your earth will change.'

'How will it change?'

'It is living in the Anomaly,' said an old man, further down the table. 'The society of the brass books is on borrowed time. It will go into the wine press, and good wine will come out for the people.'

'I marvel, Comrades, how you know so much about Our Side,' I said. 'Most people there know little of yours.'

'We have been peasants on Your Side and hungry on Your Side,' said the old man. 'You see, we are better Adepts than your Losian friends – we are serious about it.'

'There will be time for the Losians later,' said the younger man.

'Work first, play afterwards: before the Four are united we have a harvest to get in, and trash to burn. On Your Side, much trash. Those who take other people's blood and use it to buy toys for themselves. Those who take the name of change and use it to make themselves tyrants. All of them, into the wine press, and we will dance on the grapes.'

And then, without any sense of a key change, they were onto less dangerous subjects – how we fared in the Empty Quarter, Rosanna's Tharmian jewels and good wishes for our journey. Clearly, they took us for Adepts of the kind that they approved. It was getting hot, and we learned that at this season in Luvia one sleeps in the afternoon and resumes work at night. We were shown to a clean chamber with straw mats and woven blankets, and slept until after dark.

12

Her Shadow, Vala, Builded by the Reasoning Power

The guesthouse, or whatever the place was, had two entrances – one by way of the room where we had eaten, from which stairs led to a gallery; the other end of the gallery had an external wooden stair to the street, like a fire escape, and from the gallery opened our sleeping room. The Tetrarch was moored, after feeding, to the post of this external stair, so it was natural that when we prepared to leave I should go down to him by the nearest way, carrying such of our baggage as we had taken up with us. Rosanna came a little later, and I saw her go down the other stair. She did not, however, appear in the street. In a few moments I saw that she had remounted the inside stairs and was hurrying down by the way I had come.

'Let's go,' she said.

'Anything wrong?'

'I don't know. The whole of that dining room is full of women. They're absolutely silent, and they're waiting for me.'

'Or for us?' I said.

'No,' said Rosanna, 'for me.'

I looked in the window of the lower room, which was glassless. It was exactly as Rosanna said. The room was full of the Luvian women, standing in complete silence. All of them faced the door where Rosanna and I would have to appear. The two girls who had spoken most at table were closest to the door. One held a small silver cup, the other a folded curtainlike cloth. Two torches fixed in brackets lit the room. The faces I could see were expectant. One woman held in her arms a black cockerel.

'Odd conventicle,' I whispered. 'You're right – it's a reception committee. And a ritual.'

'I know,' said Rosanna. 'I heard people and I peeped through the boards of the door. I'd have gone in, but I saw that bird. It's a sacrifice, and they want me to be part of it.'

'These folk won't hurt us,' I said. 'You talked to them. It's likely a farewell ceremony and we'll hurt their feelings.'

'No,' said Rosanna, 'wrong vibrations. There's something they want me to do. And beside the chicken, there's a knife and a mirror.'

Two of the women, indeed, held these objects.

We could not mount the Tetrarch where we stood, because he stood under a low platform which was the first landing of the stair. He could be as silent as a shadow, but on this occasion his claws sounded, as I led him out, like seven league boots. The reception committee spun round and flowed into the street, and we, at the Tetrarch's head, met them as they threw open the door. Light poured out.

'Don't go,' said one of the girls, she of the silver cup. 'Sister, we want you to join with us. You have not seen our ceremony. The brother can wait with the asva. It will not take long.'

'What ceremony, sisters?' said Rosanna.

'Only to drink the wine in the cup,' said the other girl, 'and put on the veil of our Goddess. We want to honor you, who come from the Other Side. Won't you preside?'

And she handed Rosanna the little cup. Rosanna half-turned to me. I shook my head slightly, recalling Thapsis's instruction. Rosanna played for time.

'Is that the veil of Vala your Goddess?' she said. 'Surely I should not wear it?'

'Yes,' said the girl who carried it, 'oh, yes – look!' And she part opened the folded thing which she carried. It was like a pool of fire. Even the small part of it which we saw was breathtaking, for the Luvian weavers had covered the transparent silk with closely packed peacock eyes. Rosanna gaped at its beauty.

'Edward . . .' she began, 'perhaps I ought – perhaps we should . . .' The Luvian girl smiled and held out the little cup.

'Watch it, Ros,' I said.

'Be quiet, Brother, this is a woman's mystery,' said the veil carrier.

Rosanna took the cup in her hand. The veil bearer let the whole swath of it fall and raised it like a bridal veil to place on Rosanna's head. It was internally luminous like the mandalas of Adambara, a torrent of eyes. Rosanna seemed hypnotized by it. She raised the cup.

As she did so, a rough pink tongue reaching over her shoulder lifted the little cup from her hand. The Tetrarch closed his mouth and munched. Cup and all had disappeared down his throat. Then without ceremony he gave his prefatory whinny and moved forward. The Luvian women fell back. The veil carrier gathered up her burden and it went out as if a cloud had gone over it – she of the black rooster dropped it and it flapped off squawking. I mounted, grabbed Rosanna and pulled her up unceremoniously behind. 'Bad medicine,' I said, 'take his word for it. Geeup!' They were after us like Tam O'Shanter's witches, shouting, laughing, some angry, some ridiculing our flight. She of the cup clung to one of the saddlebags.

'You will come back!' she yelled. 'You will wear the veil, sister. You will carry the knife and the mirror. Wait and see!' She let go and fell behind. We were down the street and out of the Luvian village in short order. We saw women jump back to let us pass – not a male was in sight.

'Ros!' I said, 'wake up. That thing freaked you out. I don't know what that was about, but the asva did.'

'I know,' said Rosanna, 'or part of it. I would have known what to do. I would have worn the veil, and later I would have had to sacrifice something.'

'Probably the black cockerel,' I said.

'I think so.'

'That fantastic veil was a sort of aegis. You must have been closer to it – it didn't work on me.'

'It wouldn't,' said Rosanna. 'Somehow it had all of womanhood in it, and it was unholy, and I would have liked to have worn it even so.'

'Womanhood isn't unholy,' I said. 'What the hell are you

talking about? It's a good thing you didn't drink that stuff, whatever it was. I only hope it doesn't freak the Tetrarch out. He ate the cup as well.'

'Womanhood isn't unholy, but this was.'

We were out of the village and going steadily along a straight stretch of causeway. There was enough light to see hills ahead. We passed three pointed rocks in a field. I watched the Tetrarch with apprehension; though I doubted the efficacy of any Luvian potion on his vast frame, I recalled the sad fate of an Indian elephant who took a swig of country spirit and charged a high tension pole. I hoped that asvaya had no similar susceptibilities. And indeed, he began to act strangely. Something was bothering him. We were coming abreast of three rocks – I thought we had passed them a few minutes before, but they were still ahead. It was only when we prepared to pass them for the third time that I began to share the Tetrarch's uneasiness. He turned and whinnied. He liked the performance no better than I.

'Ros,' I said.

'Yes,' she said, 'I see them.'

'We're in some kind of a time loop. We're replaying. Hold everything.'

I reined the Tetrarch. He stood, pawing, swinging his head from side-to-side as if attempting to locate the cause of the trouble. I urged him forward. He moved cautiously. There was a kind of inner click in my head, and the rocks were coming abreast again. He stopped.

'We're in trouble,' said Rosanna.

The Tetrarch continued to search, as if he were tracing the source of a sound. I thought I heard suppressed laughter behind us. Then with an air of having resolved a problem, the Tetrarch stretched his neck back and inspected the left front saddlebag. He looked at me. I opened it, groped in it, and a flashing piece of veil, studded with the peacock eyes of Vala, slipped from it like a bright snake and lay on the ground. He backed carefully, put a foot on one end of the glowing thing and spread its full length with the other. Then, backing further, he stood facing it, and foot by foot stepped over it. I felt the click in my head repeated as we did so. We breasted the line of rocks and passed them. The strand of the veil lay glowing in the roadway until it became a bright point.

'That,' I said, 'is the first time we have tangled with a śakti, in her dark aspect. Why the Luvians? It seems not to fit. You can thank the Four you didn't put the thing on.'

'I don't understand either,' said Rosanna. 'Thapsis said they were complex. On earth they'd be high-minded Maoists, until Urizen caught up with them. Here it's different. Vala too is passion.'

I was about to say that it was fortunate that the Tetrarch was a stallion asva, not a mare, but held my peace. Rosanna read my mind, however.

'Goddesses frighten me too,' she said. 'I don't know why. But I'm cowardly, Edward – there was another knowledge in that veil which I should have had.' And she looked back at the burning point behind us.

We passed no more villages. At the end of the straight causeway, there was a scent of flowers which became stronger, and we saw away to our left rounded trees, moonlit lawns, choreb moving about and great vines with white bells so large that we could see every flower in the moonlight. It must, I thought, be the garden of Vala. A road ran into it under arched trees, and in a little shrine was a veiled image, decorated with more flowers in garlands. Before it stood little votive pots, and in its hands were the knife and the mirror. We passed it by. If it had not been for the affair of the veil, I think we should have gone in. Rosanna peered into the shadows of the grove, where a choreb dam and its lamb stood watching us, speckled with more but paler eyes from the leaf-mottled moonlight. We passed it by.

'You know,' said Rosanna, 'they were right. I shall have to go back and meet with Her some time. But not now.'

It struck me that although we had not gone in through the gateway, we were not going to be able to avoid the garden. It was coming to meet us. Trees at its confines arched over the road. The white bellvines were getting more numerous – first one or two, climbing into the branches at the roadside, then overhead, then hanging down in ropes. They began to touch us. The smell of tuberose and datura was overwhelming. The Tetrarch evidently disliked it. Rosanna put up her hand to touch one of the white, waxy bells as it brushed her face, and it came away in her hand. Next time I looked back she had put it in her hair. Moreover the carpet of large, pale peacock eyes cast by the moon was starting to invade the road, to move over the Tetrarch's back, over Rosanna herself and over me. 'Watch it,' I said.

'There's no danger now,' said Rosanna, as if she was sure.

The avenue of trees ran out. We were indeed in Vala's garden – clumps of dark trees and bushes covered with the vines, patches of lawn clipped level by choreb, pairs of choreb. And though the overshade had gone, the flicker of eyed light on the Tetrarch's back and on our skin continued. When we looked up northward, towards the Empty Quarter from which we had come, the sky was full of bright moving drapery. The Northern Lights had no business in so tropical a place.

'I want to get down,' said Rosanna.

I wasn't so sure, and I wished the Tetrarch could talk. He seemed to have had the measure of the dangers inherent in that veil. For all I knew we could still get stuck in some other singularity of time, or run into some of the unpleasantnesses we'd avoided before.

'*There's no danger now,*' said Rosanna again. And the Tetrarch, without orders, stopped, looked around him and knelt with his hind legs to let her get off. Not having anyone else to consult, I had to rely on his judgment. He was obviously in charge, for as soon as Rosanna had slipped off his back, he stood up in a businesslike manner, sauntered over to the nearest bush and started noisily pulling down and eating flowers. I was on the outside of this whole transaction. It appeared in some way to be Rosanna's property. Rosanna was nearly out of sight across the lawn – the choreb moved away as she passed them, and she disappeared among the flowering bushes. There was a dark blotch halfway across the lawn – Rosanna's clothes, lying where she had dropped them in a heap.

Time passed, the Tetrarch munched steadily, the choreb

moved about and the veils of light in the sky came and went. I knew, though I can't imagine why, there was no way I could lose Rosanna here – there was power at large in the place, but the threat we had felt before was withdrawn. Something was going on – I did not know what, only that it was none of my business.

It must have been a full half-hour before I saw her coming back, walking slowly between the flower-laden clumps, the eyes of light moving on her skin, so that she looked like a paler choreb – crossing the lawn, picking her clothes up and putting them under her arm. The Tetrarch stopped munching flowers, backed off and knelt for her, and I dismounted and went to meet her.

'That's done,' said Rosanna. 'Don't touch me – not yet.'

She was a little out of breath, and looked very much as she did when she had been making love. Then she came to me. 'There was a little temple,' said Rosanna, 'and it was quite easy.' Clearly it was not a time for questions. She put an arm round my neck. 'I expect you were worried,' she said. 'I told you there was no danger. That was the right way to do it.'

'Do what?'

Rosanna shook her head. 'We'll come back another time. We can wander about here as we did in Beulah, but it would be different – deeper. I'd be a woman, not a lascivious child.'

'What do you want now, Ros?'

'You could either love me, or worship me. It's my garden,' said Rosanna.

I thought of a mode suitably expressive of both, leaned her against one of the vine-covered trees and knelt down. When we'd finished, choreb were standing round watching – Rosanna had one hand in my hair and her other arm round the Tetrarch's neck. He was about to push his head between us. The Tetrarch was usually blunt when he thought it was time to move.

'Thank you,' said Rosanna, 'that was absolutely right. I didn't know you were imaginative about this kind of feeling.'

'Are you going to tell me what happened?' I said.

'I don't know. Not now – not until I know what happened

myself. Completeness. Being a part of Her. Not being a part of you. You don't mind that?'

She was dressed again: I helped her into the rear saddle. The veil of lights had contracted into a corner of the sky as if its wearer were leaving, but it was still moonlight.

'No,' I said, 'of course I don't mind. I never thought you were a part of anything but you. Certainly not a part of me.'

'Not your emanation,' said Rosanna, 'as some of these Losians seem to think?'

'Certainly not.'

'Which was why I needed to worship Vala. Not like those Luvian witches. In my own way. I was starting to wonder if the Losians were right.'

I mounted and the Tetrarch prepared to move off. I didn't press Rosanna about the nature of the worship – it seemed to be feminine property.

'Goddesses frighten men,' said Rosanna. 'I can see why. They frighten us too until we know who we are. Let's go, Edward – She gave me a sort of safe conduct, but it's running out.'

Back on the road she began to laugh. 'Poor Edward,' said Rosanna, 'sitting there waiting. As if I'd gone to the ladies' room. Thinking, either she's a spiritual part of me or she's dangerous. It's scary to have a Feminine Will running around on its own. You did think I was going to turn out to be part of you, didn't you?'

'No,' I said, 'quite honestly I didn't.'

'Good,' said Rosanna, 'because I'm not.'

The veil of lights was beginning to come back. The Tetrarch started to hurry. We left the garden and moved into open country – out of that domain.

13
In the Ship of Erzulie

We rode on. We were entering the hills and the limit of cultivation, for the garden is at the fringe of the woven landscape of Luvia, which we were now leaving. After a while we left matters to the Tetrarch and slept in our saddles like asvin, and when we woke he was loping steadily towards a lightening dawn sky. The ground ahead was crossed by moldering, overgrown fortifications. The road traversed them through gaps where arches had fallen. We saw a few sleeping reed houses, choreb, a boat by the roadside on a cart. We were entering the port of Glossa. Beyond it we saw for the first time, and began to smell, the Tharmian sea. Soon we passed a reedy arm of it. It was like no other sea – waveless, a complete silver mirror turning gray and lemon as the sun approached its rising point. Before it rose, we were in streets of reed and stone houses with nets hanging before them, and over all was the sweet, rotten smell of weed. People of all kinds began to move – Luvian carts, Tharmians with flocks, Losians carrying hammers and anchors, the shipwright smiths of Glossa and many of the fisherfolk of the town itself – black people with the look of Africans, men carrying nets and women with headscarves and flat baskets. The quayside, when we came upon it, was wide and ancient – nothing in the World of the Four appears newly built – ending in a great brazier which served as a sailing mark, and in which the fire was dying down, for it was now full daylight. Losian inns were opening their doors. Outside one stood a long cart drawn not by choreb but by two asvaya, small dark asvaya of Thalmi, only half the stature of the Tetrarch, and into it from an inn there mounted a small crowd of people wearing the white bathrobes and black sashes we had come to dislike on past adventures. Two Losians were riding herd on these tourists as couriers.

'Verulans,' I said.

'Being taken,' said Rosanna, 'on a tour of the Four Worlds to broaden their minds. Those two youngsters are from the Rehabilitation Corps.'

The tourists had earthly-looking cameras, and looked as if they owned the place.

'Let's get past them,' said Rosanna.

The dockside was packed with the reed-built sampans and boats of Tharmian design. Only one craft in the whole harbor looked as if it might convey us and our mount. It lay towards the end of the mole, a wooden vessel shaped like a slice of pumpkin, with high pointed prow and stern, a deep hold amidships and small thatched cabins fore and aft. It had no rigging, but there was a stubby mast painted spirally with two climbing snakes, and a long spar like a bowsprit ahead from which tackle hung. Under the after cover sat two black people, a girl and a young, bearded man. He was playing a guitar, and she was listening. They watched us approach, and the music stopped.

'Ma'p di ou bonjou,' said the girl, 'côté ou pr'allez?'

'To the Shore of the Plains,' said Rosanna. 'Will you take us in your boat?'

On Our Own Side, our rings had proved useless on earthly languages, but here they seemed effective.

The girl consulted with her companion.

'Oh yes,' she said, 'if the big horse will come in our boat. You are Adepts?'

The word she used was 'houn'sihs'.

'Yes,' said Rosanna. 'Greetings.'

'I am Ramise, he is César. We shall leave tonight, when there is a full moon again. We can set you down on the Shore of Plains. If you are houn'sihs, why do you not come with us?'

'Where are you going?' I asked.

'To Ifé.'

I wondered how we should pay them for our voyage. Ramise read my thoughts. 'You give me your moon earrings,' she said, 'and bring perfume for Erzulie. It is her boat. Come to us tonight, then.'

'Does your boat sail, then?' I asked her. 'I see no mast.'

They burst out laughing. 'No sails – I will call,' said César. 'Tonight.'

'Who are they?' I asked Rosanna, as he returned to his music.

'Haitians. Ifé is their spiritual city. They have to go there to become priests.'

Our rings must still have been switched on. 'You know well,' said Ramise. 'All the Four live there, and many others. You are Tharmians?'

'No,' said Rosanna, 'we are from Your Side too, but we are Losians here.'

'The moon earrings?' said Ramise.

'I was in a Tharmian city,' said Rosanna.

'Moon earrings are for Tharmas and Enion? We call them Agoueh and Erzulie – whom you call Zoas, we call Loas. This you know?'

'Yes,' said Rosanna.

'Good,' said Ramise, 'then you can sail with us.'

At a Losian inn, we ate on the porch, the Tetrarch dining on more pineapples in the yard. He had taken the measure of the magic boat, and viewed it with resignation.

'Oh yes,' said the Losian girl who waited on us, 'they came in yesterday. They are going to be made Adepts according to their way. We often see the ships going to Ifé. They are great Adepts, the black people who come in ships – they can speak to the Four and be possessed by them, and they know about us as if we had told them.'

While the Tetrarch took his ease, Rosanna and I walked in Glossa. It was a kind of crossroads, we found, where all manner of people congregate who have voyages to execute in the World of the Four. Not only the Four themselves but many other objects of veneration had shrines here; though the town, being devoted to the sea, was in spirit Tharmian, only the herd boys were naked in the Tharmian manner. The Verulan educational tour, we were pleased to see, had left. The shops dealt not only in the gear of shipping and of fishing, but also in objects of initiation and pilgrimage – gourd rattles, iron scepters, woven bags containing consecrated things: even the leaden medals of Christian saints. At one such we bought for Erzulie, Loa of the sea, a rose-patterned pot of a pink flower confection, sweetly scented, which is made from the large cabbage roses of Glossa, and for Agoueh her consort a white china lamp. 'You go to Ifé?' said the shopkeeper. 'You don't look African.'

The day wore on, the sun set, the beacon was lit, and still the water of the Tharmian sea was as flat as a mirror, windless and timeless. We brought the Tetrarch to the pierside as the moon rose out of the hills behind Glossa. Ramise and César were waiting. Stout planks had been laid from the quay to the edge of the hold, and the Tetrarch, talking morosely under his breath to himself, let us lead him, a footstep at a time, to his station in the hold, from which his neck soared like a mast. César picked up the planks as if they had been toothpicks and cast off the boat.

'Though you are Adepts,' said Ramise, 'stay here, in the rear deck-shelter. Do not come forward – you do not know the prayers.'

She took the two offerings.

On the foredeck, César had traced in white powder a complex diagram, a combination of curled lines and a heart like that on a Victorian pincushion. It was repeated on a woven flag at the stern. These were the vèvès of Erzulie. César lit the white lamp and set it amidships.

'You chose your offerings well,' he said. 'Here we need no drummer – we shall sail well.'

He poled the boat slowly out into the fairway, past the beacon and on into the darkening Tharmian sea. We could see the lights of Glossa turning behind us. Ramise leaned against the post with its snake pattern, gesturing with a tiny magical oar. After a while César shipped the quant pole and went forward to the long sprit, from which he hauled up two rings of cane and leatherlike yokes, and then lowered them into the water, one on each side. Both began to chant. Then César put a conch shell to his lips and sent a series of long booming notes across the water. For a moment nothing happened, and then the water stirred, two white clouds of fishy-smelling steam rose side-by-side ahead of us, and two shiny backs fell under our counter. As if engines had been started the boat began to move, faster and faster, like Kishmul's galley, without visible means of propulsion. César began to shake his calabash rattle, calling his thanks to Agoueh and to Erzulie la Baleine.

'Not verras,' I whispered to Rosanna, 'pilot whales, by the look of them.'

We left a long wake in the mirror calm as they bent to their task.

14
In Which the Tetrarch Makes His Own Likeness

'We can't go closer,' said Ramise. 'They need deep water. But your big horse will swim.'

The Shore of the Plains was a long, gray, waveless strand, littered with white bones of tree trunks, lying about a hundred yards from us.

It had been a magical journey, during which we talked little: Ramise and César had sat together under the fore-shelter, we under the aft. They had sung for us, shared meals, made much of the Tetrarch. Most of the time, on this waveless sea, the boat of Erzulie had seemed to be hanging at the center of a sphere or sailing in air, through a night and a day and a night. Our two friends were gentle, preoccupied, magically remote, intent on their pilgrimage.

We gathered our goods: they embraced us gently – the Tetrarch craned over the edge of the hold and looked into the water without enthusiasm. Long weeds rose up towards our keel. We urged him onto the after-deck. His leap set the boat of Erzulie rocking – there was a vast splash, and his head came level with the gunwale and rose above it as he brought his back alongside.

'See, he knows,' said Ramise. 'Who is he on Our Side, your big horse? And who are you?'

'I can't tell you who the Tetrarch is, other than himself,' I said, 'and we are Edward and Rosanna.'

César shook his head. 'There are many we do not know. But we shall know you if you come again.'

It struck me that for them we two were spirits, and the asva a mortal "horse" whom we had possessed, and who would, in real time, resume a human shape as some houn'sih who had invoked us by accident. But it was no time for explanations – we were mounted, our feet touching the water, the Tetrarch turned and swam: we saw them wave, the two curved shiny backs bent to the harness, and the boat of Erzulie, with a bone in her mouth, resumed her voyage to Ifé and vanished into the sea mist, carrying the two young people bound for the spiritual Africa where the spirits of their religion have their homes in the *grand bois*.

'I think they'll try to call us,' said Rosanna. 'It wouldn't surprise me if one day we found ourselves here because they brought us, and not of our own choice.'

The Tetrarch found footing, and clambered up the beach. His huge prints crossed the gray blade of sand which ran left and right as far as we could see, passed between the driftwood skeletons, and we were on the Plain of Cities once more. Not half a mile away ran the paved asva road.

All day we followed it. After twenty miles it divided – the left fork was marked with the stone figure of an asva, the right with a new pillar bearing a sun and two open hands, the road to Verula. What the pillar had formerly borne we did not know. We took the left hand fork, passed over higher ground, and suddenly came to the edge of the hollow plain of Or-Cu. As far as the eye could see, tall necks moved like sails, hundreds upon hundreds of asvaya moving in tended flocks. The Tetrarch was coming home. He showed no emotion, but began to munch. Another asva passed us on the road, with one of the short Or-Cu herdsmen, my old troopers, in the saddle. We exchanged greetings with him, and the Tetrarch with his mount. Soon we passed others, and before long we rode into the square of Or-Cu, filled with tethered asvaya, shouting cowboys, drinking troughs, carts of hyasa meat. It had the air of a Wild West frontier town, dwarfed by the size of the beasts which were its main concern. At the inn, the Tetrarch was led off by a boy who had forgotten more about asvaya than I had ever learned from Takis. I saw him fetch up before a crib full of hyasa meat. The host was an old trooper.

'He's a fine one,' he said. 'Losian cavalry. Would you be an officer, Sir?'

'Colonel Eda, Losian asvin. Were you in the Service?'

Instead of answering, he yelled in the language of Or-Cu, and we were surrounded. Or-Cu seemed entirely filled with retired Losian servicemen anxious to shake our hands, provide us with herb tea, blach and yellow bread, and ply us with questions.

Finally mine host asserted himself. 'Let them alone, boys,' he bellowed. 'Colonel, Lady, our house is honored. Our village is honored. You men, hats off. These are the Adepts who cleaned up Verula. Take a look at them, youngsters. These are the kind of people you'll serve under, if you're lucky. Take a look at their mount, because you won't see another like him. Single-handed he killed five hundred armed men . . .'

'Where, incidentally, is our mount?' I said, as soon as I could stem the flow of military exhortation.

'In the lines, Sir,' said our host, 'or at least . . .'

But he was not. The crib of hyasa meat had been eaten, but there was no Tetrarch. The crowd of admiring Cossacks broke up to look for him. Boys ran and graybeards hurried. Rosanna and I got up to follow. As we rounded the end of the inn building, a cheer and a roar of laughter went up. There were two or three stone-walled paddocks behind the inn yard. In the furthest was the Tetrarch. Without benefit of a love bed, he was in enthusiastic coition with a comely black asva mare. The Or-Cu men waved their hats and yelled their approval.

'Son of a bitch!' said our host, 'that's *my* mare. He didn't waste time. I shall have the finest asva foal in Or-Cu. That's the best gift I've had in many a long year.' He slapped my back and led us back in triumph to resume the press conference. Or-Cu men packed the little eating-house; Or-Cu boys swarmed in the unglazed windows.

'Don't thank us,' I said. 'It was entirely his idea – he was born here.'

'You hear that, men? A true son of Or-Cu. Now Sir, Lady, will you make your boast for us?'

'Our boast?' I said.

'Yes, Sir. Your boast.'

And we repeated our story for a fourth, a fifth and a sixth

time, telling of the ride to Verula and the journey through the Empty Quarter. There were more rounds of herb tea and more pipes of blach. The air thickened steadily with smoke. Rosanna, who had rarely before spoken of Verula, boasted more easily than I, but in doing so made our story the boast of the Tetrarch rather than of the two Adepts. He meanwhile had returned, munching and rather out of breath, with an air of having seen a foundation stone well and truly laid. Cowboys walked round him and admired his points – the Or-Cu women gathered round Rosanna, treating her as the Colonel's lady, but with no false deference. Finally all hands had been shaken and all pipes smoked. I was about to ask our host how far it was to the asvin base which was our rendezvous when I heard the familiar sounds, the pounding and the asvin trumpet, and a squadron went through at the canter. We were coming home.

'It's not far, Sir,' said the innkeeper. 'They've been coming through all day. May I ask you a favor, Sir?'

'Ask away,' I said. 'I'd be happy to do what I can.'

'My boy, Sir. May he ride with you to enlist?'

'Of course.'

The boy was pushed forward, another short, dark, sturdy youth. He saluted me as if he were already in uniform.

'He's the youngest, Sir. His brothers will have the herd. He rides well, when he pays attention.'

'We'll make an asvin of him,' I said. 'Trooper!'

The boy jumped to attention.

'Mount my asva and bring him around.'

'Sir!' He was off like a bullet.

'Thank you, Sir. And the foal?'

'What about it?'

'It's name, Sir.'

'If it's a boy, call it Minoru. And if it's a girl . . .'

'Call it Erzulie,' said Rosanna.

'And if it's twins, Sir?'

'We'll cross that bridge when we come to it,' I said. 'Trooper, kneel him to mount. What do we owe you, Sergeant?'

'Nothing, Sir. You're our honored guests, Sir.'

And so, behind the young volunteer, we rode out of Or-Cu, and the Tetrarch, sensing a prentice hand, behaved himself better than when I first rode him. He seemed well pleased with the day's work, and before dusk we saw the walls of the desert fort, the asva lines and the hammer flag of Los, and drew rein before the asva gate, and Faesto himself came out to meet us. I handed over our recruit and we saluted like strangers. Faesto despatched the lad to find Sergeant Takis, closed the door, embraced me and then Rosanna, and they fell into each other's arms, one of her hands remaining somehow in mine.

15
The Form of the Design

'We won't stay here,' said Faesto. 'It's been bedlam for a week. I know a place out of town.'

'You and Rosanna go,' I said. 'You have time to make up together.'

'No, Blood Brother – it's a joint operation. Unless Rosanna wants . . .'

'I want you both,' said Rosanna. 'That's how it's always been with us.'

We left in a choreb cart. Faesto took the reins. Outside the gate we passed asva lines – row on row of draft asvaya as well as beasts of war, row on row of carts, Verulan powered earth-moving equipment, poles and girders laden upon bogies, covered mandalas, supplies, field kitchens. Simurgh came and went in a constant stream.

'I'm glad to be out of that command post,' said Faesto. 'They need a quartermaster or a computer, not a soldier.'

'How about a Smith of the Smiths?' said Rosanna.

'They'll need that. Kari took in the police column,' said Faesto. 'He's going to restore some kind of order. The physicians sent a head-changing team in with him. I wish 'em all luck – simpler to have put Dormouse over and sent the whole bunch to sleep until we got there. We'll give them a couple of weeks and move in with the civil engineering column.'

'To do what?' I asked.

'Well, the first objective is a new pipeline – we switch the emigrants out of the badlands. We march asvaya ten abreast through that damned forest, and we put in the Adeptic Highway – from their touchdown point to Tarnindhupura.

Once that's in, there'll be public transport to meet every batch.'

'And take them into Beulah?'

'Correct.'

'Do you reckon Beulah's ready for them? Or they for Beulah?' I said.

'Oh well, we won't be dumping them there cold,' said Faesto. 'From the present plan of action, there'll be a holding area – clean them up, get them out of their clothes, let them mix with the Tharmians.'

'You think they'll be able to take that?' said Rosanna. 'Our Side people pitched into Beulah – when they're on a guilt trip, or they wouldn't be headed across Acheron?'

'Your guess is as good as mine, Rusana. But the intelligence we have is that they'd understand Beulah better than Adambara. We had every shrink in the College of Physicians in on the planning, and that's what they came up with.'

'And Hell itself?'

'Well, we're going to throw a bridge over Acheron and run the highway to Limbo, and from there we play it by ear. Kari's going straight in. He's got orders to round up everyone and collar every son of a gun who has made himself into any kind of chief. They'll go neck and crop into the de-Veruliza-tion program: the rest we'll feed and put in tents, and hope the college can sort them out. Most of them can be shipped out to Beulah once the road is finished.'

'You could use Verulan reconnaissance ships,' I said.

'We've got a couple. But we don't want to start them on Your-Side technology again. A Tharmian love-in is a technology they might just understand. It's about the only gate to perception some of your folk have left themselves, according to Thapsis.'

'Thapsis is your source of information about Our Side?' said Rosanna.

'Yes, indeed. That's why he was on reconnaissance there,' said Faesto. 'It's not a new suggestion, for dealing with Hell as an institution. An Adept called Bosch made it years and years ago. I've got my settlement team studying his blueprint in detail. The Earthly Paradise, he called it. These folk don't need formation-flying angels and singing virgins – they need permission and nonpossessive love – follow me?'

I never ceased to marvel at Faesto. When I knew him as a Smith, his cover as a conventional jealous husband, earth style, had been perfect. As a soldier in clandestine operations he was as hard as a nail and as cool as a dill pickle. Now he was talking like Fritz Perls.

'Oh well,' he said, 'in the Smithy, we learned a lot about melting them down. I hope it works. We're only taking the first two circles, as you know.'

'The rest go to the Luvians?'

'Correct. Kari's scouts report they're in already, in force, and they're turning people back at the pass. So Hell is partitioned.'

'So what happens there?'

'The Four know what will happen. You never know with Luvians.'

Our adventures in the badlands he already knew. Rosanna told him the affair of the veil. Faesto shook his head.

'Could go any way. There's more than one way of climbing out of Self. The Luvians use social conscience – or sorcery, or both. The Tharmians use a king-size love bed. Both work. Pity we can't mix 'em. If I had my way I'd send all Tharmians for a stint in Luvia, learning to plant potatoes and be angry over injustice – and all Luvians for a holiday in Tarnindhu-pura. Make 'em leave their blue fatigues at the border. But that, as you probably realize, is your assignment.'

'Ours?'

'Well, it has to be done on Your Side, not ours. You must know by now why we got you here. Rusana knows.'

'I have a feeling,' I said, 'that when this is over, we'll be seconded to Our Side and not allowed to come back.'

'I don't think so,' said Faesto. 'You know your assignment now. Come back for a refresher, or when you have questions. But your project is where you came from. Understood?'

'We'll go over it later,' said Rosanna to me. 'It seems we've completed our training.'

'Have we, Faesto?'

'Don't ask me, Colonel; I'm not an Adept – or at least I

wasn't until Rusana made me one, and according to the Tharmian rite at that. No soldier ever finishes training, any more than a dancer. But you know your objectives and you've studied your equipment. Now all you need is to go and do the job. Here's our place. I've given orders to call me if war breaks out with Luvia, and for no other reason.'

'I was looking,' I said, 'for a model of the implicate order.'

'That's the easy bit,' said Faesto. 'I thought your physics people had it. If not, they'll soon get it. Your job's showing them what it means – fourfold style.' The word was aenpada.

We turned into the little, flowery court. 'This is Sephora's place,' said Faesto. 'She runs it all by herself, since Sutun killed her husband.'

At dinner we told our story again. We spoke kindly of Agrippa. Sephora, who had waited on us, joined our table as hostess – there were no other travelers in the inn – a handsome woman in her late forties or early fifties, by Our-Side chronology, she was naturally one of us, and when Rosanna spoke of Agrippa it was natural that we should join hands fourfold.

Faesto was asleep on Rosanna's shoulder, Sephora on mine.

'So that was it,' Rosanna whispered. 'I thought we were headed for our own perfection. We needn't worry about mystical fusion – that wasn't the target.'

'How shall we begin?' I said, taking care not to wake Sephora with the resonance of my voice in her ear.

'We shall see that. Begin by living as we know.'

'We still haven't seen all four worlds. Verula was the world of Sutun, not Urizen. Shouldn't we see his world too?'

'We have,' said Rosanna, 'that's where we operate. It's a big assignment.'

'And without the Tetrarch to protect us?'

'I think,' said Rosanna, 'he was always around. I laughed when the Haitian Adepts thought we were spirits possessing him. You're the Tetrarch's "horse" – particularly in your gang-busters frame of mind. He possesses you, if anyone does.'

'And you?' I whispered.

'I think,' she said, 'that I am Vala's. That's why I was afraid of Her.'

We could hear Losian transport beginning to move on the causeway outside. As we fell asleep again, the convoys were moving, headed for the steep slope leading out of the plains, into the Tharmian uplands and on towards the tangled forest which lies between Beulah and the immigrant point at Acheron – tools, beams, asvaya, road-building gear, great plows and rollers from the Forges of Adambara.

'The fourfold clangor of the Arrows of Intellect,' murmured Rosanna, as she turned away into sleep.

We were listening to the end of the religious institution which had outlived its meaning.

16

In Regenerations, Terrific or Complacent

We spent two nights with Faesto, and Rosanna a whole day alone with him, and on the last morning we saw him leave, raising his hand, at the head of his squadron, and all the while the convoys of heavy Losian equipment rolled westward. The fort emptied of all but its permanent inhabitants. We saddled the Tetrarch, took the road to Adambara and reached it by the following afternoon. Takis took charge of our mount.

'That was a bright recruit you sent us, Sir. Have a pleasant evening,' said Takis. 'I hear the operation's going like clockwork.'

Once more we walked through the streets of Adambara to the room beside the Rotunda, and opened the door of our Losian home. It was as we had left it. Even our bath was ready. I picked up Rosanna and lifted her over the sill.

'That was a nice thing to do,' she said. 'We're home. No mergers. And there is a Feminine Will in eternity, in spite of the Great Adept.'

For several days we came and went at leisure, walking in Adambara, worshipping in the temple of Enitharmon, going once or twice to the House of Play. The warm nights and the dusty light were timeless. I do not know how many days passed before Thapsis came back. He sent us a message, came to dine in our room, bathed with us, shared the love bed. It was on the love bed, indeed, that we reported to him what we thought we had learned. It was a little like a report of clients to a marriage counselor into the insights we had gained. Thapsis said gravely that we seemed to have found the journey profitable.

'Are we now finished?' said Rosanna.

'Finished in what way?' He stretched and looked puzzled. 'Are we complete?'

Thapsis remained silent. Then he said, 'Nothing, you know, has so far ever really withstood you – you realize that? You've been tested but in superior force. If you mean, are you ready to tackle real opposition, you're as ready as you ever will be. A time will come for that, for real opposition.'

I thought of Verula and the frantic spirits of the Empty Quarter. There had been no real opposition. As in dreams, we had been in superior force. Thapsis read my mind.

'Preparation,' he said, 'and you were equipped. There is combat which isn't preparation, and opposition which isn't play.'

'You mean the real-time mission will be really hairy,' I said.

'Oh, yes – that,' said Thapsis, 'it probably will. But warring against flesh and blood is pretty much like dealing with Verulans. There is other opposition.'

'I know there is opposition,' said Rosanna. 'The veil of the śakti on the way to Glossa?'

'She too was playing with you. But that is closer.'

'From whom,' I said, 'is the opposition? Is it from one of the Four?'

'From one, or all.'

'Even if they are united? Even if we reverence all of them?'

'If you go into the desert without water,' said Thapsis, 'and the sun dries you to a skin, that is hardly the fault of the sun. Yet there is opposition to your going there.'

'*Is* there an enemy?' said Rosanna.

'It will seem so,' said Thapsis. 'You'd probably do best to say that there is. Call him, or her, or it, simply "the enemy" if you wish, but use the tessaract – there's no Losian word: we simply say "that which has no name."'

'The Unnameable?'

'Precisely.'

'Thapsis, are you talking knowledge or skull-knowledge? Have you met this opposition?' said Rosanna.

Thapsis shook his head.

'So we are to do something you haven't done?'

'Yes. Or I would have done it myself. General Kari never fought a battle, but he trains asvin.'

'Who don't fight battles either,' I said.

'There,' said Thapsis, 'the analogy breaks down. I think you will have to face this one. Being an archimage is easy. After that, and for people of both worlds, the opposition begins.'

'The struggle – can be won?' said Rosanna.

'Won or drawn. It's uncharted. No enterprise carries built-in success, unless it's play. You have outgrown play I think.'

And by a kind of mutual consent we pursued the matter no further. It was plain to both of us that there would be another journey but never one fully armed and guided by our mentors, never one with the equipment of Adambara or the stage management of Thapsis, never one with blank ammunition or constant contact with base.

Rosanna did, however, ask him a last question, before she got up and led the way to the onyx bath.

'We can come back?' she said.

'Of course. As often as you wish, if you wish. This is your home. We all need reflection. Don't you ever go back to your old university? Come here at will – go to Tarnindhupura and sail in the reed boat. Go back to that village and put on the peacock veil – no, don't be afraid, you've worn it often without being aware of it. But when you do go back to your old university it isn't as a sophomore. That happens once only.'

And he followed Rosanna to the bath, taking her hand, and I followed them.

Matters seemed to have come to an end. I felt that Adambara was waiting for us to return home. I asked Rosanna if we should go now.

'I think,' said Rosanna, 'that there's more. There is no shape to it if we leave now. We shall know when to go, and how.'

So we continued the gentle, waiting life of Adambara, ate at the Iron Choreb, went home to the love bed. In the morning I made my way to the asvin barracks, exercised the

Tetrarch, lunched in the mess. Rosanna had gone to the College of Adepts.

I was walking out of the barrack arch when someone called. It was Sergeant Takis, the farrier and riding master.

'Excuse me for shouting, Sir, but I saw you leaving.'

He stationed himself as if loath to continue.

'Well?'

'It's the Tetrarch, Sir. Did you notice anything about him?'

'No – he seemed tetchy this morning, but that's the Tetrarch: any problems?'

'I think he's becoming fey, Sir.'

'He's what?'

'Well, Sir, he's an old asva. How old we don't know, but he wasn't young when . . . when you first rode him.'

'All right, Sergeant, you can say it – when he ran away with me.'

'Yessir. Now he seems normal to you, Sir, but when an asva gets old he's got some way of knowing when he's running out of wick – don't ask me how they know, Sir, but they do. And when that happens, there's nothing for it but to turn them loose. They know what to do. It's like an Adept making a pilgrimage, if you'll forgive the expression.'

'How do you know he's fey? He didn't say anything to me,' I said.

'No, Sir, he wouldn't. But he's stopped drinking. An asva never stops drinking when there's water. Not unless he's fey.'

'I hope you're wrong,' I said, rather stunned. It seemed suddenly that there would be little point in returning here for enlightenment without that vast spotty back to mount.

'I hope so too, Sir,' said Takis. 'But I'm not, Sir.'

'How long do you give it?'

'Sir?'

'Until we have to turn him loose.'

'He'll ask, Sir, when he's ready.'

'I'd like to go with him,' I said, 'we've been in a few things together.'

'Yessir. But I don't think he'll permit that. I've tried to follow them, but they've always given me the slip. They head towards Or-Cu, but there's a line of hills where they just seem to disappear. Must be a boneyard somewhere, but I've ridden every inch and never found it.'

I went back disconsolate.

'Whatever is the matter?' said Rosanna.

'Takis says the Tetrarch's fey. He's preparing for his last roundup.'

'Oh, no!'

'Well, I hope not. But Takis knows asvaya, and he's sure. I saw nothing wrong with him – a bit preoccupied, perhaps.' The thought hung heavy over the remainder of the day.

We were asleep, on the love bed, and it must have been halfway through the night when a noise woke me. It was a thump. It was repeated more loudly. Somebody was knocking unhandily at the door of the stairway leading to our room. Then the thump was repeated again. It was thunderous and was doing no good to the door.

'Rosanna!'

'It's him,' she said. 'He wants to come in.'

I ran down naked and opened the door. It was indeed the Tetrarch. In the moonlight he seemed white rather than spotted. His tether was broken. He had no saddle.

'He's come,' I said, 'to say good-bye.'

Asvaya do not nuzzle or sentimentalize. He looked at each of us, with a steady gaze. Then he knelt.

'He wants us to mount,' said Rosanna.

'Naked, in the middle of the night, with no saddle, on a one-way trip into the desert?' I said.

'Trust him. He's paying you the supreme compliment,' said Rosanna.

'I'm obliged to him, I'm sure, but hadn't we better get dressed?'

The Tetrarch plunged and whinnied. Rosanna made no answer. She mounted him, in the fore-saddle position, where the asvin saddle would be.

'Are you coming, or not?' she said.

I mounted behind.

The Tetrarch traversed the night streets like a ghost. Apart from our ride with the recruit I had never ridden him behind another asvin. He seemed now to be Rosanna's mount, not mine. We passed the Hall of Record, and were coming to the wall of Bowmen. I felt him shovel on coal. The gates were permanently open now, but he would leave Adambara in style. I felt his soaring takeoff, and, as on the first ride I had had upon him, he cleared the wall and the canal, landed, picked up his step and headed into the desert towards Or-Cu, and all so smoothly that we rose and landed with him. Rosanna held to the hair of his shoulders, and that was all. Fey or not, there was no sign of age in his gait. He moved faster than an express train. Hyasa scuttled off, but he had forgotten lizard meat. His round ears lay back, his muzzle above us pointed straight into the hills. He had never gone so fast. It seemed little time before the outliers of that line of hills moved out to meet us. They were hummocks only – if this were his destination, there was no place in it to hide a graveyard of asvaya. I knew the place, having ridden through the line of hummocks before. It separated the now distant lights and watchtowers of Adambara from a dry flat which had the look of a saltpan. There was nowhere there to hide a rat, let alone an asva. The Tetrarch did not pass between the hummocks, as I had expected. He slowed and mounted one. As he breasted it I could see over the top, and caught my breath. The saltpan had vanished, and its place was taken by a shining lake, or by a mirage, for there was clear moonlit water where I knew that there should be desert, and yet the desert bushes could be seen, sunk in it like weeds. I could smell salt.

'There was no lake here,' I said.

On the flat top of the mound he halted and knelt. We did not move. He knelt again, reached back his head and snapped gently at us.

'This is where we get off,' said Rosanna. Reluctantly I followed her. The Tetrarch stood again, backed a few paces, then reared, flailing his forefeet, whinnying out scream after scream of greeting and farewell. Then he turned, descended the sand slope, and like a bather entered the water. I saw it splash around him. In twenty yards he was waterborne and swimming. Before long he was a wide running ripple, an arrow with a huge head at its point, and at that moment the first of a small file of clouds passed over the moon. We stood in silence. Rosanna held my hand. The cloud completed its work, and as the moon came out again we saw that the lake surface was unbroken.

'He's gone,' I said. 'May the Four be with him.'

The next cloud began to encroach on the light.

'I'm glad he took us into his confidence,' I said. 'It's a long step back, but luckily it's warm. We'd better go, Ros. I don't have anything to fire a volley with.'

'Look,' said Rosanna.

The moon was clear of the cloud again. At first I saw nothing, for I was looking for the huge bow-wave of the Tetrarch, and I missed a smaller arrow, far out, which was coming steadily our way.

'Must be a hyasa swimming,' I said. It gave me a pang – if my old friend had postponed his journey by only a few minutes, he could have had his favorite meal before departing. The swimming object continued towards us.

'No, Ros,' I said, 'you can see it's far too small for an asva.'

Small it was, but at its point was a rounded head, and behind the rounded head, an arched neck and a barrel-shaped back. On the neck, in contrast to the Tetrarch's matted neck-hair, stood a bristly rocking-horse mane. It swam steadily in, grounded, splashed out of the shallows and shook irritably with the gesture I knew. It was only pony-sized, leggy but sturdy, its spots were augmented by the dark juvenile streaks which fade in the adult asva, but it had the huge forequarters and the heavy testicles of a stallion. In its eye was sagacity which boded ill for somebody in the future. It was an asva foal. It saw us and shied, springing back towards the water and scaring itself a second time with its own splash.

An asva foal within a few hours of birth is a mixture of whipcord, gunpowder, teeth and claws, which can take six of the tough Or-Cu herd boys to lasso, and which can distribute gashes and broken ribs enough to make them cautious in going anywhere near such a capture. I have seen such a little devil hauled in, kicking and screaming his defiance, unwillingly to school. But this foal did not bolt. It stood in two minds as if reasoning with itself, and then receiving instructions, it seemed, from somewhere, it began to move towards us, until it stood in the footprints left by the Tetrarch when he had reared his farewell. Then it too reared and gave a youthful imitation of that animal's mighty, screaming whinny – soprano as yet but none the less formidable. Then, walking delicately like Agag it approached Rosanna. She put out her hand.

'Watch it, they bite,' I said.

It put out a large pink tongue and licked her. Then it turned to me. I think it sensed my suspicion, for instead of repeating the gesture of good will it spun round, backed a few paces, seemed to bow, then went into furious military action against invisible enemies. It snapped right, snapped left, spun, kicked, trampled and rolled on an unseen verra. It reared and yelled victory. Then it stood quite still, eyeing me, as if to say, 'Satisfied, thick-head?'

I was fully satisfied.

'I wonder,' said Rosanna, 'if he should have a new name?'

'Son of the Tetrarch?'

'Don't be ridiculous – it's not his son.'

I think if an asva could have laughed, that one would have done so. Instead, with a military bearing, he turned flank, and stood.

'Down,' said Rosanna, and he knelt for mounting. Rosanna climbed on the rocking-horse back.

'Come,' she said, 'he's my asva now. I'm the first to mount him.'

I got up behind her. It was like getting into a mini-car after a ten-wheeler. He found us heavy, but still he stood. Then, without any command, he turned down the slope. His feet slipped in the sand of the dune bank. Then he entered the water, deeper and deeper. Our feet were immersed, but it was like air, not water, and warm. I felt him quit the bottom. Water came to our thighs. He swam steadily, and as we moved I saw the desert bushes and stones under us, at the bottom of the airlike lake.

'Where to?' I whispered. Rosanna's head was close to my mouth. I could smell her hair.

'Taking us home,' said Rosanna.

And as I put my arms round her more firmly, the swimming ceased, the airlike water splashed to our waists, and for a moment I felt that the two of us and our mount were a single androgynous centaur having its own existence as a single being, as in reverse we traversed the brief suspension of thought which marks the passing of the fringes of Vala's veil. And we were where we had been when we set out; my hands were over her breasts, Rosanna was sleeping. I had a brief image of the Tetrarch, renewed in youth, passing from under us and turning away into some other dimension. I slipped my hand from under her, rose a little and pulled the wraps over us both.

BOOK FOUR
The Fourth Journey

. . . Is in Real Time

ta s urva la ma rga enpa d a

Appendix

The Losian Religion

As Expounded by William Blake

(With Acknowledgments to Professor Northrop Frye)

Man and His Anima
(Albion)   (Jerusalem)

Contain

Eternal Name	Luvah (Passion)	Urizen (Reason)	Tharmas (Sensation)	Urthono (Imagination)
Earthly Name	Orc (Revolution)	Satan (Opacity)	Covering Cherub (Selfhood)	Los (Creativity)
Bride (Śakti)	Vala (Nature)	Ahania (Nirvana)	Enion (Generation)	Enitharmon (Spirituality)
Quality	Passion	Knowledge	Fusion	Prophecy
Negative	Hate	Doubt	Despair	Dullness
Beast	Bull	Lion	Eagle	Man
Cakra	Genitals	Head	Heart	Spirit-Self
Metal	Brass	Gold	Silver	Iron
Symbol	Stars	Sun	Moon	Mountain
State	Generation	Eden	Beulah	Ulro
Compass Points	East	South	West	North
Son of Los	Palambron (Pity)	Rintrah (Wrath)	Theotormon (Jealousy)	Bromion (Terror)
Śakti	Elynittria	Ocalythron	Oothoon	none
City	London	Verulam	York	Edinburgh
Occupation	Weaver	Plowman	Shepherd	Smith

Four Mighty Ones are in Every Man; a Perfect Unity Cannot exist but from the Universal Brotherhood of Eden, The Universal man, to Whom be Glory Evermore.

Losian Grammar

The Losian language has three numbers – singular, plural and tasurat (tessaract), the last of these peculiar to Losian. The use of the tessaract is confined to: (1) things or persons in fours; (2) nouns denominating religious, transcendental or timeless things or persons; and (3) as an honorific (see text).

Typical Losian nominal declensions are as follows:

asva, *m.* steed

SINGULAR	PLURAL	TESSARACT
Nom. as-va	-vai, -vaya	-vat
Acc. -vamh	-vash	-vat
Gen. -vaih	-vabhi	-vati
Dat.)	-vabhyah	-vabh
Instr.) -var		

choreb, *f.* Losian sheep-llama

Nom.	choreb	chrebu	chrbut
Acc.	chrebumh	chrebush	chrbut
Gen.	chrebih	chreburhi	chrebuti
D/I.	chrebur	chrebhyuh	chrebubh

Losian verbs have two tenses only: present and past-future, used for all non-present events. Sentences in the past-future where tense is emphasized end in the particulate adverb aenpada (not-now). The vector sense of time is conveyed where the context obliges it by specification: 'last year', 'tomorrow', 'recently', 'soon', etc., omitting aenpada.

The Losian here described is that of Adambara. The Losian

spoken in Or-Cu is a hybrid with a local patois which resembles Ionic Greek with simplified grammar but is written in Losian characters, the supplementals, e.g., ϕ, ξ, being Greek.

The Losian Script

A	B	Ch	D	E	G	H	H asp.	I	K	L

M	N	O	Th	P	R	Ṛ	S	T	U	X asp.

J	Y	V	Z

Thus in Adeptic Losian:

s a t u j a y a t e v e n p a d a

In cursive Losian, medial 𝈀 is omitted as in Sanskrit:

or ,

sₐ t u ja Yₐ t e v e n pₐ d a

A Losian Vocabulary

aenpada   *partic. adv.* Sign of past future (follows sentence). *adj. indecl.* Not now; divine, religious, transcendental. [a-privative + enpada.]

agurh   *adj. indecl.* Ageless, long-lived, immortal. [a-privative + gurh.]

astra   *n. masc.; pl.*: astraya; *tess.*: astrat. Weapon, arm, device. [Skr. astra: weapon.]

asva   *n. masc.; pl.*: -ai, -aya; *tess.*: -at. A steed, *Chalicotherium* (*Hipposcylax*) *chemosit*. [Skr. aśva: horse.]

asvin   *n. masc.; pl.*: asvin; *tess.*: asvit. Hussar, asva rider, mounted infantryman. [Skr. asvin: horseman.]

blach   *n. neut. indecl.* Herb used for smoking: *Piper calpalata*. [?]

chhot, -a, -u   *adj.* Lesser, small, trifling. [Hindi: chhota: small.]

chitru   *n. Neut.; pl.*: chitrur. Pictures. *tess.*: chitrut. Magical or transcendental pictures. [Skr. citra: colored, varied.]

choreb   *n. fem.; pl.*: chorebu; *tess.*: chrbut. Sheeplike domestic animal, sheep-llama: *Ovicapra choreb*. [?]

enpada   *partic. adv.* and *adj.* Now, underfoot, secular, base. [Gk. empodōn: underfoot, present.]

ev   *partic.* Indeed, verily. [Skr. eva: surely.]

gurh   *n. fem. irreg.* Old age. [Skr. root gu: old.]

hyasa   *n. masc.; pl.*: -ai; *tess.*: not in polite usage. Large scavenging lizard, *Pseudamblyrrhynchus porcinus*, considered unclean by Losians: filthy person, swine. [?]

intru   *n. neut.; pl.*: ——; *tess.*: intrut. Mandala, active diagram. [Skr. yantra: implement, mandala.]

jayen   *v. tr.* and *intr.* Conquer, triumph, be victorious. [Skr.

397

jaya: victory.] *Pres. tense*: jayu, jayus, jayat: *pl*.: jayum, jauti, jayun; *tess*.: jayut, jayuh, jayun.

lata   *n. fem.*: Plant, creeper; *pl*.: latai; *tess*.: latat. [Skr. lata: creeper.]

parakiyamarga   *n. fem.* Ritual insemination of slave by person other than owner. [Skr. word: way of other woman.]

pursa   *n. comm.* Person; *pl*.: pursai. People; *tess*.: pursat. Sages. [Skr. purusa person.]

saktu   *n. fem.* Spear, power; *pl*.: saktur. Spears; *tess*.: saktut. Powers. [Skr. śakti: spear, energy, female emanation.]

satu   *n. fem.* Right, justice, fair dealing. [Skr. satya: truth.]

sidar   *n. masc.; pl*.: sidri. A coin of Adambara. [?]

simurgh   *n. comm. indecl.* Message eagle (*Haliaeetus nuntius simurgh*). [Pers. simurgh: mythical bird, roc.]

siddhi   *n. fem.; tess.* siddut. Magical device, tour-de-force by Adept. [Skr. word: success, magical side-effect of yoga.]

tacho   *adv.* Quickly, at once. [Gr. tachu: swiftly.]

tas, ta, sti   *rel. pron.* Who, that, that which.

tasur   *num. indecl.* Four [Gk. tessara: four.]

tasurat   *n. masc.; tess.* (T) The Four: Luvah, Urizen, Tharmas and Urthona; Quaternity of the Losian pantheon; Fourness, Essence. (t) *grammat.* The tessaract number (tasur).

tichan   *n. fem.; pl.* and *tess*.: tichan. Art, skill, device. [Gk. techne: skill.]

-vala   *nom. suff.* In charge of, having, costing. Thus simurgh-vala: person in charge of s.; blach tasur-vala sidrih: blach costing four sidri; blach-vala: person having blach, blach seller. Cf. Eng. use of 'wallah'. [Hindi: wala: same usages.]

PHRASES

sat kam'yaste   'Love well! Did you love well?' The normal Losian greeting to an adult person or couple: good day, greetings, farewell.

The Adeptic version is 'sat viddhayaste?' (know well) or more popularly 'viddhat sat kamayaste' (knowing, love well).

sanpitur Either 'brother' (one who shares a father) or 'co-father'. Form of address by one male to another with whom he has shared the favors of a woman. Losian philologists favor 'co-father' as a derivation predating the discovery that conception can result from a single act of intercourse.

The phrase between women is *sammutr*, 'sister': one with whom a woman has shared a man.